Conserving
Carolinian Canada

This publication is sponsored by:

 WWF World Wildlife Fund

Union Gas

 The Ontario Heritage
Foundation

Cloverleaf Foundation

Conserving Carolinian Canada

Conservation Biology in the Deciduous Forest Region

edited by

Gary M. Allen, *Ontario Ministry of Natural Resources*
Paul F.J. Eagles, *University of Waterloo*
Steven D. Price, *World Wildlife Fund*

University of Waterloo Press

ISBN 0-88898-102-3

University of Waterloo Press
Porter Library
University of Waterloo
Waterloo, Ontario, Canada N2L 3G1
Phone: 519-885-1211, ext. 3369
FAX: 519-747-4606

Design by Graphic Services, University of Waterloo

Printing and binding by T.H. Best Printing Co., Toronto, Ontario

Canadian Cataloguing in Publication Data

Main entry under title:

Conserving Carolinian Canada

Includes bibliographical references.
ISBN 0-88898-102-3

1. Natural areas – Ontario.   2. Natural areas –
Research – Ontario.   3. Endangered species – Ontario.
4. Forest ecology – Research – Ontario.   I. Allen, Gary Michael,
1952-   .   II. Eagles, Paul F.J. (Paul Franklin
John).   III. Price, Steven D. (Steven Douglas), 1956-   .

QH77.C3C66 1990   333.78'09713   C90-095232-6

Printed on acid-free paper, 50% of which is recycled, post-consumer waste.

Acknowledgements

The editors would like to thank the many people who took the time to review one or more of the papers in this book. Their constructive and thoughtful comments brought out many important points and helped enrich the papers. They are: Mark Brundrett, Peter Carson, Daryl Coulson, Terry Crabe, Bruce Duncan, James Duncan, Linda Dupuis, Dave Euler, Mary Gartshore, Joyce Gould, Quimby Hess, James Kamstra, Kevin Kavanagh, Donald Kirk, Ben and Brenda Kulon, Jeff Larson, James Levenson, Paul Pratt, John Riley, Donald Sutherland, Art Timmerman, Steve Varga, Yvette Wells, and Natalie Zalkind. Special mention must be made of Mike Oldham, Paul Smith, Mirek Sharp and Phil Taylor, whose collective expertise was invaluable in improving several of the papers.

We relied on Dave Balser, Noel Burbidge, Barbara Crowe, and Paul Smith for their computer advice and trouble shooting capabilities. Margaret McLean is thanked for her cartographic skills. Peter Tallon did much of the word processing and Jennifer Ballantine helped with style editing. Gloria Smith advised on various aspects of production, and David Bartholomew designed the book. Parks and Recreational Areas Section, Ministry of Natural Resources, Central Region, generously provided office support which was critical to the publication.

The pen and ink drawings which grace the cover and the text help convey the essence of Carolinian Canada. We sincerely thank Daryl Coulson, Suzanne House, Ron Ridout, Steve Varga, and Zile Zichmanis for contributing their art work. Craig Campbell kindly provided the drawings by the late Shelley Logier.

Dedication

To the thousands of Carolinian Canada landowners, past and present. Their love of the land has been critical in maintaining these "islands of green", Canada's most endangered ecosystem. Their foresight will reap priceless conservation dividends, in perpetuity, to future generations.

Contents

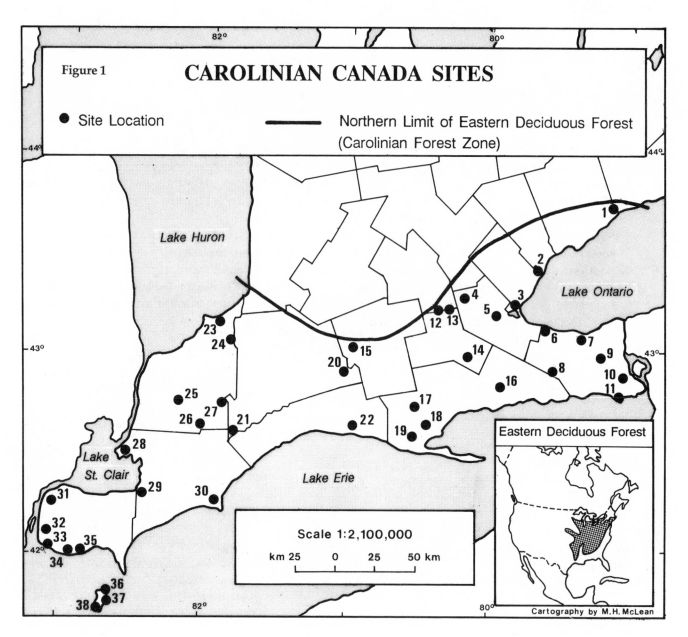

Figure 1

CAROLINIAN CANADA SITES

● Site Location ———— Northern Limit of Eastern Deciduous Forest (Carolinian Forest Zone)

Lake Huron

Lake Ontario

Lake St. Clair

Lake Erie

Eastern Deciduous Forest

Scale 1:2,100,000

km 25   0   25   50 km

Cartography by M.H. McLean

1 Rouge River Valley

2 Iroquois Shoreline Woods

3 Sassafras Woods

4 Beverly Swamp

5 Dundas Valley

6 Grimsby – Winona Escarpment and Beamer Valley

7 Jordan Escarpment Valley

8 Caistor – Canborough Slough Forest

9 Fonthill Sandhill Valley

10 Willoughby Clay Plain

11 Point Abino Peninsula Sandland Forest

12 Sudden Bog

13 Grand River Valley Forests and Spottiswood Lakes

14 Six Nations Indian Reserve Forests

15 Embro Upland Forest

16 Oriskany Sandstone and Woodlands

17 Delhi Big Creek Valley

18 St. Williams Dwarf Oak Forest

19 Big Creek Valley – South Walsingham Sand Ridges

20 Dorchester Swamp

21 Skunk's Misery

22 Catfish Creek Slope and Floodplain Forest

23 Port Franks Wetlands and Forested Dunes

24 Ausable River Valley

25 Plum Creek Upland Woodlots

26 Shetland Kentucky Coffee-tree Woods

27 Sydenham River Corridor

28 Walpole Island Indian Reserve

29 Lake St. Clair Marshes

30 Sinclair's Bush

31 Ojibway Prairie Remnants

32 Canard River Kentucky Coffee-tree Woods

33 Big Creek Marsh

34 Oxley Poison Sumac Swamp

35 Cedar Creek

36 Middle Point Woods

37 Stone Road Alvar

38 Middle Island

Introduction

The Deciduous Forest Region of Ontario has long been recognized by naturalists as a special place. The warm and dry southern climate is ideal for ecosystems that are not found elsewhere in Canada. More endangered species are contained here than in any other Canadian life zone.

This Deciduous Forest Region, nicknamed the Carolinian Zone, was first described by researchers in the late 1800s, however not until a series of papers in the 1950s by Sherwood Fox and Joe Soper (1952, 1953, 1954), did the significance of the zone gain public attention. Foresters have long noted the area as a unique zone (Hosie, 1969) due to the presence of dominant forest tree species that are not known from elsewhere in Canada. Ontario's Deciduous Forest is part of the much larger Eastern Deciduous Forest that extends well south into the United States (Figure 1).

Since the last century, various public and private groups have undertaken conservation efforts in the Carolinian life zone. As a result, very significant natural communities have been brought into conservation ownership. Point Pelee National Park (Canadian Parks Service), Rondeau Provincial Park (Ontario Ministry of Natural Resources), Big Creek National Wildlife Area (Canadian Wildlife Service), Backus Woods Conservation Area (Long Point Conservation Authority), Cootes Paradise (Royal Botanical Gardens), and Spooky Hollow Nature Sanctuary (The Hamilton Naturalists' Club) are examples of Carolinian areas that are protected by a conservation agency or group.

Nevertheless, the Carolinian life zone contains the most urbanized and most intensive agricultural area of Canada. Indeed, 25% of Canada's population is supported by this relatively tiny area, which occupies only 1/4 of 1% of the country's land mass. As a result, a steady loss of natural land and the associated species in this Carolinian Zone has made for a rising tide of concern in conservation circles.

In 1984 the World Wildlife Fund (Canada), in concert with the Ontario Heritage Foundation, the Nature Conservancy of Canada and the Richard Ivey Foundation launched a conservation program in the Carolinian life zone. This was part of WWF's policy move to concentrate their conservation actions within clearly defined areas and themes.

The WWF Carolinian Canada Program has three components:

I. A Carolinian Conservation Strategy will be prepared by a steering committee representing the major conservation agencies and universities in Southwestern Ontario. This work plan will identify and rank the critical natural areas which must be protected, as well as recommend an agency and method of protection to secure each area.

II. Wildlife Conservation Projects, under the auspices of WWF Canada, will address the most important wildlife and wildlife habitat work that needs to be done in the Carolinian zone. Emphasis will be on endangered, threatened, rare and extirpated species and their habitats, but would not exclude other species requiring attention that are harvested as a natural resource.

III. A Natural Areas Protection Program will pursue the protection of the priority areas identified in the Strategy from Component I. In some cases, this will involve acquisition of lands, but it will also include the use of many of the non-purchase methods of securing natural areas identified by the Natural Heritage League. This emphasis recognizes that most of the remnants of Carolinian habitat are in private ownership, and that public funds will not be sufficient to secure the areas (Price, 1984).

In addition, the conservation program has a fourth objective of encouraging the development of an interagency management policy structure to govern activities of different agencies in the Carolinian life zone in the future.

The first goal of the program, a lucid conservation strategy for the life zone, has remained an elusive goal. However, the many individual actions do add up to a useful set of conservation actions.

The second goal of the program is fulfilled with the publication of this book. The WWF funded a large number of research projects on various aspects of the flora and fauna of the Carolinian life zone (Table 1). On January 15, 1988 a summary of the results of most of the research was presented to a workshop at the University of Waterloo. This book contains papers supporting those presentations.

Table 1

Wildlife and Habitat Projects Funded by the World Wildlife Fund

During the 1984 to 1986 period the World Wildlife Fund provided funds for a number of research projects. This Table contains a summary listing of all projects funded. Those projects with papers in this document are marked with an asterisk. Projects funded by the $3.6 million Carolinian Canada Fund are not listed here.

Project Title	Total Funding
A) Mammals	
* 1. Echo-locating Endangered Bats in the Carolinian Zone – Dr. Brock Fenton, Carleton University	$ 10,000
* 2. Determining the Status and Life History of the Southern Flying Squirrel – Mr. Mark Stabb and Dr. Paul Aird, University of Toronto	$ 5,000
B) Birds	
* 3. Rare Birds of the Carolinian Zone – Michael Cadman, Ontario Breeding Bird Atlas and the Federation of Ontario Naturalists	$ 9,000
* 4. Reintroduction of the Wild Turkey – Dr. David Ankney, University of Western Ontario	$ 2,500
* 5. Reconstruction of the Bird-banding Station at Long Point (Ontario) – Ms. Erica Dunn, Long Point Bird Observatory	$ 2,500
* 6. Reintroducing the Endangered Bald Eagle to Southern Ontario – Mr. Bruce Duncan, Taquanyah Nature Centre, in cooperation with the Hamilton Naturalists Club	$ 2,500
C) Reptiles and Amphibians	
7. Conservation of the Eastern Spiny Soft-shelled Turtle – Dr. Martyn Obbard, University of Guelph	$ 4,500
* 8. Preparing a Summary of the Reptiles and Amphibians of Ontario – Mr. Michael Oldham, Essex Region Conservation Authority	$ 11,000
* 9. Determining the Status of Rare and Endangered Butterflies in Southern Ontario – Dr. Laurence Packer, York University in cooperation with the Ontario Ministry of Natural Resources	$ 15,000

Table 1 (continued)

Project Title	Total Funding
D) Invertebrates	
10. *Discovering the Life-cycle of the Karner Blue Butterfly* – Dr. Dale Schweitzer in cooperation with the Lambton Wildlife Inc. and the Ontario Ministry of Natural Resources	$ 2,000
* 11. *Importance of Seepage Springs for Aquatic Insects* – Dr. Stephen Marshall, University of Guelph	$ 2,500
* 12. *Cataloguing Rare Mollusks and Other Aquatic Invertebrates in the Sydenham River* – Dr. Gerry Mackie, University of Guelph	$ 5,000
E) Plants	
* 13. *Population Ecology of the Tulip Tree* -Mr. Kevin Kavanagh, in cooperation with the University of Toronto	$ 5,250
* 14. *Effect of Woodlot Size on the Diversity of Carolinian Forests* – Dr. Richard Reader, University of Guelph	$ 1,860
* 15. *Improving the Germination and Cultivation of Rare Ontario Orchids* – Mr. Allan Anderson, University of Guelph	$ 500
* 16. *Reproductive Biology of Rare Plants in Southwestern Ontario* – Dr. John Ambrose and Dr. Peter Kevan, University of Guelph	$ 22,000
17. *Mapping of Rare Carolinian Plants to Determine Critical Habitats* – Mr. Brian Klinkenberg, University of Western Ontario	$ 5,000
F) Natural Areas	
18. *Determining the Ownership of Priority Natural Areas* – Mr. Lloyd Mayeda, Nature Conservancy of Canada	$ 5,000
* 19. *Determining Conservation Priorities on Walpole Island* – Mr. Gary Allen, Mr. Wayne Rowe and Mr. Allen Woodliffe, in cooperation with the Ontario Ministry of Natural Resources and Lambton Wildlife Inc.	$ 15,000
* 20. *Protecting Environmentally Significant Areas in the Counties of Elgin and Kent* – Ms. Rose Klinkenberg, Long Point Foundation in cooperation with The Lower Thames Conservation Authority and the Ontario Ministry of Natural Resources	$ 14,000
21. *Rehabilitation of Sand Dunes on Lake Erie* – Dr. Anwar Maun, University of Western Ontario	$ 13,400
* 22. *Identifying and Protecting Environmentally Significant Areas in the Regional Municipality of Haldimand-Norfolk* – Mr. Michael Bradstreet, Norfolk Field Naturalists	$ 23,500
* 23. *Encouraging Land Owners to Conserve Private Natural Areas* – Dr. Stewart Hilts, University of Guelph and the Natural Heritage League Stewardship Program in cooperation with Wildlife Habitat Canada	$ 10,000
* 24. *Natural Area Assessment of Sassafras Woods* – Ms. Kathy Lindsay, in cooperation with The Ontario Heritage Foundation	$ 1,975

Table 1 (continued)

Project Title	Total Funding
G) Status Reports	
25. *Determining the Status of the Red Mulberry in Canada* – Committee on the Status of Endangered Wildlife Canada (COSEWIC) – Dr. John Ambrose, University of Guelph	$ 1,000
26. *Status of the Illinois Tick-trefoil and the Blue-eyed Mary* – COSEWIC – Mr. Brian Klinkenberg, University of Western Ontario	$ 1,700
27. *Status of the Large Twayblade* – COSEWIC – Mr. Gary Allen, Chatham, Ontario	$ 1,000
28. *Status of the Dense Blazingstar* – COSEWIC – Mr. Gary Allen, Chatham, Ontario	$ 850
29. *Status of the Silver Shiner* (update) – COSEWIC – Ms. Betsy Baldwin, Ontario	$ 200
30. *Status of the Small-flowered Hemicarpha* – COSEWIC – Mr. Michael Oldham, Essex, Ontario	$ 850
31. *Status of the White-fringed Orchid and the Pink Milkwort* – COSEWIC – Ms. Vivian Brownell, Ottawa, Ontario	$ 250
32. *Status of the Hoary Mountain Mint and the Few-flowered Club-rush* – COSEWIC -Mr. William Crins, University of Toronto	$ 200
33. *Status of the Spotted Wintergreen* – COSEWIC – Mr. Donald Kirk	$ 1,700
H) Strategy Committee	
34. *Publication of a Special Edition of "Seasons" Magazine Featuring the Carolinian Zone* – Ms. Judith Parsons and Mr. Mike Singleton, Federation of Ontario Naturalists	$ 10,000
35. *Publishing the Final Report "Critical Unprotected Natural Areas in the Carolinian Life Zone of Canada"* – Dr. Paul Eagles, University of Waterloo	$ 4,184
36. *Strategy Committee for Carolinian Canada* – Mr. Steven Price, WWF Canada, in cooperation with the Nature Conservancy of Canada and the Ontario Heritage Foundation	$ 33,286
Total	**$254,205**

In addition to those papers listed in Table 1, a few other papers that provide important research findings but were not funded by the WWF program are also included. The goals and operations of the Conservation Data Centre effort of the Nature Conservancy of Canada are outlined in papers by George Francis and by Phil Hoose and Susan Crispin. The use of distributional data in assessing species significance is outlined for five species of rare Carolinian breeding birds by Karen McColeman and Paul Eagles. The status of rare Carolinian plants is detailed by Mike Oldham. Steve Varga and Gary Allen report on the efforts of many individuals to keep records on the plants in each county in the life zone. Craig Campbell,

Daryl Coulson and Andrew Bryant provide details on the rare butterflies of this area. These papers were chosen because of the significance of this research to Carolinian Canada conservation.

Most of the papers in this book deal exclusively with Carolinian topics. But in true ecological fashion several of the topics and many of the recommendations have implications well beyond the immediate area of concern. Each author gives a summary of the research findings and a list of the most important implications for conservation.

The third goal of the Carolinian Canada program was initiated with the publication of the document; *The Critical Unprotected Natural Areas in the Carolinian Life Zone of Canada* (Eagles and Beechey, 1985). This document identified 36 priority sites for action. Later two more sites were added. These sites have served as a basis for a considerable amount of conservation action since 1985 (Figure 1).

The fourth goal of the WWF program was fulfilled on June 1, 1987 when then Minister of Natural Resources, Mr. Vince Kerrio, and then Minister of Citizenship and Culture, Mrs. Lily Munro, with the funding cooperation of the World Wildlife Fund (Canada), the Nature Conservancy of Canada and Wildlife Habitat Canada, signed a Memorandum of Understanding. This established a three year program with a budget of $3,600,000. The goal was to promote conservation in the Carolinian life zone, with emphasis on the 38 special sites. In order to implement the agreement, the Ontario Heritage Foundation was assigned the role of funds supervisor and a Steering Committee was established to provide the Ontario Heritage Foundation with recommendations for action.

The general approach of the three year program was to encourage cooperative conservation action of the broad range of public and private groups that have a role to play in resource management in the Carolinian area. Specifically, as of May 1990, 764 land owners have been reached by the Natural Heritage Stewardship program, which promotes conservation at the 38 sites by property owners. In addition, 419 hectares of critical habitat at ten sites have been purchased to stem the loss of natural habitat. Appendix 1 of the summary paper in this book gives a fuller explanation of the progress to date on each site in regards to land owner contact and land purchase.

This book reports on conservation research in the Carolinian Zone, the majority of which was funded by the World Wildlife Fund and its partners. Research per se was not funded during the three year Carolinian Canada program, rather, funds were chanelled toward land owner contact and land acquisition. It is important that the reader realize that these two efforts were separate but sequential in operation.

Findings presented in this book are intended for consideration by the Carolinian Canada program as well as by each of the cooperating agencies and groups. The land owners of the many important Carolinian Canada sites may find that the papers contain much relevant information to them. Our hope is that this document will stimulate reflection and further action to conserve these 38 remarkable natural areas.

References

Eagles, P.F.J. and T.J. Beechey. 1985. *Critical Unprotected Natural Areas on the Carolinian Life Zone of Canada*. The Nature Conservancy of Canada, The Ontario Heritage Foundation and World Wildlife Fund Canada. 400 pp.

Fox, W.S. and J.H. Soper. 1952. The Distribution of Some Trees and Shrubs of the Carolinian Zone of Southern Ontario: Part I, *Trans. of the Royal Can. Inst.* XXIX(II):65-84.

Fox, W.S. and J.H. Soper. 1953. The Distribution of Some Trees and Shrubs of the Carolinian Zone of Southern Ontario: Part II, *Trans. of the Royal Can. Inst.* XXX(I):3-22.

Fox, W.S. and J.H. Soper. 1954. The Distribution of Some Trees and Shrubs of the Carolinian Zone of Southern Ontario: Part III, *Trans. of the Royal Can. Inst.* XXX(II):99-130.

Hosie, R.C. 1969. *Native Trees of Canada*. Canadian Forestry Service, Queen's Printer, Ottawa. 380 pp.

Price, S. 1984. *Carolinian Canada Funding Proposal*. World Wildlife Fund Canada. Toronto. 17 p.

Soper, J.H. 1956. Some Families of Restricted Range in the Carolinian Flora of Canada, *Trans. of the Royal Can. Inst.* XXXI(II):69-90.

Soper, J.H. 1962. Some Genera of Restricted Range in the Carolinian Flora of Canada, *Trans. of the Royal Can. Inst.* XXXIV(I):3-56.

Natural Areas Inventory and Stewardship

Canada's largest wood warbler, the Yellow-breasted Chat is a rare Ontario species virtually restricted to the Carolinian Zone. It is pictured here in a patch of Prickly-pear Cactus, an endangered species which occurs naturally at only two Canadian locations, Pelee Island and Point Pelee National Park.
Artist – Ron Ridout.

The Natural Areas Inventory of Haldimand-Norfolk Regional Municipality

Michael S. W. Bradstreet Norfolk Field Naturalists
P.O. Box 995, Simcoe, Ontario N3Y 5B3

Abstract. *During a two-year inventory of candidate natural areas in the Regional Municipality of Haldimand-Norfolk, 41 Significant Natural Areas and 32 Significant Sites were identified. Areas and sites were chosen on the basis of nine selection criteria. The two volume report presenting the results of the inventory has been used to document the regional status of rare species and to bolster arguments for the protection of significant natural areas through municipal planning.*

Introduction

The Regional Municipality of Haldimand-Norfolk contains many areas of great biological significance. Long Point is recognized as one of the finest dune systems in North America, and contains one of the most important wetlands on the Great Lakes. Other important areas of national significance include Turkey Point and Backus Woods. Many rare species are found in the region and some are found nowhere else in Canada. The floral and faunal assemblage is diverse, including species with northern and others with southern affinities.

The Need for an Inventory

The Official Plan of Haldimand-Norfolk, passed in 1979, designated 30 "Environmentally Sensitive Areas" (ESAs) in the region; these areas were given certain safeguards in the plan. The designations were based on unpublished IBP (International Biological Programme) reports, the results of brief reconnaissance studies, and other information provided by the Ministry of Natural Resources, Conservation Authorities, naturalists, and local experts. The designations were not based on detailed studies, no selection criteria were employed, and the areas were not delineated. In 1985, the region initiated a process of Official Plan review. Rectifying the inadequacies of the ESA designations was one of two major reasons for undertaking the Natural Areas Inventory of Haldimand-Norfolk. The other was the regional conservation program, called Carolinian Canada, initiated by the World Wildlife Fund, Canada (WWF). WWF and other agencies realized that while most of the Carolinian Zone had benefitted from surveys of important natural areas, Haldimand-Norfolk, Kent, and Elgin had not, and they set out to rectify this deficiency.

In response to these two driving forces, the Norfolk Field Naturalists acted as sponsor of a two-year inventory of the natural areas of Haldimand-Norfolk. The club raised $130,000 for the inventory from five government agencies, seven funding bodies, and several private individuals.

How the Inventory Worked

Candidate areas for study were selected using a predetermined set of six criteria. Original field data were collected and these data and other reliable information were then used to determine whether an area met a set of nine selection criteria. If an area met the requirements of two to nine criteria, it was designated as a **SIGNIFICANT NATURAL AREA.** If only one criterion was met, the area was designated as a **SIGNIFICANT SITE.** The selection criteria employed were a hybrid of the ESA and ANSI (Areas of Natural and Scientific Interest) criteria used in other studies (Table 1), but all five ANSI criteria were used. Forty-one Significant Natural Areas and 32 Significant Sites were identified in the region and are described in Volume One of the report. Volume Two is essentially an annotated checklist that provides supporting information for the selections made.

Table 1

Criteria used to evaluate candidate natural areas.

Key No.	Criterion	Explanation
1	Significant species	Species which are rare, threatened or endangered nationally, provincially or locally.
2	Significant communities	Associations of species of plants and/or animals which are poorly represented on a national, provincial or local level.
3	Significant Landforms and soils	Landforms and soils which are unique or are poorly represented on a national, provincial or regional basis. Landforms which have a high potential for supporting important biotic features are included.
4	Absence of disturbance	The site remains close to its original state due to lack of human disturbance. The site is not adjacent to areas which might compromise its quality.
5	Diversity	A high degree of natural diversity of biotic and abiotic features is found in close proximity on the site. This criterion may be applied at the species or community level.
6	Linkage	Areas are connected to other important natural areas through woodlots or river valleys which may, in turn, facilitate gene flow.
7	'Representativeness'	The area is locally important and contains a good representation of the expected flora, fauna, communities, soils and landforms of the region.
8	Size	The area is large enough so that its significant biotic features can maintain themselves indefinitely and are less prone to disturbance or extinction.
9	Migratory stop-over	The area is a significant stop-over for large numbers of wildlife on migration.

The 41 Significant Natural Areas identified are mapped in Figure 1, and the selection criteria met by each site are given in Table 2. The results of the study can benefit the protection of species and important areas in Haldimand-Norfolk and the Carolinian Zone.

Table 2

Selection criteria fulfilled by significant natural areas in Haldimand-Norfolk*

Map No.	Significant natural area	Selection criteria fulfilled‡									Total
		1	2	3	4	5	6	7	8	9	
31	Attercliffe Station Slough Forest	•	•						•		3
13	Backus Woods	•	•		•	•	•	•	•		7
35	Big Creek Bend	•	•				•	•			4
29	Caistor-Canborough Slough Forest	•	•	•				•	•		5
9	Clear Creek Old Growth Forest	•						•			2
3	Courtland Swamp	•	•			•			•		4
10	Cultus Forest	•	•					•	•		4
7	Deer Creek Valley	•	•			•	•	•	•		6
5	Delhi - Big Creek Valley	•	•	•		•	•		•		6
4	Delhi Kettle Bog	•	•					•			3
40	Dunnville East Forest	•	•			•		•	•		5
33	Dunnville Grand River Marshes	•	•				•	•	•	•	6
41	Dunnville Northwest Forest	•	•								2
11	Fairground Forest	•	•						•		3
2	Langton Woods	•	•								2
1	Little Otter Creek Valley	•	•			•	•	•	•		6
16	Long Point	•	•	•	•	•	•	•	•	•	9
18	Lower Young Creek Valley	•					•	•			3
19	Monroe Landon's Woods	•	•					•			3
28	Mount Healy Woods	•	•								2
34	Mohawk Island	•	•	•							3
25	Nanticoke Hemlock Slough Forest	•	•					•			3
26	Nanticoke Heronry Woods	•	•		•						3
32	North Cayuga Slough Forest	•	•			•			•		4
30	Oriskany Sandstone Formation	•	•	•				•	•		5
36	Pine Grove Forest	•	•				•				3
37	Rotala Field	•	•								2
38	Salem-Rockford Rocklands	•	•	•				•			4
27	Sandusk Creek Floodplain Woods	•	•					•			3
14	Spooky Hollow	•	•		•	•	•		•		6
15	St. Williams Forest	•	•			•	•	•	•		6
6	South Walsingham/Big Creek	•	•			•			•		4
20	Trout Creek Valley	•	•		•		•		•		5
12	Turkey Point	•	•	•		•	•	•	•	•	8
24	Varency Woods	•	•								2
22	Vanessa Swamp	•	•			•					3
8	Venison Creek Valley	•	•				•	•	•		5
17	Walsh Carolinian Forest	•	•				•	•	•		5
39	Waterford Ponds	•	•								2
23	Wilsonville Cedar Swamp	•			•			•			3
21	Windham Centre Sandy Swampland	•	•				•		•		4

* Use map no. to locate area on Figure 1.

‡ See key no. on Table 1.

5

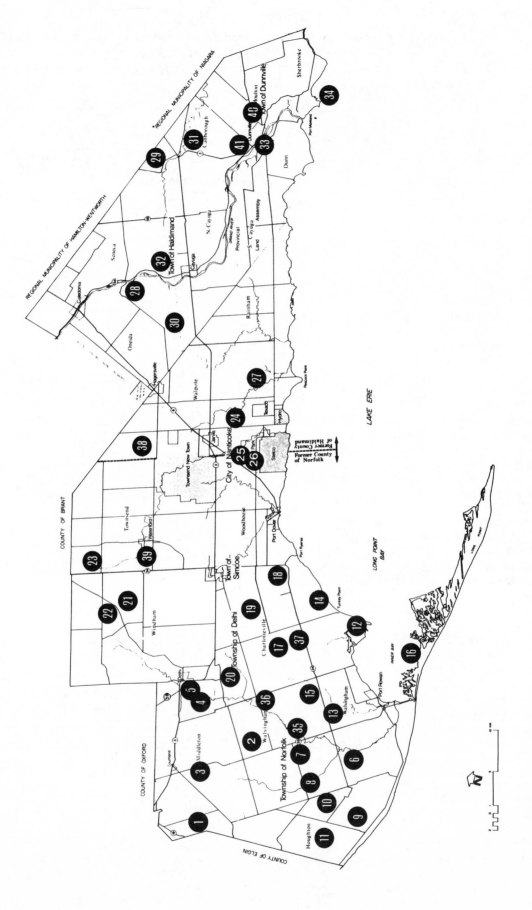

Figure 1: Significant Natural Areas in the Regional Municipality of Haldimand-Norfolk. Areas are keyed to Table 1.

Following Up On Inventory Results

The Committee on the Status of Endangered Wildlife in Canada (COSEWIC) prepares reports on the status of candidate species. These reports are used to determine whether species are rare, threatened, endangered, extirpated, extinct, or not in any of those categories. Twenty-six of the plant species found during the inventory occur on ten or fewer sites in Canada. These plants should be considered for addition to COSEWIC's candidate list. Likewise, results from the inventory suggest that three mammals (Least Shrew, Pine Vole, and Eastern Pipistrelle) and seven birds (Northern Bobwhite, Chuck-will's-widow, Red-bellied Woodpecker, Acadian Flycatcher, Tufted Titmouse, White-eyed Vireo, and Yellow-breasted Chat) should also be added to the candidate list.

While designation as threatened or endangered under COSEWIC may have some moral suasion, the only legal protection offered in Ontario applies to species listed in regulations under the Endangered Species Act. But even here there are problems. Recently, Cucumber Magnolia was listed under the Act. But it turns out that the property descriptions given for all three cucumber sites in Haldimand-Norfolk by the MNR were incorrect, and thus the species had no legal protection. This is especially unfortunate since recently, magnolias have been damaged at two of the three sites. This situation has now been corrected.

Somehow, we must establish procedures for monitoring the population levels of rare, threatened, and endangered species throughout the Carolinian Zone. In Haldimand-Norfolk, these species include but are not limited to about 35 plants, mammals such as Least Shrew and Badger, and birds like King Rail, Acadian Flycatcher, Prothonotary Warbler, Hooded Warbler, Louisiana Waterthrush, and Chuck-will's-widow. Some of these species are now monitored by naturalists, but many are not, and some are difficult to monitor at all. At present, much useful information is privately held, where it is likely to stay. We definitely need a central repository for such information as is now done with herpetological records, and is proposed for rare breeding birds.

The need to develop recovery plans for endangered species is obvious, but the same is true for threatened species, for simple economic reasons. The costs associated with preventing a species from becoming endangered, are likely to be less than those of bringing it back from the edge or extirpation or extinction.

One of the main reasons for undertaking the inventory was to provide the regional government with technical information that would help them refine their selection of natural areas requiring protection. There was little concordance between the original ESA list and the results of the inventory. Not surprisingly, well-known areas like Long Point, Turkey Point, Backus Woods, and Spooky Hollow, were jointly identified. But of the 17 remaining original ESA sites, we accepted only seven as Significant Natural Areas, and a further five as Significant Sites. Five of the original ESAs did not fulfil a single criterion of the inventory study. We proposed an additional 30 Significant Natural Areas, and an additional 27 Significant Sites for the Region's consideration.

The Regional Municipality has indicated that they wish to involve the Norfolk Field Naturalists in designating natural areas during the Official Plan Review. We are pursuing this course of action but it is not without problems. For example, Regional Council passed an amendment to its Official Plan permitting new development next to the Long Point marshes without environmental review. This is contrary to the protective safeguards already in place in the Official Plan. We are thus in a difficult position. On the one hand, we are trying to move the Region forwards, toward extending environmental safeguards to additional areas, many of which are privately owned, while on the other hand, we are objecting to their policies concerning the Region's most outstanding natural area. We have a long way to go, I believe, in building a bureaucratic, political, and public commitment for the protection of natural areas in Haldimand-Norfolk.

One obvious step that needs to be undertaken is the ranking of natural areas in the region as to their relative importance. This process is fraught with problems, but in my opinion is unavoidable. It was not within the mandate of the inventory to provide such rankings, but it is clear that unless this is done, regional planners and politicians may use the large number of significant areas and sites in the region as a reason in itself to maintain the status quo.

Many of the Significant Natural Areas in Haldimand-Norfolk are in public ownership, being contained within National Wildlife Areas, Provincial Parks, Conservation Areas, Authority Forestry Properties, or as Crown Land. But even in cases where Significant Natural Areas are publicly held by organizations with a conservation mandate, there have been, are, and probably will continue to be, conflicts over the management of these sites. It seems very clear that in order to reduce the potential for future conflict, management plans which consider natural values should be prepared for those significant areas now largely or totally in the public sector.

Management plans have been prepared for much of the federal property at Long Point, and for the Long Point Region Conservation Authority's (LPRCA) Backus Woods. Oak parkland, bog areas at Turkey Point Provincial Park, and the wet meadows at Long Point Provincial Park, have been classified as Nature Reserve Zones under the Ministry's Park Management Planning exercise, but these designations will not be official until approved by Ministry personnel. No management plans have been prepared for these Nature Reserve Zones. There are management problems. Does the use of trailbikes in the Turkey Point bog need to curtailed? Do the wet meadows at Long Point need to be burned or mowed periodically? The answers may be clear, the required action obvious, but the best way to deal with these problems, and perhaps the only way when dealing with government agencies, is to prepare a master plan which can then be implemented and monitored.

There are also concerns about some of the properties held by Conservation Authorities. One area identified during the inventory is slated to be flooded if a proposed dam is built. Several LPRCA properties, managed as commercial forests, contain reproducing populations of rare flora and fauna. I do not believe that these forested properties will all be managed as Nature Reserves, nor need they be. Nor do I think that protection of rare species and commercial forestry practices are mutually exclusive. But I do think that sites with species features need to be treated in special ways. It behooves the Conservation Authority as owners of these properties, and the MNR as managers, to develop plans for these areas that give due attention to their special features.

Of the 41 sites identified as Significant Natural Areas by the inventory, only eleven are classified as ANSIs by the MNR. This is somewhat surprising given that both studies used similar selection criteria. There is a need to re-examine, and probably increase, the number of ANSI sites on the Norfolk Sand Plain and on the Haldimand Clay Plain. Obvious candidates for inclusion in the ANSI program are the Manester property at St. Williams and the crown land present near the tip of Long Point. Both properties are highly representative of the site district in which they occur, are diverse, and contain features unprotected in the Provincial Parks system.

The Manester property near St. Williams is critically important. It is being increasingly degraded by off-road vehicle use, and yet it contains Canada's only known population of Frosted Elfin, one of only two Canadian populations of Karner Blue Butterfly, and it is one of only three sites in Canada with Dwarf Chinquapin Oak. The recent addition of the Manester property to Carolinian Canada's list of 36 critical sites permitted a key access to acquisition funds. Fortunately, the site was purchased with Carolinian Canada funds. It is now being managed by the MNR.

Another site identified as critical under the Carolinian Canada program was the Attercliffe Station Slough Forest. Inventory results indicate that better examples of slough forest complex are present in the Caistor-Canborough Slough Forest and the North Cayuga Slough Forest, and serious consideration should be given to altering the critical list to reflect this fact. Landowner contact was undertaken at Attercliffe. This investment of time and money did not prejudice the protection of the best example of slough forest available in the Carolinian Zone. Fortunately, the Carolinian Canada program acted upon these recommendations.

Landowner contact should be undertaken for all Significant Natural Areas in Haldimand-Norfolk, not just for the presently identified critical sites, although this is a good beginning. Our experience has indicated that once private landowners are aware of the natural values of their properties, they are usually willing to protect them. And informed and agreeable landowners are the key to the protection of many natural areas in the region. More landowner contact needs to be done, and naturalists share the responsibility to see that it gets done.

While there are continuing problems in protecting important species and natural areas in Haldimand-Norfolk, there have been some remarkable successes. Bald Eagles and Wild Turkeys have been reintroduced. Long Point has largely been set aside as a National Wildlife Area. The LPRCA has agreed to manage Backus Woods as a de facto nature reserve and is planning to build a Carolinian Conservation Education Centre. The MNR has negotiated an agreement with a private developer that provides good protection for an important ANSI site, and they have prepared a vegetation management plan for Turkey Point Provincial Park which will return pine plantations to native Black Oak parklands. The Ministry is preparing a management plan for the St. Williams Forestry Station which is sensitive to the site's natural features. And through the Ontario Heritage Foundation, the Norfolk Field Naturalists have acquired part of a critical Carolinian site as the club's first nature reserve.

These are all good accomplishments, but we must continue to demand and expect the best of each other. Most importantly we need to keep our head of steam. We must all realize that more work needs to be done at all levels: conducting inventories, monitoring, ranking, selecting, contacting landowners, re-evaluating designations, educating politicians, and purchasing and otherwise protecting sites in the Carolinian Zone, in order for the momentum to be maintained. We must strive to ensure that a diversity of natural areas is maintained in this intensely agricultural and steadily urbanizing part of Canada.

Acknowledgements

The Natural Areas Inventory of Haldimand-Norfolk was sponsored by the Norfolk Field Naturalists. Sincere commendation must be given to the authors of the final report, Mary Gartshore, Don Sutherland, and Jon McCracken, for their dedication to this project. Without their collective expertise and commitment, the inventory would have fallen short of its goals. It is also appropriate to thank the many funders of this study. Thanks to: World Wildlife Fund, Long Point Foundation for Conservation, Ontario Heritage Foundation, Stelco, The Royal Canadian Geographical Society, Hamilton Naturalists' Club, The Regional Municipality of Haldimand-Norfolk, Ontario Ministry of Natural Resources, Long Point Region Conservation Authority, Ontario Ministry of Skills Development, Employment and Immigration Canada, Federation of Ontario Naturalists, and private benefactors. Copies of the 547-page, two-volume inventory, can be ordered by sending a cheque or money order for $44.00 to: Natural Areas Inventory, P.O. Box 424, Waterford, Ontario N0E 1Y0.

Summary Report on the Kent – Elgin Natural Areas Survey

Rose Klinkenberg
Jane M. Bowles*
Michelle Kanter

* RR #3, Thorndale, Ontario N0M 2P0

Abstract. *Kent and Elgin Counties were identified as two counties in southwestern Ontario for which no complete natural areas survey had been done. The aim of this project was to identify natural areas critical for the maintenance of natural diversity in both counties. During early groundwork in 1985, 66 sites in Elgin and 35 sites in Kent were selected for study. Fieldwork, which was the major source of data for the study, was completed in 1986.*

Based on nine natural areas criteria discussed in our final report, the sites were reduced and combined to 43 Significant Natural Areas, including nine Top Sites, in Kent. Top Sites met six or more of the natural areas criteria. An additional six sites in Elgin and five in Kent which did not meet sufficient criteria to be Significant Natural Areas, were designated as Special Areas.

Introduction

Kent and Elgin Counties lie in southwestern Ontario within the Carolinian Zone of Canada, and reflect the astonishing diversity of communities and species which is the essence of this area. The variable physiographic conditions in the two counties range from clay plains in west Kent to sand plains with deeply incised valleys in east Elgin. A spectrum of habitats, including open prairie remnants, lakeshore marshes, large and small ravine systems, a large river system, upland and lowland woods, and shoreline cliffs, is present. In addition, agricultural, industrial, and urban development, are intense and have resulted in fragmented natural areas and have threatened the natural diversity of the region.

This project consisted of a Natural Areas Survey of the two adjoining counties (Figure 1). Kent and Elgin were identified as two of the few remaining counties in southwestern Ontario for which no complete natural areas survey had been done. Previous published and unpublished information on the natural features of the two counties includes Stewart (1982), Stewart and James (1969), Brooman (1954), Bowles *et al.* (in prep.), International Biological Programme Reports, Ontario Ministry of Natural Resources ESA report, Site District Reports, and Life Science Inventories, Lower Thames Valley Conservation Authority Wetland and Conservation Area surveys, forest stand information gathered by Paul Maycock of the University of Toronto, and rare and endangered species status reports. In addition, a number of local experts and naturalists contributed material including recent records of the flora and fauna of both counties. None of the former surveys in either county has comprehensively assessed the natural areas and compiled existing information on the flora, fauna and vegetation.

The aim of the project was to document the full range of communities and habitats present, and to identify those areas critical to the maintenance of natural diversity in both counties. Our recommendations are aimed, as far as possible, at protection of all elements of diversity.

Figure 1: Study Area

Methods

"Natural Areas" represent a very small proportion of the total land surface in Elgin County and even less in Kent (Figure 2). Originally, 66 sites in Elgin County and 35 sites in Kent County were selected for study. Preliminary selection was based on air photo interpretation, topographical map work, and advice from naturalists and biologists familiar with the counties.

Early groundwork was done in 1985 and included land owner contact, air photo mapping, and some reconnoitre. Fieldwork was completed by the end of 1986.

Other than fish the major source of information for this study was the field-work, but data from government files, published material, and records from local experts were also used. A team of botanists, zoologists, and geographers, headed by Jane Bowles (Botany), Michelle Kanter (Zoology), and Marti Mockler (Geography), was responsible for most of the fieldwork which involved site visits for vegetation, faunal, and soil surveys. In addition, plant collecting, small mammal trapping, herpetofauna surveys, birding, and some butterfly work, were covered in the field. All these data were augmented with existing records. Fish information was obtained entirely from extant files.

Criteria

Sites were evaluated based on natural areas selection criteria. The nine criteria were used to analyze the natural areas in the two counties. The criteria are adapted from Eagles and Adindu (1979) and are explained in full in our final reports. They are presented in summary form here:

1. Presence of regionally, provincially, or nationally significant landforms.

2. Linkage with other natural areas.

3. Special ecological consideration such as good buffer, integrity, unity, watershed intactness, etc.

4. Presence of significant plant/animal communities or significant flora, fauna, or habitats.

5. Presence of a high diversity of habitats, communities, or species.

6. Size of site.

7. Regional biogeographical representativeness of site features and habitats.

8. Good site conditions/low disturbance.

9. Site is a natural area or has high natural value for wildlife viewing, unique county location for a significant species, etc.

Results

As a result of our work, and based on the natural areas selection criteria, the preliminary sites were reduced and combined to 43 Significant Natural Areas in Elgin (Figure 3) and 19 Significant Natural Areas in Kent (Figure 4). Significant Natural Areas met at least three of the nine criteria.

In addition, six sites in Elgin and five in Kent were designated as Special Areas. These met only one or two of the criteria, but had outstanding features which deserved particular recognition or protection.

An example of a Special Area is Hawk Cliff on the north shore of Lake Erie in Elgin County. This does not meet enough of the criteria to rank as a Significant Natural Area, but has a special importance for wildlife study in Ontario, and the rest of North America as a raptor migration viewing point.

The two reports, one for each county, contain a summary for each site which includes an overview of site conditions, physical features (landforms, hydrology, and soils), a detailed description of the vegetation and animal communities represented, and annotated lists of significant flora and fauna. General introductions to the natural features of each county are given, and annotated checklists of birds, mammals, herpetofauna, butterflies, and significant plants of the county, are included.

In each county a number of "Top Sites" which meet at least six of the criteria have emerged. These include protected sites, such as Provincial Parks, recognized critical natural areas such as Areas of Natural and Scientific Interest (ANSIs) and Conservation Areas, one site targeted for protection as a Carolinian Canada site, and a number of completely unprotected sites.

There are 15 Top Sites in Elgin including one Provincial Park, three ANSIs, one Conservation Area and ANSI, one Carolinian Canada site, one Wildlife Management Area, and eight unprotected sites. These sites are listed in Table 1.

Eight Top Sites in Kent (Table 2) include two Provincial Parks, two ANSIs, one Wildlife Management Area and ANSI, and three unprotected sites.

Some of our Top Sites in both counties are complexes of fragmented woodlots rather than single continuous sites. This fragmentation made assessment more complicated than the evaluation of single large areas. However, we feel that the complexes provide community diversity and important wildlife habitats which are not represented by single sites in either county. In terms of the present landscape, fragments and islands are more typical of both counties than large continuous nat-

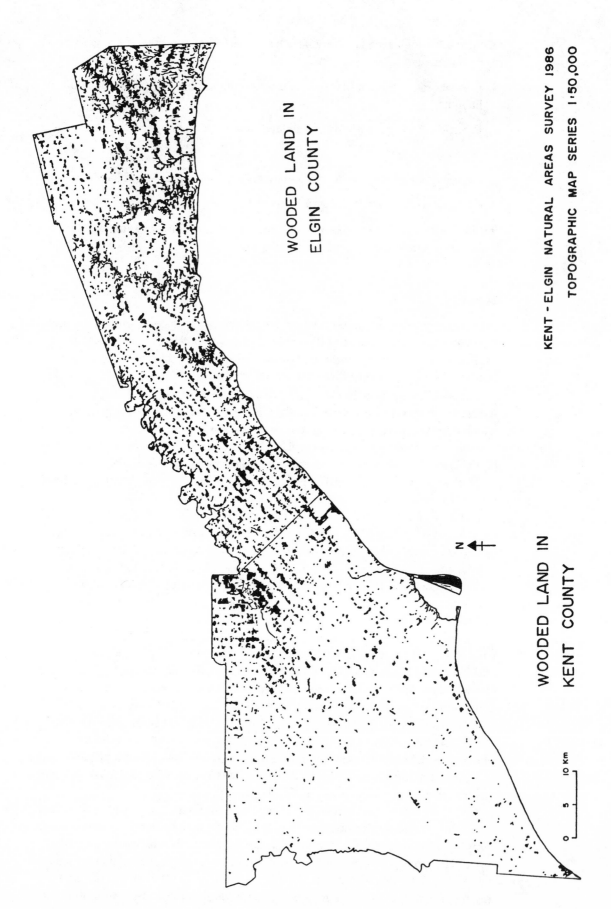

WOODED LAND IN
ELGIN COUNTY

KENT - ELGIN NATURAL AREAS SURVEY 1986

TOPOGRAPHIC MAP SERIES 1:50,000

WOODED LAND IN
KENT COUNTY

N

0   5   10 Km

Figure 2

14

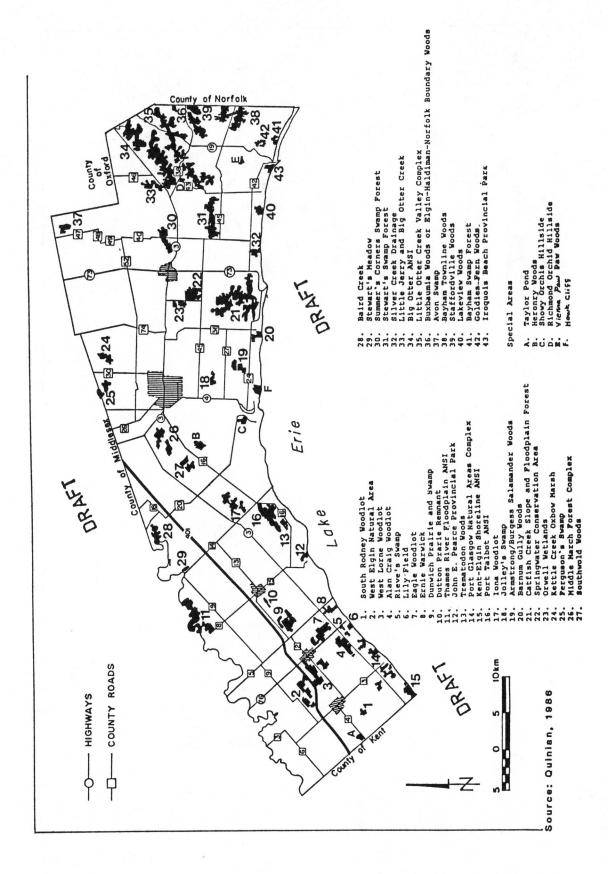

Source: Quinlan, 1986

1. South Rodney Woodlot
2. West Elgin Natural Area
3. West Lorne Woodlot
4. Alan Craig Woodlot
5. Rieve's Swamp
6. Lily Field
7. Eagle Woodlot
8. Ernie Warwick
9. Dunwich Prairie and Swamp
10. Dutton Prairie Remnant
11. Thames River Floodplain ANSI
12. John E. Pearce Provincial Park
13. Trematodon Woods
14. Port Glasgow Natural Areas Complex
15. Kent-Elgin Shoreline ANSI
16. Port Talbot ANSI
17. Iona Woodlot
18. Jolley's Swamp
19. Armstrong/Burgess Salamander Woods
20. Barnum Gully Woods
21. Catfish Creek Slope and Floodplain Forest
22. Springwater Conservation Area
23. Orwell Wetlands
24. Kettle Creek Oxbow Marsh
25. Ferguson's Swamp
26. Middle March Forest Complex
27. Southwold Woods

28. Baird Creek
29. Stewart's Meadow
30. Summer's Corners Swamp Forest
31. Stewart's Swamp Forest
32. Silver Creek Drainage
33. Little Jerry and Big Otter Creek
34. Big Otter ANSI
35. Little Otter Creek Valley Complex
36. Buxbaumia Woods or Elgin-Haldiman-Norfolk Boundary Woods
37. Avon Swamp
38. Bayham Townline Woods
39. Staffordville Woods
40. Lakeview Woods
41. Bayham Swamp Forest
42. Goldies-Fern Woods
43. Iroquois Beach Provincial Park

Special Areas

A. Taylor Pond
B. Heronry Woods
C. Showy Orchis Hillside
D. Richmond Orchid Hillside
E. Vienna Paw Paw Woods
F. Hawk Cliff

Figure 3 Biologically Significant Natural Areas in Elgin County

15

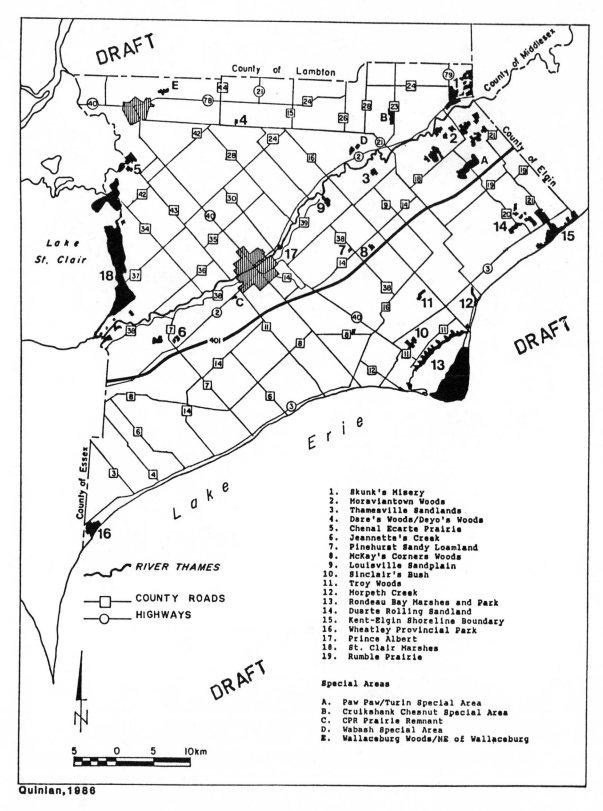

Figure 4 Biologically Significant Natural Areas in Kent County

Within the figure:

DRAFT

County of Lambton

County of Middlesex

County of Elgin

Lake St. Clair

Lake Erie

County of Essex

DRAFT

DRAFT

RIVER THAMES

☐— COUNTY ROADS

◯— HIGHWAYS

N

5   0   5   10km

Quinlan, 1986

1. Skunk's Misery
2. Moraviantown Woods
3. Thamesville Sandlands
4. Dare's Woods/Deyo's Woods
5. Chenal Ecarte Prairie
6. Jeannette's Creek
7. Pinehurst Sandy Loamland
8. McKay's Corners Woods
9. Louisville Sandplain
10. Sinclair's Bush
11. Troy Woods
12. Morpeth Creek
13. Rondeau Bay Marshes and Park
14. Duarte Rolling Sandland
15. Kent-Elgin Shoreline Boundary
16. Wheatley Provincial Park
17. Prince Albert
18. St. Clair Marshes
19. Rumble Prairie

Special Areas

A. Paw Paw/Turin Special Area
B. Cruikshank Chesnut Special Area
C. CPR Prairie Remnant
D. Wabash Special Area
E. Wallaceburg Woods/NE of Wallaceburg

ural areas. In addition, some of the typical plant community types (eg. prairie) in Kent and Elgin may require only small areas to be biologically self-perpetuating (Reznicek, pers. comm.).

Table 1

Preliminary List of Top Sites for Elgin County

Site Name	UTM*	Status
Port Burwell Provincial Park	150215	Provincial Park
Big Otter Creek	195415	ANSI
Thames River Floodplain	540320	ANSI
Talbot Creek	695220	ANSI
Springwater Forest	980320	Conservation Area and ANSI
Catfish Creek Slope and Floodplain	985258	Carolinian Canada Site
Steward Swamp Forest (Calton Swamp)	085296	Unprotected/Wildlife Management Area
Little Otter Creek Valley Complex	190350	Unprotected
Dunwich Prairie and Swamp	545195	Unprotected
Little Jerry and Big Otter Creeks Valley Complex	165365 and 125355	Unprotected
Bayham Townline Woods	200265 and 220280	Unprotected
Port Glasgow Natural Area Complex	491062	Unprotected
Middle March Forest Complex	780357	Unprotected
Alan Craig Woodlot	520120	Unprotected
West Lorne Woodlot	485165	Unprotected

* UTMs are approximate and will be centred in the final report.

Table 2

Preliminary List of Top Sites in Kent County

Site Name	UTM*	Status
Rondeau Bay Marshes and Provincial Park	270820	Unprotected/ Provincial Park
Wheatley Provincial Park	805605	Provincial Park
Kent-Elgin Shoreline	420000	ANSI
Sinclair's Bush	229855	ANSI/Carolinian Canada Site
St. Clair Marshes	845915	ANSI/Wildlife Management Area
Skunk's Misery	305195	Unprotected in Kent
Moraviantown Woods	275130	Indian Reserve/ Unprotected
Deyo's Wood	999149	Unprotected

* UTMs are approximate and will be centred in the final report.

Preliminary Conservation Recommendations

Although our reports are not yet finalized, we have a number of preliminary recommendations which are directed to sites in both counties. These are:

1. **That the 43 Significant Natural Areas in Elgin County, and the 19 in Kent, be incorporated directly into County and Township Official Plans as soon as possible.** In addition, they should be added to, or updated in, the MNR District Landuse Guidelines. Conservation Authorities with jurisdiction over sites should flag the areas in their watershed plans.

2. **That Skunk's Misery ANSI be extended into Lambton and Kent Counties** (Figure 5). This would incidentally extend the site into two new MNR Districts (Wingham and Chatham). The expanded, presently unprotected part of the Skunk's Misery Complex should at least be recognised as a Carolinian Canada site and preferably as part of the ANSI.

   Effective protection for Skunk's Misery is urgent to control the effects of forest management practices, logging, draining, and spraying in the area; activities which negatively affect the natural diversity, site evolution, and species composition.

   Selective experimental logging is scheduled to take place in part of the ANSI during the winter of 1988-1989. Active logging and some clearcutting was occurring in the expanded portions of the site during the 1986 field season.

   We recommend an advisory committee be set up consisting of both ecological experts and planners. This committee should work with a research committee to help direct the use and conservation of this site. Guidelines for research in top Carolinian Canada sites and ANSIs are clearly needed. All

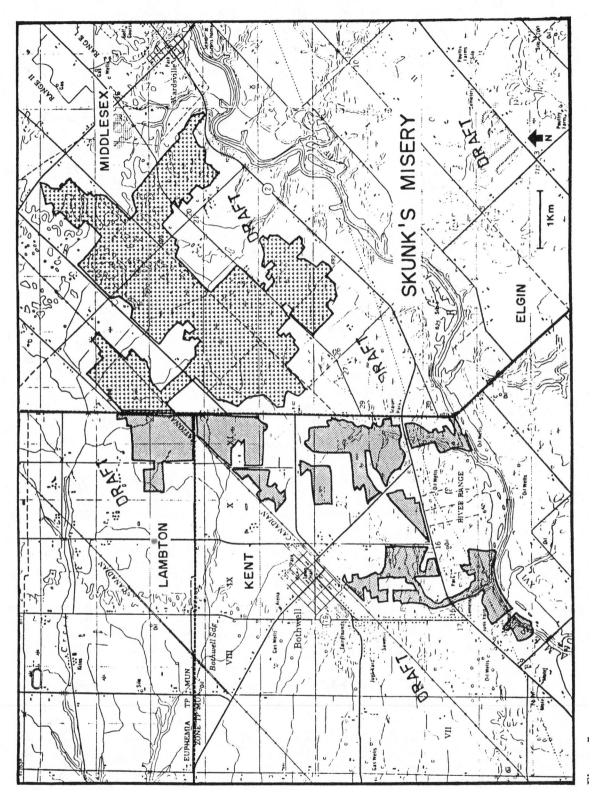

Figure 5

19

research proposals for such sites should be reviewed by a technical committee. It is essential that any experimentation in the site be holistic in approach, looking at the effects of potential activities on all ecological components. For example, butterfly populations are often ignored in planning and research.

Skunk's Misery is of both Provincial and National importance. We will be submitting a special write-up on this site to Carolinian Canada and including our recommendations.

3. **That Deyo's Wood, in Kent County, be adopted as a Carolinian Canada Site** (Figure 6). This site (like most of the wooded areas in Kent) is very small, but it appears to be a natural areas "hot spot". A number of rare plants and birds have been found here. Based on the coverage so far there is a good potential for further finds. It is probably a unique area, and is certainly the best woodlot in west Kent.

4. **That Little Otter Creek Valley Complex should be adopted as a Carolinian Canada Site** (Figure 7). This complex ranks with the Catfish Creek Slope and Floodplain Carolinian Canada Site, which is one of the best Elgin sites. There is a good diversity of habitats and a number of rare plants and birds. This area should at least be considered as an alternate site to Catfish Creek.

5. **That Stewart's Swamp Forest should be given at least ANSI status** (Figure 8). We have named this area in honour of Bill Stewart, in recognition of his outstanding work on the natural history of Elgin County.

The site consists of three contiguous sections. At present, the only protected part of the site is the eastern portion which is a Wildlife Management Area known as Calton Swamp. To the west are two more sections of equivalent size which make up one of the largest tracts of non-ravine woodland in the county. The whole site merits protection, preferably as an ANSI, both as representative habitat and for the number of significant species it supports.

6. **That unexplored sites in both counties should be examined.** We recommend that some funding, or focus of Government staff time, should be directed towards examining remaining unknown sites in both Elgin and Kent Counties. These sites were identified as potential Significant NAtural Areas late in the field season. Limited time did not permit a thorough examination of them.

Of particular interest is a complex of sizable woodlots south of Moraviantown in Kent and some areas in Elgin south of the Thames River. The sites in question are highlighted in our report. They have been given a preliminary write-up based on the material available from brief visits.

7. **That consideration be given to rare species protection in Kent and Elgin Counties.** This recommendation concerns rare species in Kent and Elgin County which have few or no protected populations elsewhere in Ontario or Canada. Populations of these species should be identified. In particular, areas of concentration of rare species should be addressed. Locations of some such populations may require protection as ANSIs, or at the very least, as ESAs in County and Township Official Plans. Rare species are often indicators of rare or unusual habitats which should perhaps also be scheduled for protection. By nature, this seems to be material for an MNR project.

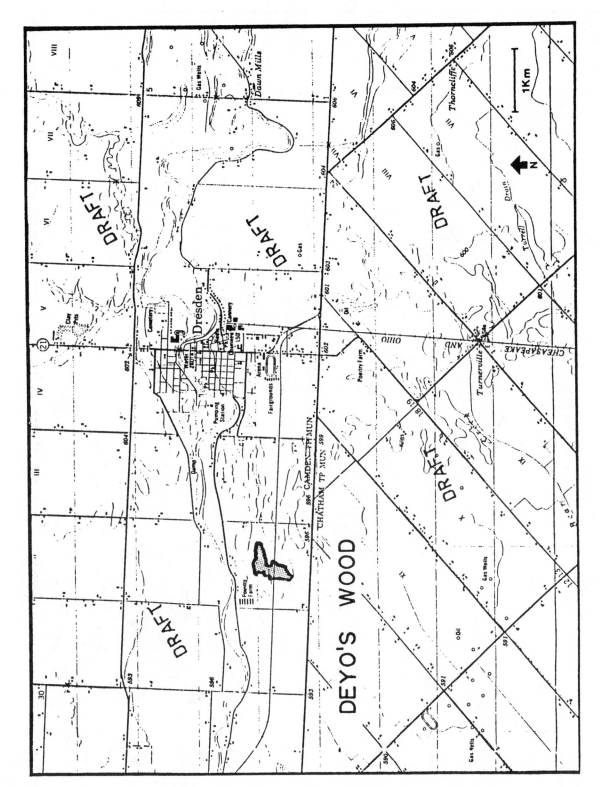

Figure 6

21

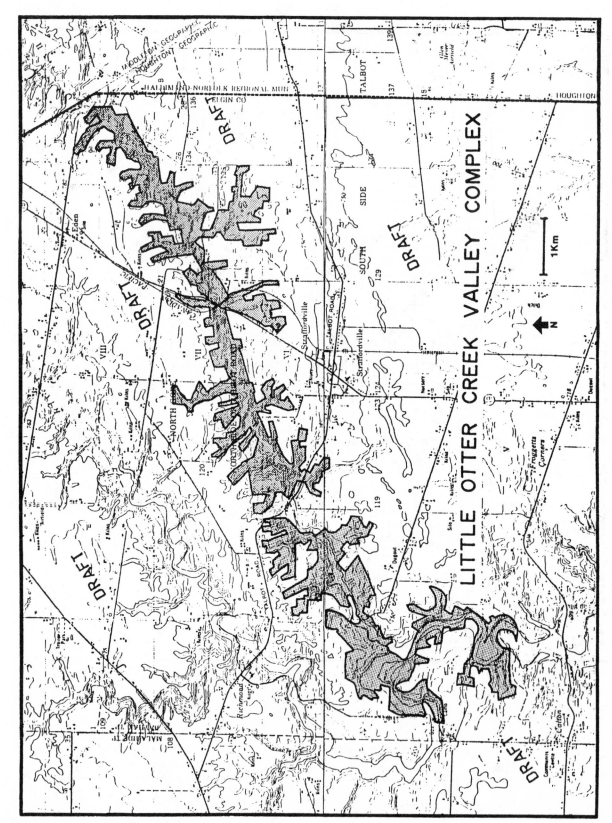

LITTLE OTTER CREEK VALLEY COMPLEX

Figure 7

22

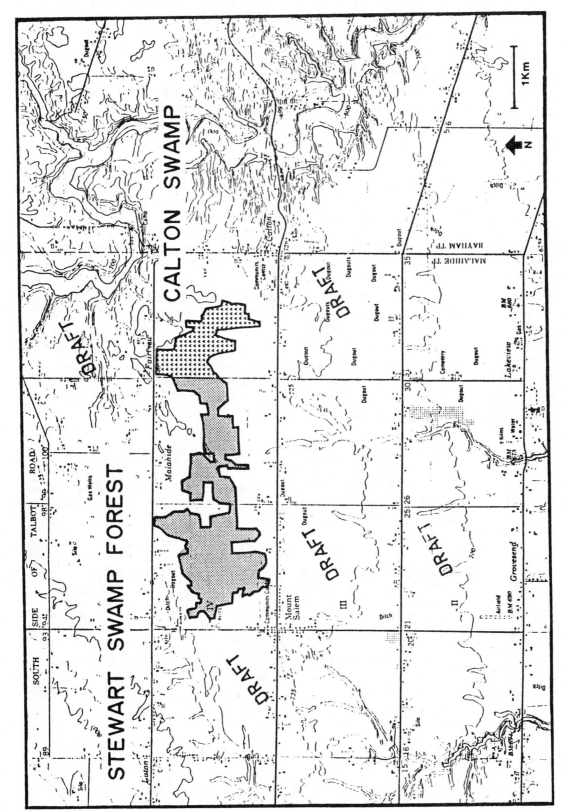

Figure 8

23

Protection for rare species in the Carolinian Zone in Canada is especially important. If they cannot be protected under a coordinated project like Carolinian Canada, they have little chance of protection elsewhere.

8. **That a Carolinian Canada-led committee should be established to address directly the scarcity of some faunal groups in the two counties.** Other researchers have identified low population levels in both counties of some faunal groups such as flying squirrels and bats. Immediate attention must be paid to the activities, such as forest management practices and natural areas reduction, which have led to these losses. Therefore, we recommend that the committee should consider:

    i) the changes in forest management practices which are needed to restore key species. In particular, increased numbers of mature and "over-mature" den trees are needed throughout the two counties.

    ii) the current tree-cutting by-laws for each county. The minimum native woodlot coverage needed to sustain existing faunal populations, and to provide a base for restoring declining or missing faunal groups, should be recognised in each county. Limits to further clearance of woodlots should be established and set as part of the by-laws. Township and County Official Plans should directly regulate further woodlot clearing and encourage re-establishment of wooded areas in both counties via natural succession. These regulations need to be directly aimed at established minimum requirements for species maintenance. Input from other researchers will be needed in order to establish minimum woodlot availability for the maintenance of populations of the various species concerned.

9. **That a Carolinian Canada-led committee address roadside spraying and railway verge maintenance activities which may have serious impacts on floral and faunal populations in the two counties.** Particular attention should be paid to roadside and railway edge prairie pockets and butterfly populations throughout both counties.

10. **That special measures by taken to protect the best prairie sites in both counties.** Obviously absent from the Top Sites for Kent is representation of prairie habitats. Most of the prairie sites in both counties are small disturbed remnants at road junctions, along railway tracks, and in small parcels of land which have not been cultivated. Prairies are certainly representative of native habitats in certain areas of Kent and Elgin. Often they contain a number of unusual or significant species. However, as Significant Natural AReas, they often do not satisfy any additional criteria. We recommend that the Carolinian Canada Committee should address this issue as soon as possible. The recommendation ties in with recommendation #9 above.

Discussion

In addition to our recommendations there are some other points which we feel should be addressed in the context of protection of habitat in these two counties.

There is a characteristic and strong gradient from west to east across the two counties. This gradient reflects topography and land use. Sites on the clay plains in west Kent tend to be small, isolated, uniform, and species poor. The best woodlot, Deyo's Wood, is only a few hectares in area. Working eastward onto the sand plains of east Kent and into Elgin, the natural areas become larger, more diverse in habitat, and support a larger number of plant and animal species. Among our richest and most diverse sites are the incised valleys and wooded ravines of east Elgin which fall on "waste" land.

The ecological principles which govern the criteria for selecting significant sites suggest that protection measures should concentrate on the larger, richer, more diverse sites in the east. On the other hand, land use patterns in Kent indicate that it is the sites here which are imminently threatened. A small woodlot in Kent may, in fact, be more important from the point of view of the natural diversity of the county and region than a relatively unthreatened, much larger ravine system, in east Elgin.

Several sites, or portions of sites in Kent County were clearcut or lost to agriculture during the survey. These included parts of Skunk's Misery and Moraviantown Complexes, a prairie site on Prince Albert Sideroad Prairie in Chatham, a sandplain woodlot south of Thamesville, and Thamesville Moor.

Conclusions

Natural areas in Kent and Elgin Counties, in keeping with the rest of the Carolinian Zone, support a high diversity of species, communities, and habitats. Because of intense agricultural, urban, and industrial pressures in the region, this natural diversity, and therefore the strength of our wildlife populations, is threatened. .

Our assessment of the remaining natural areas in both counties has resulted in a list of the Significant Natural Areas representing the **minimum** number of areas which are **critical** for the maintenance of *status quo*. These sites need to be highlighted in County and Township Official Plans, MNR District Land Use Guidelines, and Conservation Authority Watershed Plans.

In spite of major natural area losses in Kent and Elgin, few species so far have actually been extirpated. However some species such as the Southern Flying Squirrel are in jeopardy in both counties because of specific habitat loss. Special attention must be paid now to both plant and animal species which have been lost in the region or which are in serious decline. Changes in current forest management and agricultural practices are necessary to restore these species and to maintain remaining populations.

Protected populations of all rare species should be established throughout the Carolinian Zone, and areas of concentration of such species should be highlighted and protected as special habitats.

Based on our survey, a number of sites have been proposed as new Carolinian Canada Sites or ANSIs. Gaps in the coverage still exist however. These gaps need to be addressed. Features of the most outstanding sites should be added to the matrix of habitat representation for each county if they represent previously omitted habitat coverage.

We appear to be at a stage in both counties where major species and habitat losses are imminent. Because of the critical state of natural areas in Kent and Elgin and the national significance of natural features they support, Carolinian Canada-led committees should be set up to address all environmental planning issues.

All planning agencies in the two counties should immediately reconsider current maintenance activities. Where possible, detrimental activities should be altered to minimize impact on the floral and faunal groups.

Acknowledgements

Funds for the project were obtained from several sources and sponsors (Figure 9). A rather large number of people have been directly involved with the project, including volunteers, Section 38 workers, and experts under special contract (Figure 10). William and Eileene Stewart deserve special acknowledgement. Bill Stewart formulated the initial list of potentially significant sites in Elgin County and surveyed several sites. Both he and Eileene are responsible for, and provided, many of the significant species data summarised in the Elgin County report.

Note: Please refer to our final reports for Kent and Elgin to obtain full recommendations and conclusions.

References

Bowles, J.M., R. Klinkenberg, B. Klinkenberg *et al*. In prep. *The Plants of Kent County.*

Brooman, R.C. 1954. *The Birds of Elgin County, Ontario.*

Stewart, W.G. and L.E. James. 1969. *A Guide to the Flora of Elgin County, Ontario.* Catfish Creek Conservation Authority. 118 pp.

Stewart, W.G. 1982. *Mammals of Elgin County, Ontario.* The St. Thomas Field Naturalist Club, St. Thomas, Ontario. 125 pp.

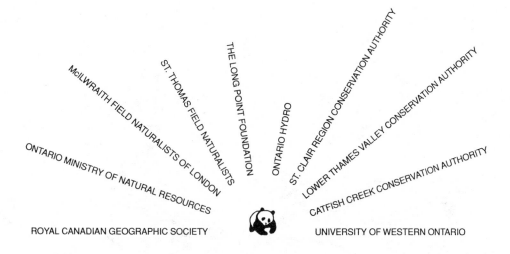

ST. CLAIR REGION CONSERVATION AUTHORITY

LOWER THAMES VALLEY CONSERVATION AUTHORITY

THE LONG POINT FOUNDATION

ST. THOMAS FIELD NATURALISTS OF LONDON

McILWRAITH FIELD NATURALISTS

ONTARIO HYDRO

CATFISH CREEK CONSERVATION AUTHORITY

ONTARIO MINISTRY OF NATURAL RESOURCES

ROYAL CANADIAN GEOGRAPHIC SOCIETY

UNIVERSITY OF WESTERN ONTARIO

World Wildlife Fund

Ontario Heritage Foundation
Federal Employment Development Branch

Thank you to the Staff and Members of these organizations for their time and support.

Figure 9 Project Sponsors

Project Co-ordinator
Rose Klinkenberg

Botany Co-ordinator	**Physical Geography Co-ordinator**	**Assistant Project and Zoology Co-ordinator**
Jane Bowles	Marti Mockler	Michelle Kanter

Assistants
Bill Lamond   Wendy Laberee   John Parish   Cathy Quinlan
Mike Matheson   Lisa Needham   Robert Bergman   David Stevenson

Typist
Karen Rip

Assistant Co-ordinator – Fund Raising and Mapwork
Yvette Wells

Volunteers
Bill Stewart

		Contracts
Gary Allen	Janet Lambert	Al Wormington (birds)
Ross Brown	Paul Pratt	Ian MacDonald (botany)
Bill Crins	Susan Reznicek	Dave McLeod
Brian Klinkenberg	Tony Reznicek	
Bob Moos	Winnie Wake	
Mike Oldham	Allen Woodliffe	

Figure 10 Kent-Elgin Natural Areas Survey Personnel

An unusual inhabitant of rich floodplain
woods, the Green Dragon is a close
relative of the Jack-in-the-Pulpit.
Artist – Zile Zichmanis.

Reconnaissance Biological Inventory of Sassafras Woods, Regional Municipality of Halton, Ontario

Katherine M. Lindsay   88 Levendale Rd.
Richmond Hill, Ontario L4C 4H2

Abstract. *Sassafras Woods represents southern deciduous forests associated with the south-facing, lower Queenston shale slopes of the Niagara Escarpment. This remnant natural area of deep, forested ravines and adjoining wooded uplands was evaluated using the Ontario ecological framework and criteria for the evaluation of Areas of Natural and Scientific Interest (ANSIs), and was considered provincially significant.*

Introduction

Sassafras Woods is a 125 ha natural area lying south of the Niagara Escarpment cliffs, north of Highway 403 and east of Waterdown Road, in the municipality of Burlington, Halton Region. Deciduous and mixed forests line four ravine systems along tributaries of Falcon and Grindstone Creeks, ravines which are cut deeply into the broad zone of Queenston Shale slopes below the escarpment cliffs. The vegetation has many southern species typical of the Carolinian Life Zone.

Sassafras Woods was identified in 1978 as an Environmentally Sensitive Area in the Regional Municipality of Halton (Regional Municipality of Halton 1978). It is also one of the 36 natural areas selected in the multi-agency study of "Critical Unprotected Natural Areas in the Carolinian Life Zone of Canada" (Identification Subcommittee of Carolinian Canada 1985). The need for further inventory and analysis of Sassafras Woods was recommended in that study.

This interim report on Sassafras Woods assembles biological information from background research and fieldwork carried out in the fall of 1986, into the life science inventory check-sheet format used by the Ontario Ministry of Natural Resources. It also provided boundary mapping of the proposed Area of Natural and Scientific Interest (ANSI) at 1:10,000 scale for the Ministry of Natural Resources.

The terms of reference for the rest of this project called for further work at Sassafras Woods and an assessment of natural areas in Site District 7-3, to be continued in 1987, if funding permitted. Additional fieldwork at Sassafras Woods was proposed for the spring and summer seasons, to allow further documentation of biological features and mapping of vegetation, sensitivity, and significant features at 1:10,000 scale. Another part of this project proposed for 1987, was the assessment of natural areas in the part of Site District 7-3 lying east of the Niagara Escarpment and extending from Hamilton to Georgetown. Site District 7-3, the Grimsby Site District, takes in an area between the Niagara river and the Georgetown vicinity and includes "The Niagara Escarpment with lower slopes and adjacent clay plain" (Hills 1959; 127). Much of this site district was covered during a study of significant natural areas along the Niagara Escarpment (Cuddy *et al.* 1976). The remaining portion of Site District 7-3 is the only area in the Carolinian Forest Region of southern Ontario (Site Region 7) which has not yet been evaluated in terms of provincially significant ANSIs. It is a priority for inventory because of the current conservation focus on Carolinian Canada.

Bedrock and Surficial Geology

Sassafras Woods is underlain by shales of the Queenston Formation, Ordovician Period (Guillet 1967; Karrow 1963, 1983). Bedrock is exposed along the four stream valleys which dissect the area. Surficial deposits are mapped as Halton Till, a clay or silt till with a reddish-brown colour.

Physiography

Sassafras Woods falls within the Niagara Escarpment physiographic region defined and described by Chapman and Putnam (1973; 177) as, "In this region, a rather broad belt of red shales is exposed and the long lower slopes of the escarpment are highly eroded." Within the natural area, elevations slope down 75 m, from 190 m near the escarpment cliffs at the north end of the site, to 115 m near Highway 403. Four valley systems, holding tributaries of Falcon and Grindstone Creeks, rise along the escarpment cliffs and cut across the natural area in a southeasterly direction. These ravines are deepest in the north part of the site (to 30 m deep) and less so in the south (ca. 10 m in depth). As a result, the topography of the natural area consists of plateaus, separated by a series of four steep-sided ravines.

Soils

The soils of the upland plateaus within the natural area are classed as Oneida loam by Gillespie et al. (1971). These soils are developed on fine-textured glacial till composed of ice-ground materials from the underlying Queenston Shale bedrock. The ravines crossing the site have cut through the soil and glacial deposits into Queenston Shale bedrock.

Condition

The forests growing on the ravine slopes and bottomlands of Sassafras Woods are relatively mature and undisturbed in most sections. In contrast, the woodlands of upland sites are variable in age, mainly young or intermediate-aged, with scattered larger trees. There are a few mature stands on the plateaus. Several utility corridors dissect the site – hydro, telephone, and gas pipeline. Trailbike and pedestrian trails cross parts of it and are causing erosion problems in some locations. The noise from Highway 403 and North Service Road penetrates the southern part of the natural area.

The Burlington Landfill Site lies along the east side of Sassafras Woods, adjacent to Falcon Creek. Some garbage collects along the slopes of the creek valley and there is the possibility of leachate from the landfill entering the valley and stream. Noise from this landfill operation carries into the eastern part of the natural area. One section of this valley, the west-facing slope adjacent to the southern part of the Burlington Landfill Site, has been excluded from the ANSI because it is cleared land, and is badly eroded and gullied.

NAME	MAP NAME	MAP NUMBER	UTM REF.
Sassafras Woods	Hamilton-Burlington	30M/5	920965

COUNTY, DISTRICT or REGIONAL MUNICIPALITY	LAT.	LONG.	ALT. MIN. MAX.
Halton Regional Municipality	43° 19´N	79° 48´W	ca. 115m – 190m

LOCALITY
2 km southeast of Waterdown

TOWNSHIP   LOTS   CONCESSIONS

Burlington City Municipality

1:50,000 NTS MAP SHOWING AREA BOUNDARIES   1:250,000

AREA
ca. 310 **acres**   ca. 125 **ha**

OWNERSHIP
Private

ADMINISTRATION
Private

FOREST REGION AND DISTRICT	SITE REGION AND DISTRICT
D-1	7-3

MNR REGION AND DISTRICT	CONSERVATION AUTHORITY
Central-Cambridge	Hamilton Region

AERIAL PHOTOGRAPHS   BASE MAP:

YEAR	ROLL	FLIGHT LINE	NUMBERS
1978	53	4322	450,451
1978	29	4323	30,31

PHYSICAL AND BIOLOGICAL FEATURES

At Sassafras Woods, deciduous and mixed forest follow four deep, impressive, raving systems, cut into the lower Queenston shale slopes of the Niagara Escarpment southeast of Waterdown. Deciduous woods cover the plateaus between these ravines. The vegetation of Sassafras Woods has a number of Carolinian or southern elements such as: rue-anemone (Anemonella thalictroides), poke milkweed (Asclepias exaltata), sweet chestnut (Castanea dentata), horsebalm (Collinsonia canadensis), blue beech (Carpinus caroliniana), yellow mandarin (Disporum lanuginosum), witch-hazel (Hamamelis virginiana), spice bush (Lindera benzoin), whorled milkwort (Polygala verticillata), fragrant sumac (Rhus aromatica), sassafras (Sassafras albidum), American columbo (Frasera caroliniensis), and sand violet (Viola fimbriatula).

The forests of the ravine slopes and bottomlands are relatively mature and undisturbed in most sections. Associations of sugar maple with red oak, white oak, white pine and beech are found on the slopes. A variety of forest stands cover the valley bottomlands, for example, sugar maple–red maple–basswood–white ash–dead elm–shagbark hickory; sugar maple–shagbark hickory–white ash–white oak; sugar maple–white ash–beech. The uplands between the ravines support dry mesic woods of red oak and sugar maple with white oak, shagbark hickory, ironwood and scattered white pine; mesic sugar maple woodland with occasional shagbark hickory, white ash and white oak, and a variety of other associations. Crins (1984) described Sassafras Woods as "... the best example of southern deciduous woods (Carolinian Forest) in Halton Regional Municipality."

DATA SHEETS ATTACHED

PHYSICAL DESCRIPTION	X	SUMMARY SPECIES LISTS	
VEGETATION SUMMARY		PHYSICAL FEATURES MAP	
EVALUATION SHEET	X	VEGETATION MAP	
COMMUNITY DESCRS.		BIBLIOGRAPHY	X
COMMUNITY COMP. LISTS		PHOTOGRAPHS	

MAJOR INFORMATION SOURCES

Crins,1978-1985,1984,1986; Kaiser,1984; Lindsay,16,17,23 Sept 1986,Field notes;Maycock, 1984; Regional Muncipality of Halton,1978; Sutherland,1979; Tant et al,1977.

EVALUATION AND PRIORITIES

A good example of southern deciduous forest associated with four ravines and adjoining upland sites. Proposed as a provincially significant Area of Natural and Scientific Interest.

DATE COMPILED	COMPILER
30 June 1987	K.M. Lindsay

Ontario Ministry of Natural Resources, Parks and Recreational Areas Programme, Queen's Park, Toronto, Ontario M7A 1W3

Preliminary Evaluation of the Natural Area

In southern Ontario, provincially significant ANSIs have been evaluated within the ecological framework of the site regions and districts of southern Ontario (Hills 1959). The following criteria were used for the evaluation of natural areas: representation, diversity, condition, ecological considerations, and special features (Lindsay 1984). Sassafras Woods falls within a portion of Site District 7-3 that has not yet been examined in terms of provincially significant ANSIs . Site District 7-3, the Grimsby Site District, takes in an area between the Niagara River and Georgetown vicinity and includes "The Niagara Escarpment with lower slopes and adjacent clay plain" (Hills 1959; 127).

Sassafras Woods was considered provincially significant by this study because it represents a diversity of vegetation types and sites with different exposures and moisture regimes, associated with the lower Queenston Shale slopes of the Niagara Escarpment. Much of the natural area remains in good condition due to its pronounced ravine topography. It is a sizeable natural area and is linked to the north with forests along the Niagara Escarpment cliffs. The effects of trail use and adjacent landuse, for example, the Burlington Landfill Site, should be monitored.

The vegetation of Sassafras Woods is characterized by a number of species of Carolinian affinity. As well, the area supports ten plant species considered rare in the Regional Municipality of Halton (Crins 1986), including two considered rare in Ontario (Gillett and Keddy 1983; Ambrose 1987). These species are listed in Table 1. Sassafras Woods was one of the 36 natural areas selected in the multi-agency study of "Critical Unprotected Natural Areas in the Carolinian Life Zone of Canada" (Identification Subcommittee of Carolinian Canada 1985).

Table 1

Regionally and Provincially Rare Plants Reported from Sassafras Woods

This list is compiled from plant species reported by Crins (1984), Gould (1986), Maycock (1984), and Sutherland (1979). The status of plant species in the region is based on Crins (1986), who considered a species to be regionally rare if it was found at one to five stations in the Regional Municipality of Halton.

Common Name	Latin
Rue Anemone	*Anemonella thalictroides*
Sweet Chestnut	*Castanea dentata**
Tick-trefoil	*Desmodium cuspidatum*
Tick-trefoil	*Desmodium paniculatum*
American Columbo	*Frasera caroliniensis+*
Bush-clover	*Lespedeza capitata*
Milkwort	*Polygala verticillata*
Fragrant Sumac	*Rhus aromatica*
Sassafras	*Sassafras albidum*
Sand Violet	*Viola fimbriatula*

* A provincially rare species (Ambrose 1987).
+ A provincially rare species (Gillett and Keddy 1983).

* *Carya ovalis* and *Ptelea trifoliata,* two species reported as significant in The Halton Region Environmentally Sensitive Areas Study (Regional Municipality of Halton, 1978), were excluded from this list because they require confirmation. *Sphenopholis nitida,* reported as occurring at Sassafras in the Critical Unprotected Natural Areas in the Carolinian Life Zone of Canada (Identification Subcommittee of Carolinian Canada 1985) is in error. It occurs to the west at the Royal Botanical Gardens and at the Site F landfill site directly to the east, but has never been found at Sassafras.

Acknowledgements

The author gratefully acknowledges the financial support of the Ontario Heritage Foundation and the World Wildlife Fund, who funded work on this project in 1986. Also, the Parks and Recreation Section of the Ontario Ministry of Natural Resources, Central Region (Richmond Hill), which assisted with the review, production, and distribution of this report.

Update, October 1988

Sassafras Woods is now a candidate provincially significant Area of Natural and Scientific Interest of the Ministry of Natural Resources, and will be considered as such in the next version of the Cambridge District Land Use Guidelines, subject to public review. A more detailed inventory of Sassafras Woods, proposed in the Introduction, and an evaluation of possible ANSIs in Site District 7-3, is currently being conducted by the Ministry of Natural Resources, Central Region.

References

Ambrose, J.D. and S.W. Aboud. 1986. *Status Report on Chestnut* Castanea dentata *(Marsh) Borkh., a Threatened Species in Canada.* Submitted to Plants Subcommittee, Committee on the Status of Endangered Wildlife in Canada, National Museum of Natural Sciences, Ottawa, Ontario. 24 pp.

Chapman, L.J. and D.F. Putnam. 1973. *The Physiography of Southern Ontario.* Second edition. Published for the Ontario Research Foundation by the University of Toronto Press. 386 pp.

Coulson, D.P. 1986. Fieldnotes from site visit to Sassafras Woods on 25 April 1986.

Crins, B. 1978-1985. Checklist of Vascular Plants observed and collected at Sassafras Woods on several visits (3 July 1978, 2 Sept. 1979, 26 Dec. 1982, 17 Sept. 1983, and May 1985).

Crins, B. 1984. Favourite Spots (Sassafras Woods). *The Wood Duck.* Newsletter of the Hamilton Naturalists' Club. p.174.

Crins, W.J. 1986. Vascular Plants of the Regional Municipality of Halton, Ontario. Mimeo, 27 pp.

Cuddy, D.G., K.M. Lindsay and I.D. MacDonald. 1976. *Significant Natural Areas Along the Niagara Escarpment.* A report on Nature Reserve Candidates and other Significant Natural Areas in the Niagara Escarpment Planning Area. Park Planning Branch, Division of Parks, Ontario Ministry of Natural Resources, 426 pp.

Dillon, M.M. Ltd. 1984. *Burlington Landfill Continuation – Appendix G: Environmental Impact Assessment.* Prepared for the Regional Municipality of Halton. 62 pp.

Ecologistics Ltd. 1977. *A Hydrogeologic Study of Environmentally Sensitive Areas in the Region of Halton.* Halton Region Conservation Authority, Regional Municipality of Halton, Grand River Conservation Authority and Credit River Conservation Authority. 90 pp. and appendices A to F.

Gillespie, J.E., R.E. Wicklund and M.H. Mills. 1971. *The Soils of Halton County.* Report No. 43 of the Ontario Soil Survey, Soil Research Institute, Canada Department of Agriculture, Guelph, and the Ontario Agricultural College, Guelph. 79 pp + map.

Gillett, J.M. and C.J. Keddy. 1983. *Frasera caroliniensis* Walt. 1 page in G. W. Argus and D. J. White, eds. *Atlas of the rare vascular plants of Ontario.* National Museum of Natural Sciences, Ottawa.

Gould, J. 1986. Personal communication with K. Lindsay.

Guillet, G.R. 1967. *The Clay Products Industry of Ontario.* Ontario Department of Mines, Industrial Mineral Report 22, Toronto. 206 pp. Accompanied by Maps 2130, 2131.

Hanna, R. 1984. *Life Science Areas of Natural and Scientific Interest in Site District 7-4.* A Review and Assessment of Significant Natural Areas in Site District 7-4. Parks and Recreational Areas Section, OFER 8404, Ontario Ministry of Natural Resources, Central Region, Richmond Hill. 69 pp.

Hills, G.A. 1959. *A Ready Reference to the Description of the Land of Ontario and Its Productivity.* Preliminary Report. Ontario Department of Lands and Forests, Maple. 142 pp.

Identification Subcommittee of Carolinian Canada. 1985. *Critical Unprotected Natural Areas in the Carolinian Life Zone of Canada.* Final Report. The Nature Conservancy of Canada, The Ontario Heritage Foundation and World Wildlife Fund. 400 pp.

Kaiser, J. 1984. *Overview of Forests Stand Composition in Halton ESA's.* Regional Municipality of Halton, Planning and Development Department. 27 pp. + appendices.

Karrow, P.F. 1963. *Pleistocene Geology of the Hamilton-Galt Area.* Ontario Department of Mines, Geological Report No. 16, Toronto. 68 pp. Accompanied by Maps 2029, 2030, 2033, 2034.

Karrow, P.F. 1983. Quaternary Geology of the Hamilton Area, Southern Ontario Geological Survey, Map P. 2605, Geological series – Preliminary map, scale 1:50,000.

Lindsay, K.M. 1984. *Life Science Areas of Natural and Scientific Interest in Site District 7-2 West of the Haldimand Clay Plain.* A Review and Assessment of Significant Natural Areas in Site District 7-2 West of the Haldimand Clay Plain. Parks and Recreational Areas Branch, OFER 8403, Ontario Ministry of Natural Resources Central Region, Richmond Hill and Southwestern Region, London. 129 pp.

Lindsay, K.M. 1986. *Life Science Areas of Natural and Scientific Interest in Site District 6-9.* A Review and Assessment of Significant Natural Areas in Site District 6-9. Parks and Recreational Areas Section, OFER 8601, Ontario Ministry of Natural Resources, Central Region, Richmond Hill. 71 pp.

Maycock, P.F. 1984. Life Science Inventory Checklist for Sassafras Woods. In: *Subcommittee of Critical Unprotected Areas in the Carolinian Life Zone of Canada.* Identification Subcommittee of Carolinian Canada, 1985.

Regional Municipality of Halton. 1978. *Halton Region Environmentally Sensitive Areas Study.* Ecological and Environmental Advisory Committee Planning Department, Regional Municipality of Halton. 261 pp.

Regional Municipality of Halton Planning Department. 1979. *Field Study of Environmentally Sensitive Areas in Halton.* Regional Municipality of Halton Planning Department, Ecological and Environmental Advisory Committee. 107 pp.

Regional Municipality of Halton. 1982. Phase 1. *Ownership and Access Study of Environmentally Sensitive Areas in Halton Region.* Planning and Development Department, Regional Municipality of Halton. 14 pp + cxii appendices.

Sutherland, D. 1979. *Sassafras Woods Environmentally Sensitive Area #4.* Halton Region Conservation Authority. 5 pp.

Tant, M.S., S. Varga, A. Fleming and M. A. Bryant. 1977. *Biological Documentation of Natural Features in Regional Municipality of Halton.* Regional Municipality of Halton Planning Department and the Royal Botanical Gardens. 74 pp.other associations. Crins (1984) described Sassafras Woods as "… the best example of southern deciduous woods (Carolinian Forest) in Halton Regional Municipality."

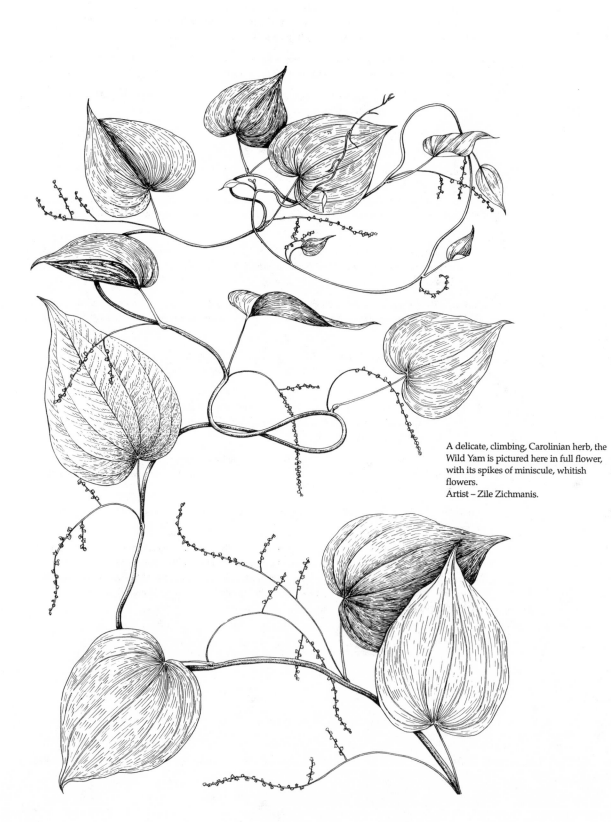

A delicate, climbing, Carolinian herb, the
Wild Yam is pictured here in full flower,
with its spikes of miniscule, whitish
flowers.
Artist – Zile Zichmanis.

A Life Science Inventory and Ranking of 30 Natural Areas of Walpole Island Indian Reserve

P. Allen Woodliffe

Ontario Ministry of Natural Resources
1023 Richmond St.
Chatham, Ontario N7M 5J5

Gary M. Allen

Ontario Ministry of Natural Resources
820 Yonge St. S.
Aurora, Ontario L4G 3G8

Abstract. *A two-year study to document and assess the highly significant life science features of the Walpole Island Indian Reserve was begun in 1985. The northern part of the island complex where extensive prairie, savannah, and hardwood communities remain, was divided into 30 areas. The southern part, consisting of agricultural lands and wetlands, was not examined. Based on intensive field study and literature search, over 800 vascular plant species are known from Walpole. Ninety-six of these are rare in Ontario, and eight are not known elsewhere in Canada. Ninety-two species of birds were confirmed as breeding. Twenty-eight are recognized as rare in Ontario, one of which is also considered to be threatened. An additional 46 bird species are possible or probable breeders. Twenty-six species of amphibians and reptiles were recorded, including five of which are rare. Twenty-four species of mammals were recorded, one of which is rare in Ontario. The results of this study confirm that Walpole Island contains the most significant tall grass prairie and oak savannah vegetation remaining in Canada. Using six criteria, the 30 areas have been prioritized to provide the native people with evidence and rationale for future conservation strategies.*

Introduction

Walpole Island Indian Reserve is part of a large delta island complex situated in the mouth of the St. Clair River at the north end of Lake St. Clair in Lambton County, Ontario (Figure 1). Approximately one-third of the delta complex is made up of more than a dozen islands on the United States side of the border. The remaining two-thirds are made up of six islands on the Canadian side, with the St. Clair International Seaway being the main dividing line between Canada and the United States.

The Canadian islands are wholly occupied by the Walpole Island Indian Reserve and cover approximately 24,000 ha. Almost 8,000 ha consist of 'dryland', of which half is devoted to agriculture, while the other half is comprised of forest, savannah and prairie. The remainder of the Reserve, almost 16,000 ha, is wetland, consisting of marshes, sloughs, interior lakes, channels, and adjacent waters of Lake St. Clair to a depth of approximately two metres.

Walpole Island has long been known for a rich mosaic of life science features, including marsh, wet woods, oak forest, savannah, and prairie. It is the last remnant of extensive prairies which in Ontario once extended from southern Lambton County into Kent and Essex Counties (Hennepin 1647, McNiff 1790, Rankin 1847).

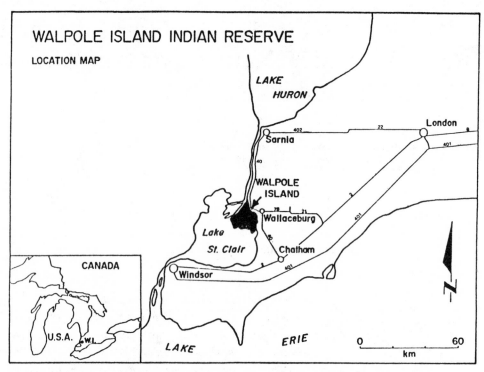

Figure 1: Regional Setting of Walpole Indian Reserve (from Hildebrand, 1985).

These prairies were largely converted to agriculture by the end of the 1800s and today remnants are confined to Walpole and the Windsor area. Today very little of the landscape of these Counties remains undeveloped, with approximately two, three, and seven percent of Essex, Kent, and Lambton, respectively, still in a natural state.

The significance of Walpole in the context of the entire midwest of the Continent – an area once dominated by the tall grass prairie biome – has also been acknowledged. Of the oak savannah which once covered some 11,000,000 to 13,000,000 ha of the midwest at the time of settlement, only 113 sites of high quality, totalling some 2,607 ha, could be located in a 1985 study (Nuzzo 1986). This represents only 0.02% of the presettlement extent of this community type. Similarly, the US Nature Conservancy has estimated that the current tallgrass reserves is 150,000 acres (60,705 ha) – about one six-hundredths of one percent of the continent's original 140,000 square miles (360,000 sq km) of tallgrass (Madson 1986).

Walpole was noted as an Environmentally Significant Area by the University of Waterloo (1980) and was subsequently selected by the Carolinian Canada Identification Subcommittee as one of the top 36 unprotected natural areas in the Carolinian life zone of Canada (Eagles and Beechey 1985). It was distinguished in fact as the only one of the 36 Carolinian sites which fulfilled all ten criteria used for selection. It is being considered for inclusion on the List of Wetlands of International Importance, the Ramsar Convention (Environment Canada 1987).

Although Walpole Island is famous for its resources, visits by naturalists have been sporadic over the decades, due to the relative inaccessibility owing to its Indian Reserve status.[1] It has been a subject of botanical interest, for example by

---

[1] The Walpole Island Reserve is under the jurisdiction of the Walpole Island First Nation. All territory within the Reserve, with the exception of public areas (i.e. roads, waterways, beaches, buildings, etc.), are not generally open to the public unless otherwise posted. As a result, off-road sightseeing is strictly prohibited unless authorized by the Walpole Island Council and/or by individual private landowners.

Dodge (1914) and Gaiser (Gaiser and Moore 1966), of preliminary biological investigations (Campbell 1974, Ecologistics 1979), and more recently, of quantitative vegetation sampling of its prairies and savannas (Chapman 1983, Faber-Langendoen 1984, Faber-Langendoen and Maycock 1987, and Bakowsky 1988). In 1985, a two-year study was initiated to compile existing information and to carry out an extensive field survey of the life science features of the terrestrial natural areas of Walpole Island.

This study was carried out with the approval and cooperation of the Walpole Band Council.

Methodology

The north half of the Reserve, encompassing all of the terrestrial communities, was subdivided into 30 natural areas, each being separated from an adjacent one by some distinct feature of the landscape, such as roads, agricultural land, or drainage channels. Each of these 30 natural areas contained some combination of prairie, savannah, and woodland. The southern half of the Reserve, consisting of marsh and agricultural land, was not surveyed as part of the present study.

Original field data was collected for five different groups: vegetation and flora, birds, herptiles, mammals, and butterflies, in the following manner:

1. Vegetation

Field visits were made into all major communities in each natural area. This was done usually at least twice, in order to compile presence lists of early to mid-season and mid to late-season species in each community, to determine prevalent species, and to obtain locations and good habitat descriptions of significant species (i.e. those species listed in the Atlas of the Rare Vascular Plants of Ontario, Argus *et al.* 1982-1987). Communities and provincially rare species were mapped on 1:10,000 air photos and described in field notes. A voucher specimen was collected for most significant or difficult to identify species and deposited at the University of Toronto, Erindale College Herbarium (TRTE). Photographic documentation of significant flora and communities was also taken.

2. Birds

Field visits were made to each area at least once during the breeding season, and the more significant areas, on two or more occasions, in order to confirm breeding. All species encountered were recorded with locations of significant species mapped on air photos and recorded in field notes. The level of breeding activity was recorded on standard breeding bird atlas cards using the standard activity codes (Cadman *et al.* 1987). Most of the data were collected in 1986 only.

3. Amphibians and Reptiles

Field visits to each natural area to search for herptiles were made in conjunction with those made for vegetation and birds. Specific searches such as turning over logs and boards were made, along with casual observations during field visits. Road-kills were also noted and a sample of these was deposited at the Royal Ontario Museum (ROM) and the National Museum. All species were recorded in field notes, with significant species being mapped on air photos.

4. Mammals

Mammal species were recorded each time a site was visited during the inventory, as a result of direct observations or other evidence (e.g. scats, tracks). In 1986, 20 traplines in eleven different natural areas were set out in the following habitats: oak savannah, oak woods, mesic prairie, wet-mesic prairie, cattail marsh, Silver Maple woods, and old field. Woodstream Professional mouse snap traps, Sherman live traps, and pitfall traps were used on these traplines for a total of 2642 trap nights. In addition, Havahart live traps were placed singly in select areas. Two hundred specimens were caught and those collected were deposited at the ROM.

Censusing for bats was conducted at Walpole in 1985 under the direction of Dr. Brock Fenton (Dewar *et al.* 1985) and obviated the need to carry this work out ourselves.

5. Butterflies

Butterfly species were recorded for each natural area during the inventory, with special emphasis in 1986 when over 180 hours of volunteer butterfly censusing was carried out. Specimens were caught and recorded. Vouchers are in the personal collections of Ben and Brenda Kulon and Gerry Clement, with significant or taxonomically difficult species also deposited at the ROM.

In addition to the above data collection, efforts were made to:

a) search the literature;

b) make contact with field naturalists or residents who had personal knowledge and information regarding Walpole Island;

c) obtain access to the breeding bird atlas data; and

d) search herbaria to attempt to substantiate historical references to species.

Results and Discussion

An impressive diversity of flora and fauna was documented during this study, and is discussed as follows:

Flora – More than 800 species of vascular plants are now known from Walpole Island. Ninety-six of these are rare in Ontario (Argus *et al.* 1982-87), the highest total for any single natural area in the province, and eight species are not known elsewhere in Canada (see Appendix I). Fully one-third of the flora is made up of grasses, sedges, and composites.

Birds – A total of 138 species of birds are now known to be breeding or potentially breeding on Walpole Island. Of these, 92 species have been confirmed as breeding. Twenty-eight species are considered rare in Ontario, and 14 of these have been confirmed as breeding. One species, Henslow's Sparrow (*Ammodramus henslowii*), is considered threatened by the Committee on the Status of Endangered Wildlife in Canada (Knapton 1982) (see Appendix II).

Herptiles – A total of 26 species of reptiles and amphibians is now known from Walpole Island. Of these, five species are considered to be rare in Ontario (Ministry of Natural Resources, 1983) (see Appendix III).

Mammals – A total of 24 species of mammals was noted during the study. Of these, the Southern Flying Squirrel is considered rare in Ontario (Stabb 1987).

Butterflies – A total of 59 species of butterflies was noted during the study. Of these, three are considered rare and two are threatened in Ontario (Campbell and Coulson in prep.) (see Appendix IV).

Vegetation – This study confirmed that there are some outstanding natural areas remaining on Walpole Island. Most significant are one 75 ha site which encompasses seven distinct prairie-savannas, six of which are linked by naturally-occurring sloughs; a 53 ha natural area which encompasses the vegetational continuum from oak woodland through to one of the largest expanses of mesic, wet-mesic, and wet prairie on Walpole Island; and three other prairie-savannah sites which range in size from 25 to 55 ha. These communities are generally in superb condition, due to the regular practice of setting fire to these areas by the island residents.

A majority of the rare flora and fauna recorded is directly or indirectly associated with prairie or savannah communities. This assemblage of rare and more common prairie and savannah species, combined with the excellent overall condition of the communities which they make up, undoubtedly gives Walpole Island the distinction of harbouring the most significant tall grass prairie and oak savannah vegetation remaining in Canada.

As a result of this study, a preliminary list and ranking of the top priority sites on Walpole Island has been produced. Of the 3649 hectares of terrestrial land on the Reserve not currently in agriculture (e.g. woodland, residential, prairie, and savannah), 638 ha of portions of the original 30 natural areas have been selected to represent the areas most in need of protection. The majority of these areas are tall grass prairie and oak savannah communities. A feasibility study, the Walpole Island Natural Heritage Protection Program, is presently underway to investigate the possibility of conserving these significant properties, through leasing or other arrangements with their respective landowners.

Conservation Recommendations

1. The Walpole Reserve continues to struggle with 60 percent unemployment. Natural area protection in most cases, is a viable option in such a milieu, only when a direct economic benefit, can be demonstrated to landowners and to the Band Council (Present annual leasing fees for agriculture run from $200 to $321 per ha).[2] Many areas are suitable for leasing, and the concept of leasing land for conservation appears to be generally acceptable to Walpole owners on the basis of a pilot landowner contact with 55 landowners in 1988 (Jacobs and Williams 1988). However, it is unrealistic to consider leasing the entire 638 ha of the top natural areas on the Reserve, and of course, leasing in itself will not be enough. A satisfactory protection strategy for Walpole's natural areas will require a mix of techniques such as:

   – private stewardship awards;

   – continued tourism dollars generated by natural history tours to the protected areas (several hundred people per year presently visit Walpole specifically to view the prairie and savannah communities);

[2] It must be noted that Walpole landowners are not affected by the new Conservation Land Tax Reduction Program, since status Indians are exempt from provincial and federal taxes.

– job creation to meet the demand from this tourism, e.g. hiring interpretive naturalists, creating exhibits, producing natural area management plans, removing exotic species, and designing and building interpretive trails;

– supplemental methods of earning income from protected sites, e.g. by harvesting and selling prairie seeds; and

– exploiting the public's present passion with the natural world, via art, books, cards, and photographs, which depict the diversity of landscapes, flora, and fauna, of Walpole.

To date, with one minor exception, credit for the existence of the natural areas of Walpole Island is completely due to their own efforts. However, in the long-term, these protection efforts will be greatly enhanced by an influx of more funds from outside the Reserve. To succeed, the Walpole Island Natural Heritage Protection Program must continue to be community-directed. The Walpole First Nation (Band Council) formally passed a resolution in 1988 accepting the roles and responsibilities as lead agency for the protection of the significant natural areas of Walpole Island. The Walpole Research Office (NIN.DA.WAAB.JIG) is the perfect vehicle for delivering this program and has demonstrated a high capacity for coordinating with others groups and agencies. The Carolinian Canada program has assisted the NIN.DA.WAAB.JIG by providing $27,000 over the past two years toward a landowner contact and protection feasibility study. This work has served to increase community awareness of Carolinian Canada generally and the significance of Walpole's natural areas specifically; has improved coordination between the Band Council, the Research Office, and the Lands Office with respect to developments potentially impacting natural areas, and has demonstrated the high level of regard Walpole residents have for natural area protection. Much work remains to be done, yet 1990 will be the last year of Carolinian Canada funding. Other funding agencies must be approached now, otherwise the progress to date may be for naught. Potential sources are the Ontario Heritage Foundation, the Ontario Wetlands Program, Ontario and Michigan Naturalist Clubs, World Wildlife Fund, Nature Conservancy of Canada, Wildlife Habitat Canada, and The Nature Conservancy (US).

2. NIN.DA.WAAB.JIG intends to formally approach the Walpole Island First Nation with a proposal to develop an Integrated Resource Management Plan for the Reserve. This will address the problem of protecting a system of natural areas on the Reserve in the absence of an official plan or set of basic guidelines to control development. This effort should be viewed as a logical extension of the presently funded Natural Heritage Protection Program, and should be supported accordingly by the various agencies.

3. A trust fund for protecting natural areas on Walpole Island would probably be popular with Conservation agencies, private organizations, and individuals, and the idea should be explored.

4. The prairies and savannas at Walpole have been maintained by quite high levels of burning regimes. Experience indicates that these open habitats are quickly 'lost' to succession in the absence of burning. Present levels should at least be maintained, keeping in mind however that there are optimal times of year for burning, and that intense fires outside of these periods can actually degrade a prairie or savannah. More research should be conducted on fire ecology at

Walpole, with the findings translated into education within the community on the importance of fire to the prairies and savannas of Walpole.

5. Several of the species at Walpole are highly significant. Some are at the very northern limit of their distributions in Canada, others are dependent on habitat types which are becoming increasingly rare in southern Ontario. Further research is required on several of these species. High priority should be given to White Gentian *(Gentiana alba)* and Oval Ladies'-tresses *(Spiranthes ovalis)*, both of which are known from only two sites at Walpole, the only extant populations in Canada. Other plants in need of work are Gattinger's and Skinner's Agalinis *(Agalinis gattingeri, A. skinneriana)*, Pink Milkwort *(Polygala incarnata)*, Fimbristylis *(Fimbristylis spadicea)*, Lace Grass *(Eragrostis capillaris)*, Panic Grass *(Dichanthelium meridionale)*, Small White Ladies'-slipper *(Cypripedium candidum)*, and Ohio Buckeye *(Aesculus glabra)*. Faunal species deserving of further attention include Henslow's Sparrow, Sandhill Crane, King Rail, and Queen Snake.

6. Allan Anderson at the University of Guelph has had success germinating in culture several of Walpole's threatened plants, thus establishing genetic insurance in the event of total extirpation of a species. Cooperation on this effort between the University of Guelph, NIN.DA.WAAB.JIG, World Wildlife Fund, and Ministry of Natural Resources, Chatham, should be continued.

7. The Walpole wetlands at 15,874 ha are the largest on the Great Lakes. The present study only considered the terrestrial portions, comprising 7695 ha of the Reserve. A comparable qualitative survey of these wetland resources should be conducted in the near future.

Acknowledgements

Funding and support for this project was provided primarily by the World Wildlife Fund and Ontario Ministry of Natural Resources, with additional assistance provided by the University of Waterloo, Lambton Wildlife Incorporated, and Walpole Island First Nation, in particular NIN.DA.WAAB.JIG. Editorial comments provided by D.M. Jacobs, M.J. Oldham, and M.C. Williams are much appreciated.

References

Allen, G.M. and M.J. Oldham. 1987. *Rare vascular plants of Walpole Island Indian Reserve.* Unpublished report. 2 pp.

Argus, G.W., K.M. Pryer, D.J. White and C.J. Keddy, eds. 1982-1987. *Atlas of the rare vascular plants of Ontario.* Four parts. National Museum of Natural Sciences, Ottawa (loose-leaf).

Bakowsky, W.D. 1988. *The phytosociology of midwestern savannah in the Carolinian region of Southern Ontario.* MSc thesis, University of Toronto. 121 pp.

Cadman, M.D., P.F.J. Eagles and F.M. Helleiner. 1987. *Atlas of the breeding birds of Ontario.* Federation of Ontario Naturalists and Long Point Bird Observatory. University of Waterloo Press. 617 pp.

Campbell, C.A. 1974. *A preliminary assessment of ecological assets and impacts on Walpole Island Indian Reserve.* Prepared for Indian and Northern Affairs, Ontario Regional Office, Planning Section. 29 pp.

Campbell C.A. and D.P. Coulson. In preparation. *Status, distribution and life history characteristics of some butterflies at risk in the Carolinian forest zone.* Proceedings of a conference on research on the Carolinian Life Zone of Canada. World Wildlife Fund of Canada.

Chapman, K. 1983. A Bray-Curtis ordination of Michigan prairies. pp. 168-169 In: *Proceedings of the Eighth North American Prairie Conference, 1982.* R. Brewer, ed. Western Michigan University, Kalamazoo, Michigan.

Committee on the Status of Endangered Wildlife in Canada. 1988. *Endangered species in Canada.* Pamphlet produced by World Wildlife Fund Canada.

Dodge, C.K. 1914. *The flowering plants, ferns and fern allies growing without cultivation in Lambton County, Ontario.* Michigan Academy of Science, Report #16.

Eagles, P.F.J. and T.J. Beechey. 1985. *Critical unprotected natural areas in the Carolinian life zone of Canada.* Final report. The Nature Conservancy of Canada, The Ontario Heritage Foundation and World Wildlife Fund Canada. 400 pp.

Ecologistics Ltd. 1979. *Biophysical Walpole Island Indian Reserve.* Unpublished manuscript prepared for Walpole Island Band Council under contract by Dept. of Indian and Northern Affairs. 54 pp. + appendices.

Environment Canada. 1987. *Draft proposed designation of the wetlands of Walpole Island Indian Reserve # 46 for recognition in the list of wetlands of international importance.* Unpublished manuscript prepared for NIN.DA.WAAB.JIG by Canadian Wildlife Service. 32 pp.

Faber-Langendoen, D. 1984. *The ecology of tallgrass prairie in Southern Ontario.* MSc. thesis, University of Toronto. 205 pp.

Faber-Langendoen, D. and P.F. Maycock. 1987. Composition and soil-environment analysis of prairies on Walpole Island, southwestern Ontario. *Canadian Journal of Botany* 65:2410-2419.

Dewar, H.J., C.L. Furlonger, and M.B. Fenton. 1985. *A survey of bats of the Carolinian Zone of Ontario.* Unpublished report prepared for World Wildlife Fund (Canada). 38 pp.

Gaiser, L.O. and R.J. Moore. 1966. *A survey of the vascular plants of Lambton County, Ontario.* Plant Research Institute, Research Branch, Canada Department of Agriculture, Ottawa, Canada. 122 pp.

Hennepin, J.L. 1683. Description be la Louisiane nouvellement découverte. *In:* E.L. LaJeunesse. 1960. *The Windsor Border Region.* University of Toronto Press. 374 pp.

Hildebrand, L. 1985. *Woodlot utilization plan for the public bush on Walpole Island Indian Reserve.* Occasional paper No. 10. Nin.da.waab.jig. 126 pp.

Jacobs, D.M. and M.C. Williams. 1988. *Walpole Island natural heritage protection program.* A proposal to the World Wildlife Fund. 18 pp. + 6 appendices.

Knapton, R.W. 1982. *The Henslow's Sparrow* (Ammodramus henslowii) *in Canada: a status report.* Prepared for The Nongame Program, Wildlife Branch, Ontario Ministry of Natural Resources. 77 pp.

Kulon, B., B. Kulon and G. Clements. 1987. *Inventory of butterflies and skippers on Walpole Island.* Unpublished report. 27 pp.

Madson, C. 1986. America's tallgrass prairie: sunlight and shadow. In: *The Nature Conservancy News* 36(3):4-9.

McNiff, P. 1791. Unpublished survey map in the files of the Surveys Branch, Ontario Ministry of Natural Resources.

Nuzzo, V.A. 1986. Extent and status of midwest oak savannah: presettlement and 1985. *Natural Areas Journal* 6(2):6-36.

Ontario Ministry of Natural Resources and Environment Canada. 1983. *An evaluation system for wetlands of Ontario, south of the precambrian shield, first edition.* Wildlife Branch, Ontario Ministry of Natural Resources and Canadian Wildlife Service, Environment Canada. 169 pp.

Ontario Rare Breeding Bird Program. 1989. *Ontario rare breeding bird program newsletter March 6, 1989.* Unpaginated.

Rankin, C. 1847. *Survey of Southwestern Ontario.*

Stabb, M. 1987. *The status of the southern flying squirrel,* Glaucomys volans *in Canada.* Unpublished report to Ontario Ministry of Natural Resources, Wildlife Branch, Toronto. 83 pp.

University of Waterloo. 1980. *Lambton County preliminary environmentally sensitive areas study.* Prepared for the County of Lambton Planning Department, Sarnia, Ontario. 243 pp.

Appendix I

Rare Vascular Plants of Walpole Island Indian Reserve
(from Allen and Oldham 1987)

*Eragrostis capillaris**	Lace Grass
Koeleria cristata	June Grass
Leptoloma cognatum	Fall Witch Grass
Dichanthelium clandestinum	Broadleaf Panic Grass
Dichanthelium leibergii	Leiberg's Panic Grass
Dichanthelium villosissimum var.*praecocius*	Early-branching Panic Grass
*Dichanthelium meridionale**	Panic Grass
Dichanthelium sphaerocarpon var. *sphaerocarpon*	Panic Grass
Sphenopholis obtusata	Early Bunchgrass
Stipa spartea	Needle Grass
Bulbostylis capillaris	Hair-like Bulbostylis
Carex bicknellii	Sedge
Carex conoidea	Sedge
Carex emoryi	Sedge
Carex formosa	Sedge
Carex gracilescens	Sedge
Carex meadii	Sedge
Carex muskingumensis	Sedge
Carex suberecta	Sedge
Carex swanii	Sedge
Carex tetanica	Sedge
Cyperus erythrorhizos	Red-rooted Cyperus
Cyperus flavescens	Yellow Cyperus
*Fimbristylis spadicea**	Fimbristylis
Scirpus clintonii	Clinton's Club-rush
Scleria triglomerata	Tall Nut-rush
Scleria verticillata	Low Nut-rush
Tradescantia ohiensis	Ohio Spiderwort
Juncus acuminatus	Sharp-fruited Rush
Juncus greenei	Rush
Aletris farinosa	Colic-root
Hypoxis hirsuta	Yellow Star-grass
Sisyrinchium albidum	Blue-eyed Grass
Aplectrum hyemale	Putty-root
Cypripedium candidum	Small White Lady's-slipper
Platanthera blephariglottis	White-fringed Orchid
Platanthera leucophaea	Prairie White-fringed Orchid
Spiranthes lacera var. *gracilis*	Southern Slender Ladies'-tresses
Spiranthes magnicamporum	Great Plains Ladies'-tresses
Spiranthes ochroleuca	Yellow Ladies'-tresses
*Spiranthes ovalis**	Oval Ladies'-tresses
Carya laciniosa	Big Shellbark Hickory
Quercus palustris	Pin Oak
Polygonum tenue	Knotweed
Cerastium velutinum	Chickweed
Hydrastis canadensis	Golden-seal
Thalictrum revolutum	Waxy Meadow-rue
Liriodendron tulipifera	Tulip-tree
Agrimonia parviflora	Agrimony
Geum vernum	Spring Avens
Rosa setigera	Prairie Rose
Baptisia tinctoria	Wild Indigo
Desmodium rotundifolium	Prostrate Tick-trefoil

Gymnocladus dioica	Kentucky Coffee-tree
Lupinus perennis	Wild Lupine
Vicia caroliniana	Carolina Vetch
Ptelea trifoliata	Hop-tree
Polygala incarnata*	Pink Milkwort
Aesculus glabra*	Ohio Buckeye
Lechea pulchella	Pinweed
Lechea villosa	Hairy Pinweed
Hibiscus moscheutos	Swamp Rose Mallow
Lythrum alatum	Wing-angled Loosestrife
Nyssa sylvatica	Black Gum
Ludwigia polycarpa	Many-seeded Ludwigia
Bartonia virginica	Virginia Bartonia
Gentiana alba*	White Gentian
Gentiana puberulenta	Downy Gentian
Gentianella quinquefolia	Stiff Gentian
Asclepias purpurascens	Purple Milkweed
Asclepias sullivantii	Sullivant's Milkweed
Cuscuta cephalanthi	Dodder
Cuscuta coryli	Dodder
Phyla lanceolata	Fog-fruit
Blephilia ciliata	Downy Wood-mint
Lycopus rubellus	Stalked Water-horehound
Agalinis gattingeri*	Gattinger's Agalinis
Agalinis skinneriana	Skinner's Agalinis
Aureolaria pedicularia	Fern-leaved False Foxglove
Veronicastrum virginicum	Culver's-root
Aster dumosus var. strictior	Bushy Aster
Aster praealtus var. praealtus	Willow Aster
Bidens coronata	Southern Tickseed
Cirsium hillii	Hill's Thistle
Coreopsis tripteris	Tall Coreopsis
Eupatorium purpureum	Purple-jointed Joe-Pye Weed
Hieracium longipilum	Long-bearded Hawkweed
Krigia biflora	Two-flowered Cynthia
Liatris aspera	Rough Blazing Star
Liatris spicata	Dense Blazing Star
Ratibida pinnata	Gray-headed Coneflower
Silphium terebinthinaceum	Prairie Dock
Solidago riddellii	Riddell's Goldenrod
Solidago rigida	Stiff-leaved Goldenrod
Solidago speciosa*	Showy Goldenrod
Vernonia gigantea	Tall Ironweed

* only known Canadian location

Appendix II

Significant Breeding Birds of Walpole Island Indian Reserve

Species	Breeding Status	Source
Horned Grebe	(+)	ORBBP
Least Bittern	*	ORBBP, MNR
Great Egret	(*)	ORBBP
Cattle Egret	+	ORBBP
Cooper's Hawk	+	MNR, COSEWIC
Bald Eagle	+	ORBBP, MNR, COSEWIC
Northern Bobwhite	*	
Canvasback	(*)	ORBBP, MNR
Redhead	(*)	MNR
Northern Shoveler	(+)	MNR
Ruddy Duck	(+)	MNR
Sandhill Crane	(*)	ORBBP
King Rail	(*)	ORBBP, MNR, COSEWIC
Little Gull	(*)	ORBBP, MNR
Forster's Tern	(*)	ORBBP, MNR
Caspian Tern	(+)	ORBBP, MNR, COSEWIC
Black Tern	(*)	MNR
Acadian Flycatcher	+	ORBBP, MNR
Tufted Titmouse	*	ORBBP
Eastern Bluebird	*	COSEWIC
White-eyed Vireo	+	ORBBP
Prothonotary Warbler	+	ORBBP, MNR, COSEWIC
Louisiana Waterthrush	+	ORBBP, MNR
Hooded Warbler	+	ORBBP, MNR
Yellow-breasted Chat	+	ORBBP
Yellow-headed Blackbird	(+)	ORBBP, MNR
Orchard Oriole	*	ORBBP
Henslow's Sparrow	*	ORBBP, MNR, COSEWIC

*   confirmed breeding in study area.

(*) confirmed breeding on Walpole Island, but not in study area.

+   possible/probable breeding in study area.

(+) possible/probable breeding on Walpole Island, but not in study area.

Sources of significance status: Atlas (Cadman and Lamond 1987)
                                MNR (1983)
                                COSEWIC (1988)

Appendix III

Provincially Rare Amphibians and Reptiles of Walpole Island Indian Reserve

Common Name	Scientific Name
Queen Snake	*Regina septemvittata*
Eastern Fox Snake	*Elaphe vulpina*
Butler's Garter Snake	*Thamnophis butleri*
Eastern Spiny Softshell Turtle	*Trionyx spiniferus*
Spotted Turtle	*Clemmys guttata*

Status according to Ontario Ministry of Natural Resources 1983.

Appendix IV

Significant Butterfly Species of Walpole Island Indian Reserve (from Kulon *et al.* 1987)

Scientific Name	Common Name	Status
Erynnis baptisiae	Wild Indigo Duskywing	Threatened
Erynnis horatius	Horace's Duskywing	Rare
Erynnis martialis	Mottled Duskywing	Rare
Erynnis persius	Hairy Duskywing	Threatened
Heraclides cresphontes	Giant Swallowtail	Rare

Status according to Campbell and Coulson 1989.

The Natural Heritage Stewardship Program

S.G. Hilts and
T.C. Moull

Natural Heritage Stewardship Program
Dept. of Land Resource Science
University of Guelph, Guelph, Ontario N1G 2W1

Abstract. *The Natural Heritage Stewardship Program, under the auspices of the Natural Heritage League, has been developing 'stewardship enhancement techniques' to help land protection organizations promote good land stewardship through the use of a range of agreements and incentives. It began as a landowner contact program in 1984, and has since primarily operated in conjunction with private owners of Carolinian Canada sites. Ontario's Natural Heritage Stewardship Award, based on a verbal, voluntary protection agreement, was developed during this period.*

To date, 277 agreements have been negotiated, covering approximately 3840 hectares (9,500 acres) of Carolinian natural area. Many of the private landowners are looking forward to the inception of the Conservation Lands Tax Rebate program, which will offer a 100% property tax rebate to owners prepared to sign a written agreement to protect their land. The program continues to develop stronger enhancement techniques, associated with stronger incentives. Ultimately, the protection agencies will have a range of techniques at their disposal.

Recommendations which emerge from our work include using the private stewardship initiatives as an example for protecting provincially significant natural areas elsewhere in the province, involving volunteers in conducting private stewardship programs, consideration for rural landscape integrity, and a continued emphasis on the private landowner as a central theme of land protection through private stewardship.

Background

The Natural Heritage Stewardship Program is an ongoing research and extension project of the Natural Heritage League (NHL), and is developing mechanisms to encourage the conservation and wise management of privately-owned, significant natural heritage areas in Ontario. These mechanisms are referred to as 'stewardship enhancement techniques', and are methods of promoting good land stewardship through the use of a range of agreements and incentives.

The NHL is an umbrella organization of 28 government and non-government groups, all having an interest in the identification, protection, and management of important natural heritage areas in the province. Our research project receives support primarily from League members, as well as some independent private foundations. Current funders include the Ontario Heritage Foundation, World Wildlife Fund (WWF), the Ontario Ministry of Natural Resources (MNR), Nature Conservancy of Canada, Wildlife Habitat Canada, Canadian National Sportmen's Shows, the Laidlaw Foundation and the McLean Foundation.

Methods

The program began as a pilot landowner contact study during the summer of 1984. At that time, the NHL was searching for new and innovative means of promoting the protection of privately- owned, significant natural areas in Ontario. It was recognized that traditional methods of protection, including acquisition and landuse regulation through the planning process, were not always financially feasible or readily accepted by property owners. The pilot was modelled after successful landowner contact programs of the US Nature Conservancy, and was seen as a means of encouraging good private stewardship of these areas, by working cooperatively with individual landowners. Essentially, landowner contact serves three primary purposes:

- It allows an opportunity for the NHL to inform private landowners of a site's biophysical significance;

- It provides the landowners with an opportunity to voice concerns about protecting the property through private stewardship;

- It provides the organizations with protection mandates important background information on the nature of a site, to assist in developing appropriate protection strategies.

There were no incentives involved in the pilot study above the provision of information to landowners. However, there was an overwhelmingly positive response to the approach, and by all accounts, it was seen as a successful project.

During that same time period, Carolinian Canada had been launched jointly by the Nature Conservancy of Canada and WWF. Thirty-six critical unprotected sites had been identified by the Identification Subcommittee, and these were predominantly in private ownership. In early 1985, Carolinian Canada, through the Natural Heritage League, elected to contact the private landowners of these sites, employing the approach developed for the pilot study the previous year.

Through 1985 and 1986, first-round landowner contact was conducted with 539 owners on 28 Carolinian Canada sites. As well as encouraging the owners to protect their properties, we also inquired as to their interest in making voluntary stewardship agreements with the NHL to protect their land. We were encouraged that over 300 of the total number of landowners were interested in hearing more about this, should a stewardship agreement program be developed.

Also during 1985 and 1986, our project was developing the Natural Heritage Stewardship Award Program, on behalf of the NHL. It was essentially designed to recognize the past and ongoing contributions that private landowners make in protecting our natural heritage. It is based on a voluntary, verbal agreement between the owners and the Natural Heritage League. We ask that the landowners:

- Maintain and protect the site to the best of their ability;

- Notify the NHL or a designated program representative of:
  1) planned land use changes that might threaten the natural heritage features
  2) other threats to the area, such as intensive lumbering or drainage
  3) intent to sell or transfer ownership of the property.

Landowners agreeing to these conditions receive a Stewardship Award plaque, signed by the Chairman of the Ontario Heritage Foundation and the Premier of Ontario. There are no provisions for public access to properties through the agreement.

Throughout 1987, our contact continued to be primarily in conjunction with Carolinian Canada, and we returned to many of the owners previously contacted to negotiate these verbal, non-binding agreements to protect their land from major disturbance. Those recontacted in 1987 had, for the most part, expressed an interest in a Stewardship Award program during the initial contact in 1985 or 1986. In many cases, this first-level incentive is all that is required.

Results

Two hundred and seventy-seven voluntary stewardship agreements have been negotiated to date, covering approximately 3840 hectares (9,500 acres) of natural area. This represents about 40% of the owners that we have discussed the program with, and also 40% of the privately owned natural area within the sites. This aspect of our work will continue on into 1988.

The new Conservation Lands Tax Rebate Program was recently announced by the Ontario government, and was developed in part by this research project. It will offer private landowners a 100% property tax rebate on designated provincially significant natural areas. These areas could be Areas of Natural and Scientific Interest (ANSIs), Class 1 to 3 Wetlands, Conservation Authority lands, and Escarpment Natural Areas along the Niagara Escarpment. It is expected to be initiated during 1988, and retroactive for the 1987 calendar year. Participating owners will be required to sign a written agreement to protect the area in question. This will result in a more tangible financial incentive that will be of interest to some owners who cannot protect a site through more simple, verbal agreements.

In 1988, stronger agreements and incentives will be investigated, particularly with respect to natural area management agreements and conservation easements.

The end result is that land protection agencies will have a range of private stewardship enhancement techniques at their disposal. At the lower end will be the provision of information through the landowner contact process, followed by the negotiation of voluntary, verbal stewardship agreements which will be associated with Stewardship Award plaques. These have proven very successful to date. The tax rebate, tied to a written agreement, may require more of a commitment from a landowner, but will correspondingly require a stronger incentive. Natural area management agreements would be based on legal, written agreements, but could provide stronger financial incentives or assistance than a general property tax rebate. Subsequently, leases or conservation easements, which could be registered on a property's title, would provide the strongest degree of private land protection, and would require the largest capital outlay by the protecting agency. A conceptual presentation of this stewardship enhancement hierarchy is found in Figure 1.

Land management agencies associated with the research project since the beginning, particularly the MNR Districts and Conservation Authorities, are now beginning to adopt some of these principles of encouraging the private stewardship of significant sites by providing landowners with an integrated resource management message. Developing voluntary agreements with landowners, through the landowner contact process, has been suggested as one means of protection in an MNR policy to protect ANSIs.

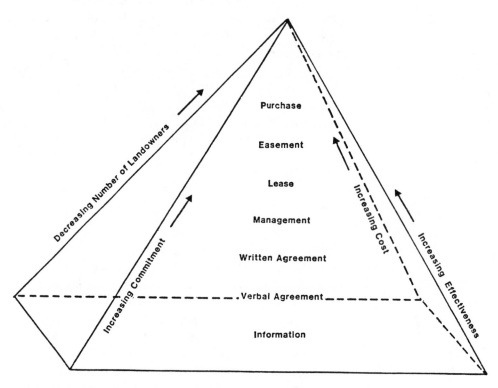

Figure 1: Hierarchy of Private Stewardship Techniques

Also important during 1987 has been the development of ways through which the program can build upon the rapport established with landowners during the first few contacts. In the short term, we are now devoting much of our time to arranging Stewardship Award presentations. Several owners have expressed an interest in receiving more specific information on their site. Some have requested that a representative of the League take them on a hike through their property to identify some of the flora. Others have become involved with various types of management assistance programs offered through the MNR or Conservation Authorities.

In the longer term, we are intending that information and processes developed through our research will be transferred to designated Carolinian Canada lead agencies over the coming year. Many will also be taking on the responsibility of following up with Stewardship Award recipients through ongoing personal contact, newsletters on natural area protection and management, and by negotiating stronger, cooperative protection agreements with individual landowners.

There is a good opportunity for the private and non-profit sectors to be directly involved with a site's protection through involvement with many of these tasks, particularly in areas where site committees headed by a lead agency have been established.

Much of our future research will evolve from an external assessment conducted during 1987. The research project was the subject of an extensive evaluation by the NHL through its member agencies, principally the Ministries of Natural Resources, and Culture and Communications. The evaluators interviewed representatives from the project, funders, Regional Natural Resources staff, and staff from Wildlife Habitat Canada. They also reviewed in detail the project's accomplishments, including the nearly 300 stewardship agreements negotiated, covering close to 4050 hectares (10,000 acres) of natural area. The conclusion was that overall the project was of high quality and has been extremely successful. As noted earlier, the MNR has incorporated the development of cooperative agreements with private landowners into its Implementation Strategy for Areas of Natural and Scientific Interest. The Ontario Heritage Foundation, an agency of the Ministry of Culture and Communications, continues to support our current activities in conjunction with Carolinian Canada. As well, the Niagara Escarpment Committee of the Foundation recently approved a pilot study to introduce these private stewardship principles to a selected sample of owners along the Escarpment.

Conservation Recommendations

Several recommendations emerge from our work over the past few years.

1. **Encouraging Good Private Land Stewardship on Provincially Significant Natural Areas:**
   Our work in Carolinian Canada should be seen as an example of the type of private stewardship initiatives which could be implemented on provincially significant natural areas in Ontario. These could include ANSIs, Class 1 to 3 wetlands, or significant natural heritage sites along the Niagara Escarpment. Most Carolinian Canada sites fit into at least one of these three categories.

2. **Application of Private Stewardship Principles to Regionally or Locally Significant Sites, or Rare Species:**
   To complement future work on provincially significant areas, these principles could also be adapted for use at the regional or local level. Several pilot stewardship projects currently underway across Canada have taken this approach, particularly in the prairie provinces and P.E.I. The protection of rare or endangered species might benefit from a landowner contact process, which could serve to inform private owners of the locations of key habitats on their properties, and provide management advice or assistance towards maintaining or enhancing a habitat's quality.

3. **Use of Volunteers:**
   In both the cases of private stewardship programs on regional or local sites, or in conjunction with the habitats of rare or endangered species, the use of volunteers would be extremely useful in conducting much of the initial contact work. Perhaps there would be naturalist groups, or volunteers associated with the Breeding Bird Atlas study, that would be available to participate.

4. **Protection of the Rural Landscape:**
   To date, encouraging good private stewardship of natural areas through this program has been confined to a small sample of provincially significant areas. Even if the program were to be expanded to include all significant provincial, regional and local sites, only a small percentage of rural Ontario would be covered. There is still a vast number of areas of lesser significance which still form key components of rural ecosystems. It will become increasingly important to encourage the good stewardship of the entire countryside, taking into consideration competing land uses, the mandates of land protection and management agencies, and the concerns of the private landowners.

5. Importance of Non-Government Organizations:

One of the most important observations from our association with Carolinian Canada is the important role played by the non- government sector. The private organizations have and continue to be a proactive force that has resulted in an extended, cooperative project, to protect significant habitat in Ontario. Undoubtedly, Carolinian Canada would not have survived three years as a quality program had it not been for the persistence and determination of the many private groups involved. Future protection programs may continue to be more successful in the long term with direct involvement of the non-government sector.

6. The Private Landowner:

The central theme of this work of encouraging good private stewardship continues to revolve around the private landowner. It is important to recognize that a significant proportion of rural landowners are already practicing good stewardship, and require little more than common courtesy and some recognition to continue to maintain the natural integrity of a site. Many are extremely proud of their properties. Others need stronger encouragement and we have tried to provide the necessary assistance whenever possible. One of the greatest real benefits of landowner contact is simply the education of the landowners.

Natural heritage protection is becoming more than fee simple acquisition or landuse regulation through planning processes. It means complementing these by working cooperatively with individual landowners, to help them appreciate what they have and why its worth protecting. There is nothing particularly new in developing an approach that shows common courtesy and respect for owners, but it is perhaps one that has been lost over the years by the numerous organizations involved in private land protection. The time now appears to be right for a resurgence of this attitude, one that is appreciated and accepted by the landowner.

Update 1990

Over the past two years, a Landowner Contact Training Manual has been produced and is currently being used as the primary teaching tool for landowner contact training sessions. Also, a newsletter for landowners has been introduced, and is being mailed to all owners associated with the program.

In Carolinian Canada, the Landowner Contact and Stewardship Award Program has decentralized to local offices of the MNR and Conservation Authorities. Several of these lead agencies have been operating their own private stewardship programs, building upon the work started earlier by the University of Guelph. There are currently 470 Carolinian Canada landowners with verbal stewardship agreements under the Award Program, owning 5,400 hectares of provincially significant natural area.

Plants

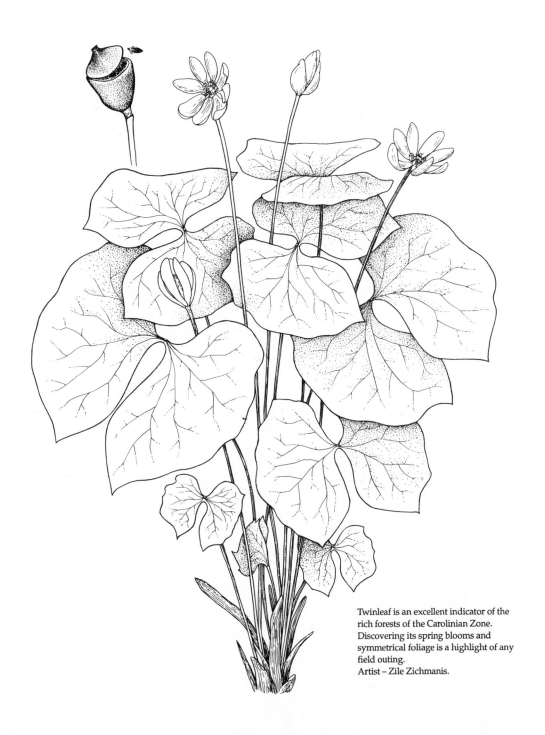

Twinleaf is an excellent indicator of the rich forests of the Carolinian Zone. Discovering its spring blooms and symmetrical foliage is a highlight of any field outing.
Artist – Zile Zichmanis.

Reproductive Biology of Rare Carolinian Plants with Regard to Conservation Management

John D. Ambrose

The Arboretum
University of Guelph, Guelph, Ontario N1G 2W1

Peter G. Kevan

Department of Environmental Biology
University of Guelph, Guelph, Ontario N1G 2W1

Abstract. *Ten rare or endangered Carolinian plant species were examined for various aspects of their population and reproductive biology. Experimental aspects of pollination, pollinator choice, and seedling establishment, were conducted. From these studies, the breeding systems, pollinator mechanisms, and means of seedling establishment were eluci-dated. This information is basic to the wise management of protected natural areas and for the recommendations to other land managers to increase the effective, available habitat, for both the species in jeopardy and the broader Carolinian biota. Threats which were recog-nized in several species include a breeding system that precludes sexual reproduction in small, isolated populations (i.e. lack of available mates), and insufficient habitat to allow a population to develop to a viable size for self-perpetuation.*

Project Objectives

The aim of this project was to investigate the reproductive and population biology of several rare or endangered Carolinian species of flowering plants. The focus of the studies was to provide information relevant to the management of significant Carolinian habitats, especially with regard to conserving biological diversity and reducing the current threat under which many species exist.

Studies Completed

During the three year duration of this World Wildlife Fund (WWF) sponsored project, studies were carried out on ten species:

1. Hop Tree (*Ptelea trifoliata*),
2. Kentucky Coffee Tree (*Gymnocladus dioica*),
3. Prairie Rose (*Rosa setigera*),
4. Round-leaved Greenbriar (*Smilax rotundifolia*),
5. Summer Grape (*Vitis aestivalis*),
6. Chestnut (*Castanea dentata*),
7. Pawpaw (*Asimina triloba*),
8. Cucumber Tree (*Magnolia acuminata*),
9. Red Mulberry (*Morus rubra*), and
10. Prickly-pear Cactus (*Opuntia humifusa*).

Some of these plants were studied as continuations of projects funded by other agencies. Studies on a few are continuing with the help of new funding.

Nevertheless, most of the information relevant to the conservation management of all these plants was gained during the time period of the WWF funding. The following narrative summarizes the findings for each species. As the detailed research reports are produced, copies will be forwarded to WWF.

Results of this Project, by Species

Dioecious Species

1. *Ptelea trifoliata* (Hop Tree) – Following our report of 1985 (Ambrose *et al.* 1985), additional observations were made on pollinator choice between male and female plants, and on gender ratios and constancy in seedling families from different known Ontario sources, under cultivation.

2. *Gymnocladus dioica* (Kentucky Coffee Tree) – Different techniques were tried for pollinating naturally occurring isolated female clones. Hand pollinations were very successful, producing abundant fruit, the seeds of which germinated into vigorous seedlings. An initial trial of hanging bottled bouquets of male flowers in high-crowned female clones was not successful, but this technique is worthy of further trial. Pollinators were observed in two populations. The confirmation of moth pollinator activity during the night, as well as bumble bees at dusk, indicates the presence of pollinators of sufficient range to account for the observed fruit set on female trees, widely spaced from male trees (up to 500 m). However, separation by kilometres, between males and females, renders the females barren. The preliminary results of an NSERC-supported study to identify clonality in Ontario stands and quantify genetic diversity were previously described (Ambrose and Carey 1987). A more detailed report is now in preparation. The confirmation of the clonal nature of most Ontario stands, and their very low genetic diversity, have implications for how their habitats might be managed, and for intervention action that in the future might be required for the long term conservation of this species.

3. *Rosa setigera* (Prairie Rose) – The early horticultural literature documented the presence of male- and female-sterile individuals, indicating the possibility of dioecy in this species. Through a high number of controlled hand pollinations, we found a clear dichotomous pattern between functionally male and female plants. In both sexes, fully formed stigmas and anthers with pollen were found to be present. However, in the female flowers the pollen is not viable, and in the male flowers even viable pollen from other male plants will not effect seed development. In all experimental pollinations, only pollen from male plants placed on stigmas of female plants, produced fruit with viable seeds. There was no evidence of other intermediate morphs. Pollination is by a variety of pollen-foraging insects, particularly bees, which gather pollen from both male and female plants. Although this species was observed colonizing recent old fields, it is almost entirely confined to Essex County in its Canadian distribution. We suspect it's seeds are dispersed by birds eating the hips.

4. *Smilax rotundifolia* (Round-leaved Greenbriar) – This is a highly restricted species of the Carolinian Zone with only four known populations. At least two of these appear to be extended single-sex clones. Only one population is known to produce fruit without human pollination intervention. Even in this latter population, natural fruit set is sparse compared to those from controlled hand pollinations. A second experimental population consisted of only female

plants which produced fruit only from the controlled hand pollinations. No natural pollinators were observed, but the small green flowers, occurring in the dark understorey, suggest small flies. The pollen from the male flowers is held together by strands of viscin.

5. *Vitis aestivalis* (Summer Grape) – Through analysis of scattered individuals in one extensive population, a clear pattern of dioecy was seen. Because of the wide clonal spread of individual plants, there often are insufficient individuals for pollination and fruit development. Their lofty position in the crowns of supporting trees makes work on this species very difficult.

Monoecious Species (including those with hermaphrodite flowers).

6. *Castanea dentata* (Chestnut) – Through pollination trials, we confirmed the self-incompatible nature of this species. Thus, isolated trees do not produce viable seeds without hand pollination with pollen from other trees. We were able to readily effect pollination and seed development through hand cross-pollinations on those few mature trees with flowers low enough to reach with a ladder. We attempted suspending bottled bouquets of male flowers into high-crowned trees, but met with only partial success. Some seeds were produced on these isolated trees that had not produced seeds previously. However, because seeds that fall to the ground are quickly picked up by foraging animals, one would need to check trees almost daily during the autumn to gather the seeds for further experimental use. A diversity of pollen and nectar feeding insects was recorded on the inflorescences. The Chestnut Blight is still the greatest threat to this species. Even some of the large trees (25-65 cm dbh) that had been observed for several years to be free of blight symptoms, are dying. 1987 appears to have been a particularly bad year, in which several new deaths were observed. Our studies were in collaboration with Dr. C. McKeen, who has confirmed the presence of hypovirulent strains of the Blight fungus in Ontario (McKeen and Ambrose 1987) and will continue this aspect of the study in 1988. Seed from our hand pollinations have been germinated and are being grown at MNR's St. Williams Forestry Station.

7. *Asimina triloba* (Pawpaw) – Through extensive pollination trials, we have determined that this species is self-incompatible. Some populations that produce very little or no fruit appear to be clonal. In one such stand, an extensive experimental regime was set up of within-stand pollinations, compared with out-stand pollinations. Only the latter produced fruit, providing evidence of the clonality of this stand. In other stands, our controlled hand pollinations produced significantly more fruit than from natural pollinations. Although a variety of beetles and flies were observed on the flowers, there appears to be too few pollinators for full fruit set. The pollen is presented in tetrads, which are, in turn, held together with viscin. Trials of *in situ* seed germination were set up in several stands. One showed almost complete germination, others showed sparse to no germination. Seedling survival will be assessed in future experiments. The occurrence of natural seedling establishment was also very variable between stands. A pair of raccoons was photographically caught, triggered by an infra-red beam, examining a large pile of ripe fruit; they are likely the primary dispersal agents at the present time. The distribution along stream and river banks, and occasionally in wet woods, leads one to question whether some (or all) of these populations were originally established by early post-glacial humans, perhaps while in transit along trails and canoe routes.

8. *Magnolia acuminata* (Cucumber Tree) – This is Ontario's only officially endangered tree, with a highly localized distribution in only two areas of southern Ontario (west of Simcoe and west of Fonthill). The flowers are extremely protogynous with the stigmas receptive only when the flowers are in the loose bud stage, with the petals expanded but still mostly closed. Selfing results in very few seeds, as do naturally pollinated flowers. In contrast, hand cross-pollinated flowers produce abundant seed, when pollinated in the loose bud stage. Pollination appears to be through a short-term, pollinator-trapping mechanism. Insects crawl into the flower through the basal gaps between the petals and try to leave by crawling up the slick inside surface of the upright petals. In their struggling, the pollinators repeatedly brush against the anthers and become dusted with pollen, or pollinate the stigmas which are recurved against the petals. All our observations were on open-grown and forest edge specimens. Natural pollination may be more successful in forest stands. However, there appears to be a serious constraint to effective dispersal beyond the few natural stands. The aril of the seeds is oily and orange and probably dispersed by birds.

9. *Opuntia humifusa* (Prickly-pear Cactus) – This endangered cactus species is extremely limited in its Canadian distribution. Two of the inland populations on cemetery grounds were recently discovered to have been established by a well-intended clergyman, and originated from the Point Pelee population. The Fish Point population is threatened by high water, and likely, by collectors as well. Thus, the large Point Pelee National Park population is very critical for the survival of this species in Canada. Pollination studies on this population revealed that *Bombus pennsylvanicus* is the primary pollinator, the flowers are receptive for only one day, and cross-pollination is required for seed set. Plots over variable microsites were set up within the population for trails of *in situ* seed germination and seedling establishment. The fruits contain a sugary pulp within which are the seeds. Birds and rodents are likely dispersers.

10. *Morus rubra* (Red Mulberry) – This species is wind pollinated, with anthers explosively dehiscing, leaving no pollen for insect foragers. There are very few populations of this officially threatened species in Canada. Further, in most populations it occurs with the alien *Morus alba*, with which it appears to freely hybridize. This alien species poses a threat through hybridization, but of undetermined magnitude. Controlled hand pollinations between individuals of each species, and the species with the putative naturally occurring hybrids, have resulted in seeds and seedlings which are being grown at The Arboretum. These will be used to better characterize individuals of known hybrid origin, and to observe patterns of segregation of morphological forms from hybrid parents. These further analyses will be necessary to quantify the hybrid dynamics of these species and the magnitude of threat that *M. alba* poses to *M. rubra*. Natural seedling establishment was observed in only two small areas of the large and extensive Point Pelee population. *In situ* germination plots were set up within different microsites (of variable moisture, shade, and organic matter in the soil), and with fruit from the spectral range of *M. alba*, hybrids, and *M. rubra*. These will require follow-up observation to assess seedling success of different *Morus* morphs over the environmental gradient.

Conservation Significance

Through a better understanding of the biology of these various rare species and their habitat requirements, action can be directed to protect and manage them wisely. An understanding of a species' breeding system is basic to its conservation. Several of these species have been confirmed to be dioecious or self-incompatible, and for these taxa it is especially important to consider the genetic diversity of populations in management.

Our hand pollinations were able to increase the amount of fruit set. Only in isolated individuals or clones was no fruit set observed in natural populations of some species. Thus, the problem appears to be more the absence of suitable mates for dioecious or self-incompatible species, than the complete absence of pollinators.

Many species have a very restricted distribution in Ontario. There appears to be a combination of insufficient dispersal agents and insufficient habitats for these species to be effectively dispersed, migrate, and in which to become established, despite a wider climatically suitable region.

Conservation Recommendations

For the conservation of our biologically diverse Carolinian biota, we need to not only protect what remnant natural areas there are, but also to consider ways to increase the effective habitat for species in jeopardy and to maintain the biological processes that support these communities. In reflecting back, the Carolinian Canada Program did a great deal to heighten public awareness and begin the process of protecting significant habitats through a creative and diverse array of means. This preservation of aggregations of threatened species and their habitats is an important first step. Now we need to look at the long term conservation of this biota. It is clear that many species are either slowly losing ground, or at best holding at equilibrium. For the long term we must do better. We should aim to not only preserve the pieces we have left, but to conserve in the sense of ensuring adequate habitat that will support populations that are large enough to respond to a changing environment, and to migrate into new sites when conditions are favourable. Much of this objective can be met by all land holding or managing agencies (e.g. Ministry of Natural Resources, Ministry of Agriculture and Food, Ministry of Transportation, public utilities, conservation authorities, municipal parks), working toward a unified goal of environmental amelioration and habitat improvement. In that context, further individual activities will have a much better chance of being successful.

To complement an improved state of critical habitats, a comprehensive program for reintroduction and population enhancement needs to be addressed. This program should include close attention to the appropriate source of stock materials and maintaining the genetic integrity and diversity within plants cultivated for later re-introduction to natural areas. This can be achieved by hand pollinations between different naturally occurring individuals, as well as by taking and propagating vegetative cuttings or offshoots. However, in the latter case, caution should be directed to avoid excessive duplication of single genotypes. The recording of sources of pollen for hand pollinations, collected seeds and vegetative propagules, and their ultimate sites for out-planting, is essential for a meaningful evaluation of the results of establishment.

A program of monitoring the status of species in jeopardy, as well as the amount and quality of habitat, should be ongoing from the basic knowledge that has now been compiled. The administrative responsibility would appear most appropriate for the Ministry of Natural Resources, under the Regional and District Ecologists, and in consultation with the researchers who have undertaken the specific studies.

Below are specific recommendations.

1. A proposal has been made to the Essex Region Conservation Authority (ERCA) to propagate material from existing stands of *Gymnocladus dioica* in highly threatened habitats which are not feasible for conservation protection (roadsides, fencerows, railroad right-of-ways), and establish stands on ERCA managed conservation lands (excluding natural areas at this time). By bringing male and female clones to within pollinator flight range, the success of natural pollination can be assessed, along with success of establishment, on different sites. These preliminary trials can provide guidance for procedures of future reintroduction or population enhancement in natural areas.

2. A species such as *Rosa setigera* could come under threat in the future if its old field habitats are brought back into cultivation and if natural areas are brought under more rigorous control, so that fields and shrub thickets succeed into closed forests. A broader management scheme, between various land holders, could ensure a diversity of appropriate habitats through a coordination of routine activities that are now carried out independently (e.g. verge maintenance, right-of-way clearing, tree planting for watershed improvement). Without any increase of land in public ownership, a coordination of management could do much to improve or create new habitats and connect existing ones within the Carolinian Zone.

3. *Castanea dentata* is a species showing a slow natural recovery from the Chestnut Blight. It was an important forest tree species in several regions of the Carolinian zone and efforts to enhance this natural recovery would be important to improving the biological diversity of the Carolinian zone, as well as increasing the economic forestry potential, and thus incentives to retain forest cover. Studies are on-going to assess the possible use of the naturally occurring hypovirulent Chestnut Blight fungus to allow recovery of trees blighted with the virulent strains. In the meantime, all efforts should be made to ensure that Chestnut trees and their habitats are protected from clearing or degradation so that a sufficient base of genetic diversity can be retained.

4. *Morus rubra* is a species threatened with extremely few populations and possible genetic erosion from introgression with the introduced *M. alba*. A proposal has been submitted to assess this latter threat so that such significant populations as occur at Point Pelee National Park and Fish Point Nature Reserve can be wisely managed.

References

Ambrose, J.D. and C.K. Carey. 1987. *Gymnocladus dioica in Canada: the biology of a rare tree at its northern limits of distribution*. Int. Bot. Congress, Berlin. 5 pp.

Ambrose, J.D., P.G. Kevan and R.M. Gadawski. 1985. Hop Tree *(Ptelea trifoliata)* in Canada: population and reproductive biology of a rare species. *Can. J. Bot.* 63:1928-1935.

McKeen, C.D. and J.D. Ambrose. 1987. The American Chestnut survives the ravages of Blight. *Working for Wildlife*. fall p. 8.

Additional papers on specific studies have been both submitted for publication and are in preparation.

The exotic-sounding Wild Mandarin is an
Appalachian species restricted in Canada
to Ontario's Carolinian Zone. Mature
forests of hemlock-beech, or dry, sandy
hardwoods are its preferred habitat.
Artist – Zile Zichmanis.

Improved Germination and Growth of Rare Native Ontario Orchid Species

Allan B. Anderson

Department of Botany, University of Guelph
Guelph, Ontario N1G 2W1

Abstract. *Seed of* Platanthera ciliaris, Spiranthes magnicamporum, S. ochroleuca, S. ovalis, S. lacera *var* gracilis, Triphora trianthophora *and* Isotria medeoloides *were obtained, sterilized, and sown on different media. All but* Isotria medeoloides *germinated.* Platanthera ciliaris, Spiranthes magnicamporum *and* S. ochroleuca *developed into plantlets and were planted in a suitable outdoor habitat and have survived overwintering.*

Background

Many previous reports on asymbiotic germination of North American orchid species have discussed the difficulty of germination and growth in culture. There have been very few successful plantings in soil. This project investigated ways to increase germination of some of our rarer orchid species and improve growth rates, with the ultimate aim of establishing plants formed by this method in suitable habitats. Seed of seven species were collected. Six of the seven rare Ontario species were germinated and three of these have now been planted in soil.

Approximately 500 man-hours were spent on this project, making up agar, sterilizing and sowing seed in culture vessels, transferring crowded plantlets to new agar, and washing old culture vessels.

Introduction

Many of Ontario's orchids are among the most threatened of our native wild flower species. Seventeen species or varieties of species are listed as rare in Ontario by Argus and White (1982) while Whiting and Catling (1986) consider 21 to be endangered, threatened, or rare in the province. In many cases, populations of these species in known locations have declined drastically over the past fifty years. Preservation of wetlands, identification and protection of environmentally sensitive areas, as well as the Endangered Species Act, are all positive steps in the attempts to stop further declines in our native orchid species.

Unfortunately, the locations of some species are too far apart to allow for cross pollination between colonies which may lead to a lack of genetic diversity in our rarer species. Others are close to their northern limit of distribution and occur only in small numbers. In some of these, seed formation is poor, possibly due to lack of suitable insect pollinators.

The natural successful establishment of a flowering orchid plant from seed is estimated by Luer (1975) to be as low as one in one million. This low success rate can be attributed to insufficient suitable habitats, predation by detrimental fungi, and the lack of suitable symbiotic fungi. It therefore has little effect on populations if a few capsules are removed for germination studies.

The 'seed' of the orchid has an undifferentiated embryo with very little food supply stored as lipids in the mature proembryo. This proembryo is protected by a light air-filled seed coat, the testa.

In nature, successful growth can only take place after a compatible fungus forms a symbiotic relationship with the germinating seed. This fungus then supplies the developing plant with carbohydrates and perhaps other materials such as vitamins (Harvais and Pekkala 1975) for continued growth of the orchid. By using an external carbohydrate source such as glucose in a suitable nutrient agar, the necessity for the symbiotic fungus can be circumvented.

Temperate climate terrestrial orchids are typically much more difficult to raise from seed than their showy epiphytic relatives (Arditti 1982). Despite the difficulties, many researchers in Europe and North America have attempted to grow them. In Europe, where this has been a relatively popular field of endeavour, many media suitable for the germination and growth of temperate orchids have been developed by researchers (Fast 1976, 1978; Luke 1976; Burgeff 1936; Borris 1969; Harbeck 1963; Voth 1976; Veyret 1969; Thomale 1954). Germination of North American species has been attempted by only a handful of researchers (Curtis 1936, 1943; Stoutamire, 1964, 1974; Harvais 1973, 1974, 1982; Arditti, Michaud and Oliva 1982; Ballard 1987; Henrich, Stimart and Ascher 1981; and Liddell 1944). Arditti (1982) provides an excellent overview of the species germinated and media used.

There are very few reports of attempts to plant orchids in soil after asymbiotic culture, but Arditti, Michaud and Oliva (1982) recommend some soil mix material from pots containing a mature plant of the same or related species be added to pots before planting seedlings.

Symbiotic germination of North American orchids has been largely unsuccessful (Currah 1987; Harvais 1973). By using asymbiotic germination techniques and testing different media it is possible to grow seedlings of some of Canada's rare orchid species until they are old enough to produce their own carbohydrates by photosynthesis. They may then be less reliant on a natural symbiont when transferred to soil.

Materials and Methods

Unopened seed capsules or seed were air dried for 48 hours and stored in the cold at five degrees C for two months before culturing. In a few instances green capsules were surface sterilized in 70% alcohol for 15 minutes and the capsules split open under sterile conditions and the seed removed for sowing on various media.

After two months or more the stored seed was added to ten ml of water with a drop of Tween 20, a surfactant, subjected to a vacuum for three hours, then brought back to atmospheric pressure and shaken. This was repeated until most of the seed had sunk to the bottom of the vial. Excess water was added to overflowing to remove any floating seed. This water was then removed and replaced by 7.5% calcium hydrochloride or 30% hydrogen peroxide. The vial was then shaken at 100 oscillations per minute for 20 minutes to two hours depending on the species. The seeds were then transferred to sterile distilled water and shaken for one hour. This step was repeated before sowing the seeds in culture vessels.

Baby food jars were employed as culture vessels as they have wide mouths, are relatively shallow, and can be sealed well. No appreciable evaporation was noted over a period of 12 months in these containers, thus eliminating the need for irrigation required in less airtight containers (Arditti 1982).

Cultures were maintained in the light and the dark at 23 degrees C. When plantlets had developed sufficiently they were thinned to four plants per jar and later to one per jar with larger plants.

Germination estimates were made by counting ungerminated and germinated seeds on three, one centimetre squares of medium.

Results

1. *Platanthera ciliaris* – Yellow or Orange-fringed Orchid: This orchid was previously known in Canada only from Essex County near Windsor and near Leamington. More recent reports have not been verified, and it seems likely that this species has been extirpated in Ontario. *Plantanthera ciliaris* was successfully germinated by Stoutamire (1964) who reported it to be one of the fastest growing of our orchids, but no germination rates were reported. Also mentioned in this paper is the discovery of leafless seedlings of this species by Mr. Fred Case in Michigan. An artificial hybrid of *Platanthera ciliaris* and *Platanthera blephariglottis* was reported to take 40 months from germination to anthesis (Stoutamire 1974). The species and hybrid were grown on Knudson's C media supplemented with peptone and solidified with 8 gm of agar per litre.

Some seed was sent by Dr. Stoutamire in March 1986. The seed had been collected in Randdolph County, West Virginia on 27 October 1984. This seed, some of which had been stored at low temperature, was sterilized for 20 minutes in 7.5% calcium hypochlorite solution, rinsed in sterile water, and sown on eight different media.

One replication was placed in the dark and the other in 12 hr light, 12 hr dark, at 23 degrees C. One percent germination was visible in four weeks in the dark. The treatments in the light were two weeks slower in showing germination. Germination ranged from 0% in a modification of Pfeffer's medium (Harvais 1982) to 80% in Fast's media (Fast 1978) with the addition of one gm of peptone and vitamins (see Table I for composition of Fast's medium with modifications). Germination was uneven with 70% of the seeds having germinated at six months and 80% at nine months. Seedlings were removed from the original culture and placed in fresh media when they reached one cm in length. Some were placed in the light at this stage and turned green within one week. Seedlings were planted outside in a moist peat area at the University of Guelph in September and October but failed to appear in the spring.

Seed was later sent from a location in Michigan by Dr. Anthony Reznicek of the University of Michigan. Seedlings from this source were planted out in early spring and produced new leaves during the summer. These seedlings have overwintered.

Table 1

Modified Fast's Medium (Fast 1978)

Macroelements		Amount per litre
Calcium nitrate Ca(NO$_3$)$_2$.4H$_2$O		65 mg
Ammonium nitrate NH$_4$NO$_3$		65 mg
Potassium phosphate KH$_2$PO$_4$		33 mg
Potassium chloride KCl		33 mg
Magnesium sulphate MgSO$_4$.7H$_2$O		33 mg
Ammonium ferric sulphate		25 mg
Trace elements stock solution (Nitch's)		
Sulphuric acid sp. gravity 1.83 H$_2$SO$_4$	- 0.5 ml	1 ml
Manganese chloride MnCl$_2$.4H$_2$O	- 2500 mg	
Boric acid H$_3$BO$_3$	- 2500 mg	
Zinc sulphate ZnSO$_4$.7H$_2$O	- 50 mg	
Cobalt chloride CuCl$_2$.6H$_2$O	- 15 mg	
Sodium molybdate Na$_2$MoO$_4$.2H$_2$O	- 1000 ml	
Vitamins		
Nicotinic acid		0.1 mg
Pyridoxine – HCl		0.1 mg
Thiamine – HCl		0.1 mg
Riboflavin		0.1 mg
Glucose		7 gm
Peptone		1 gm
Agar		6 gm
H$_2$O pH adjusted to 5.5		1000 ml

2. *Spiranthes magnicamporum* – Great Plains Ladies'-tresses: This species is restricted in Canada to the Carolinian zone of southwestern Ontario except for one disjunct location in Bruce County (Whiting and Catling 1986). In Ontario, this species is agamospermic, producing multiple embryos and often splitting the testa. Some of these embryos are expelled from the testa and some are produced as free embryos (Catling 1982).

Seed was collected by Ross Brown and Gary Allen and unopened capsules were collected later by myself, all from Walpole Island. Poor germination was quickly evident in seed sterilized with 7.5% calcium hypochlorite compared with sterilization of intact capsules. Older seed stored at five degrees C for two months also gave poor germination. An examination of seed in fresh unopened capsules revealed green, actively growing embryos, which were probably killed by sterilization. Older seed examined showed some shrivelled embryos, along with some normal ones, which would account for the lower germination rates.

Germination using fresh, unopened capsules, was evident in seven days with some treatments giving as much as 90% germination. Of the eight media tested, Knudson's C gave the best long term results (see Table 2 for composition of Knudson's medium with modifications). At five months, one medium (Fast 1976) gave larger protocorms but had about 50% mortality. Plants continued to grow and produce leafy rosettes with leaves 0.5 cm wide and two cm long after 12 months in Knudson's C, but root growth was slow. The Knudson's C medium had been supplemented with one mg per litre of benzyl adedine (BA), and 0.1 mg naphthaleneacetic acid (NAA) which had been reported to give better protocorm growth in *Cypripedium reginae* (Harvais 1982). When seedlings were transferred to media without BA and NAA, roots two cm long were produced in three months. It would appear that although BA and NAA may improve early growth, they are detrimental to root formation.

Plants 18 months and older were transferred to different soil mixes and planted outside. All survived and produced new leaves. The soil mix giving the best growth was 3/4 peat moss and 1/4 top soil; this may have been due to better moisture retention.

Some plants kept in the medium for 24 months produced large masses of embiod tissue at the base of the leaves. These developed into young plants when placed on fresh media.

There are no previous reports on the germination of this species, although Stoutamire (1964) germinated *Spiranthes cernua*, Oliva and Arditti (1984) have germinated *Spiranthes romanzoffiana* and *S. gracilis*, and Henrich, Stumart and Ascher (1981) also reported the germination of *S. romanzoffiana*.

Table 2

Modified Knudson's Media (Knudson 1946)

	Amount per litre
Calcium nitrate Ca(NO$_3$)$_2$.4H$_2$0	500 mg
Ammonium sulphate	250 mg
Magnesium sulphate	125 mg
Potassium phosphate	125 mg
Ammonium ferric sulphate	25 mg
Trace elements same as in Table 1	1 ml
Vitamins same as in Table 1	0.1 mg of each
Glucose	16 gm
H$_2$0	1000 ml
Agar Adjust pH to 5.5	6 gm

3. *Spiranthes ochroleuca* – Yellow Ladies'-tresses: This species is also restricted in Canada to the Carolinian zone of southwestern Ontario except for one disjunct location in Frontenac County (Whiting and Catling 1986). Within Ontario this species is sexual, forming normal seed (Catling 1982). Seed of this species was collected from Walpole Island and sent by Ross Brown and Gary Allen. After storage for two months, seed was vacuum treated and sterilized for 20 minutes, rinsed in sterile water, and sown on various media. Results were similar to results with *Spiranthes magnicamporum* but germination was lower at 50%. Unfortunately, a malfunctioning growth chamber resulted in the death of most of these cultures. Nevertheless, a few plants were salvaged and grown to 18 months when they were planted out. They produced new leaves during the summer and have overwintered (see Table II for medium composition).

4. *Spiranthes ovalis* var. *erostellata* – Oval Ladies'-tresses: Ross Brown, Gary Allen and Larry Lamb discovered this species on Walpole Island in 1985 and sent some seed via Wendy McNab, District Manager of the Ministry of Natural Resources in Chatham. This location is the only known site for this orchid in Canada. The seed of this species are again monoembryonic (Catling 1983) and protected by the testa. Seed were germinated in the same manner as *Spiranthes ochroleuca* and gave 25% germination on Knudson's C media after two weeks (see Table II for medium composition). Unfortunately they were in the same growth chamber as *Spiranthes ochroleuca* and all succumbed to the heat. Fresh seed has been obtained and another attempt at germination will be initiated shortly.

5. *Spiranthes lacera* var. *gracilis* – Southern Slender Ladies'-tresses: Indications are that this species is declining in southern Ontario, and Walpole Island may be one of the few remaining populations.

   Seed of this species was again sent by Ross Brown and Gary Allen and was treated in a similar manner to the two previous species. Germination only took place in the dark and was very poor, about one percent. Seedlings reaching about five mm in height were transferred to light, where they slowly turned brown and died. Oliva and Arditti (1984) reported 30% germination on full strength Curtis medium but the only germination here took place on Knudson's C (see Table II for medium composition).

6. *Triphora trianthophora* – Three Birds Orchid: This species is strictly confined in Canada to the Carolinian zone of Ontario and reproduces vegetatively by means of subterranean tubers produced on short rhizomes. Unopened capsules of this species were sent by Allen Woodliffe from Rondeau Provincial Park and some seed was collected by myself from a location outside the park. Both green pod and fresh seed were sterilized in the manner previously described, for 20 minutes. The capsule in this species is green and fleshy at the time of dehiscence, unlike most other Ontario orchids. Germination was visible in 30 days and ranged from 2% to 90% in the dark. Knudson's C medium gave the best results with no mortality at four months (see Table II for medium composition). The protocorms continued to grow and produced rhizomes with small tubers. These tubers were oval in shape and reached a maximum size of 7 mm long by 5 mm wide and turned a light brown colour at maturity. These were removed from the original plant and transferred to fresh media where they have begun to produce aerial shoots and rhizomes. *Triphora ricketii* has been germinated by Stoutamire (1964) but unlike *Triphora trianthophora*, a single tuber only is produced and it takes a number of years before any stems grow upwards to produce functional leaves.

7. *Isotria medeoloides* – Small Whorled Pogonia: Eileene and Bill Stewart first discovered this orchid in Ontario in 1977 (Stewart 1977, 1979) and it is now protected by the Endangered Species Act. This orchid failed to appear in 1983 (Stewart 1983) and may now be extirpated from Ontario. Seed of this species was obtained from Bill Brumback of the New England Wildflower Society. Despite numerous attempts at germinating this rare species using a wide variety of treatments, no germination has yet taken place. The seed still looks viable after over 18 months in the media.

8. *Isotria verticillata* – Large Whorled Pogonia: Of the three known colonies of this species in Ontario, the only one to flower in 1985 was the one in Oxford County

(Anderson and Britton 1986). Attempts to pollinate the only two flowers formed that year were unsuccessful. This species is now protected by the Endangered Species Act. Mrs. Fred Case has germinated this species on Knudson's C media (pers. comm.).

Discussion

During the WWF funding period, six species of rare Ontario orchids were germinated, four of these apparently for the first time. Three species have been transferred to soil where new leaf formation has taken place, hopefully indicating successful establishment. Germination rates are sufficiently high that a significant number could be transplanted to soil where they presumably will form a symbiotic relationship with a suitable fungus. Dependence on these fungal symbionts may be less in some species of orchids, especially those which produce chlorophyll at an early state such as *Plantanthera ciliaris, Spiranthes magnicamporum, S. ochroleuca,* and *S. ovalis. Triphora,* on the other hand, produces green leaves only for a very short time in the late summer, and therefore may be extremely dependent on a suitable fungal relationship. It may therefore be necessary to isolate this fungus from a naturally growing plant, in order to infect seedlings grown in culture before planting them into soil.

Conservation Significance

1. The sheer pressure of urbanization of southwestern Ontario has led to large reductions in suitable habitats for many of Ontario's orchids. To ensure the preservation of our unique genotypes, artificial propagation offers a partial solution.

2. By using asymbiotic techniques a sufficient number of the rarer orchid species can be raised for transplanting into suitable soil to ensure their continued survival in Canada.

3. Extirpated species can also be re-introduced by this method.

4. Ex-situ locations can be established in botanic gardens and publicly owned reserves where photographers and naturalists can photograph and view some of these rare species without disturbing their natural habitats.

5. Some of the more common showy species have also been raised by this method and established in suitable soil. If these techniques can be passed on to commercial horticultural enterprises, sufficient plants could be raised to supply the wildflower enthusiasts without resorting to the deplorable practice of digging large numbers of plants from the wild.

Conservation Recommendations

1. Some species of rare native orchids do not readily form seed and these species should be hand-pollinated annually to ensure seed production.

2. Populations need to be monitored, insect pollinators identified, fungal symbionts isolated, and ecological factors established for each species. The MNR is the most logical department to deal with some of this monitoring.

3. The establishment of new natural areas by the purchase of uneconomical farm land in the southwestern part of Ontario which may have been prairie in the past, to allow natural regeneration and planting experiments with orchids and prairie species.

4. The creation of suitable habitats by management of natural areas, especially the reduction of competition by flooding, cutting, or burning, helps in the formation of these habitats.

5. A critical number of plants of extirpated species can be grown and maintained at the University of Guelph. Plants from this stock can then be reintroduced into historical sites on an experimental basis, where they will hopefully survive and reproduce. Some modification such as burning or cutting may be required at these sites to ensure an ideal habitat for reintroduction.

Continuing Research

With some financial help from the New England Wildflower Society, the production methods for some of the more showy species are being actively pursued and enquiries have been received from three nurseries in the United States. The author intends to continue work on asymbiotic germination and growth of orchids with the intention of establishing ex-situ populations. Some species have already been planted in the Arboretum at Guelph and Peter Rice of the Hamilton Botanic Gardens has expressed an interest in growing some of these seed-raised plants.

Studies on the mycorrhizal symbionts of the more common orchids are being attempted with these seed-raised plants. Randy Currah, of the Devonian Botanic Gardens in Edmonton, has been pursuing this line of research (Currah 1987).

Acknowledgements

This work was supported by grants from the Southwestern Region of the Ministry of Natural Resources and the World Wildlife Fund Canada. I am also indebted to Ross Brown, Gary Allen, Allen Woodliffe, Wendy McNab, Bill Brumback, Warren Stoutamire, and Tony Reznicek for supplying seed, and Darren Murawski for his technical help.

References

Anderson, A.B. and D.M. Britton. 1986. *Isotria verticillata* (Muhl ex Willd) Raf. (whorled pogonia) discovered in Oxford County. *The Plant Press* 4(1):18-19.

Arditti, J., J.D. Michaud and A.P. Oliva. 1982. Practical germination of North American and related orchids – I *Epipactis gigantea* and *E. helleborine. Amer. Orchid Soc. Bull.* 50(2):162-171.

Arditti, J. 1982. *Orchid Biology.* Reviews and Perspectives II. Cornell University Press, Ithaca, New York. 390 pp.

Argus, G.W. and D.J. White, (eds). 1982. *Atlas of rare vascular plants of Ontario.* National Museum of Natural Sciences, Botany Division, Ottawa.

Ballard, W.W. 1987. Sterile propagation of *Cypripedium reginae* from seed. *Amer. Orchid Soc. Bull.* 56:935-946.

Borris, H. 1969. *Samenvermehrung und Anzucht europaischer Erdorchideen.* Ber. 2. Europ. Orchideenkongress. Paris p. 74-78.

Burgeff, H. 1936. *Samenkeimung der Orchideen und Entwicklung ihrer Keimpflanzen.* G. Fischer Verlag, Vena.

Catling, P.M. 1982. Breeding systems of northeastern North American *Spiranthes* (Orchidaceae). *Can. J. Bot.* 60:3017-3039.

Catling, P.M. 1983. *Spiranthes ovalis* var. *erostellata* (Orchidaceae), a new autogamous variety from eastern United States. *Brittonia* 35(2):120-125.

Currah, R.S. 1987. *Thanatephorus pennatus* sp. nov. isolated from mycorrhizal roots of *Calypso bulbosa* (Orchidaceae) from Alberta. *Can. J. Bot.* 65:1957-1960.

Curtis, J.T. 1936. The germination of native orchid seeds. *Amer. Orchid Soc. Bull.* 5:42-47.

Curtis, J.T. 1943. Germination and seedling development in five species of *Cypripedium* L. *Amer. J. Bot.* 30:199-206.

Fast, G. 1976. Moglichkeiten zur Massenvemehrung von *Cypripedium calceolus* und anderen europaischen Wildorchideen. *Proc. 8th World Orchid Conf.*, Frankfurt (1975). pp. 359-363.

Fast, G. 1978. Unber das Keimverhalten europaischer Erdorchideen bei asymbiotischer Aussaat. *Die Orchidee* 29:270-274.

Harvais, G. 1973. Growth requirements and development of *Cypripedium reginae* in axenic culture. *Can. J. Bot.* 51:327-332.

Harvais, G. 1974. Notes on the biology of some native orchids of Thunder Bay, their endophytes and symbionts. *Can. J. Bot.* 52:451-460.

Harvais, G. 1982. An improved culture medium for growing the orchid *Cypripedium reginae* axenically. *Can. J. Bot.* 60:2547-2555.

Harvais, G. and D. Pekkala. 1975. Vitamin production by a fungus symbiotic with orchids. *Can. J. Bot.* 53:144-155.

Henrich, J.E., D.P. Stimart and P.D. Ascher. 1981. Terrestrial orchid seed germination in vitro on a defined medium. *J. Amer. Soc. Hort. Sci.* 106:193-196.

Knudson, L. 1946. A new nutrient solution for the germination of orchid seeds. *Amer. Orchid Soc. Bull.* 15:214-217.

Liddell, R.W. 1944. Germinating native orchid seed. *Amer. Orchid Soc. Bull.* 12:344-345.

Luer, C.A. 1975. *The native orchids of the United States and Canada excluding Florida.* New York Botanical Garden. 361 pp.

Luke, E. 1976. Erste Ergebnisse zur asymbiotischen samenkeimung von Himantoglossum hircinum. *Die Orchidee* 27:60-61.

Oliva, A.P. and J. Arditti. 1984. Seed germination of North American Orchids – II Native California and related species of *Aplectrum, Cypripedium and Spiranthes. Bot. Gaz.* 145(4):495-501.

Stewart, W.G. 1977. The smaller whorled pogonia, an orchid new to Canada. *Ontario Field Biologist* 31(2):56-58.

Stewart, W.G. 1979. *Isotria medeoloides,* the smaller whorled pogonia, new to Canada. *Rhodora* 80(824):587-590.

Stewart, W.G. 1983. Status of the orchid *Isotria medeoloides* (small whorled pogonia) in Elgin County in 1983. *The Plant Press* 1(3):54.

Stoutamire, W.P. 1964. Seeds and seedlings of native orchids. *Michigan Bot.* 3:107-119.

Stoutamire, W.P. 1974. Terrestrial orchid seedlings. pp. 101-128 in C.L. Withner (ed.), *The Orchids: Scientific Studies.* John Wiley and Sons, New York.

Thomale, H. 1954. *Die Orchideen.* Verlag Eugen Ulmer. Stuttgart.

Veyret, Y. 1974. Development of the embryo and the young seedling stages of orchids. pp 223-265. In: C.L. Withner (ed.), *The Orchids: Scientific Studies.* John Wiley and Sons, New York.

Voth, W. 1976. Aussat und Kultur von *Serapias parviflora* und *S. orientalis. Proc. 8th World Orchid Conf.,* Frankfurt (1975), pp 351-358.

Whiting, R.E. and P.M. Catling. 1986. *Orchids of Ontario.* The CanaColl Foundation. Ottawa. 169 pp.

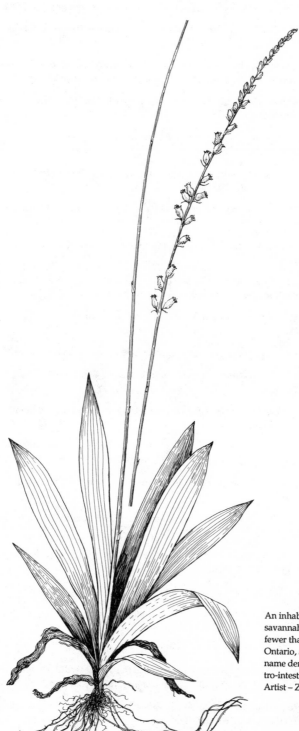

An inhabitant of tall-grass prairie and oak savannah, the Colicroot is known from fewer than 20 sites in Canada, all in Ontario, and is considered threatened. The name derives from its use in treating gastro-intestinal ailments.
Artist – Zile Zichmanis.

The Effect of Woodlot Size on Woody Species Composition and Richness

**Brad Bricker and
Richard Reader**

Department of Botany, University of Guelph
Guelph, Ontario N1G 2W1

Abstract. *Woody species present in five deciduous woodlots in each of five different size classes ($\leq 2.0, 2.1\text{-}2.5, 2.6\text{-}3.5, 3.6\text{-}4.0, 4.1\text{-}7.5$ ha) were censused to test the hypotheses that (1) maximum woody species richness occurs in woodlots of about 2.3 ha in size, and (2) that 3.8 ha is the minimum size at which interior conditions eliminate intolerant 'edge' species in favour of tolerant species. Neither woody species richness nor the frequency of occurrence of either interior or edge species changed significantly over the range of woodlot sizes examined. When small woodlots (ie., ≤ 7.5 ha) are being examined for conservation of woody species, woodlots as small as 1.0 ha could be considered since the assemblage of woody deciduous forest plants they can support may be equivalent to that of woodlots up to 7.5 ha in size.*

Introduction

Urban sprawl and the shift to larger field size in capital intensive agriculture has reduced most of the deciduous forest in southern Ontario to a series of woodlots of varying size. When forests are reduced in size their perimeter or 'edge' to 'interior' ratio increases, resulting in an increase in 'edge' habitat at the expense of 'interior' habitat. The theoretical effect of this change on the number and type of woody species present is shown in Figure 1.

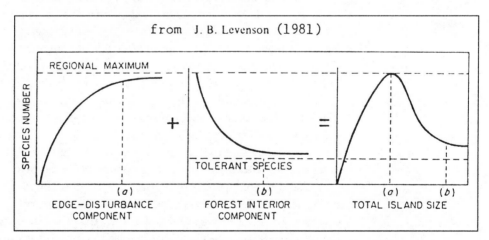

Figure 1: The relationship between the amount of edge and potential woody species richness. Left: Given enough area and variety of conditions, the number of species that could exist becomes asymptotic to the number of woody species of·the region. At some point (a), interior conditions begin to form. Center: Response of woody species to an interior environment characterized by low light levels and mesic conditions. The depletion curve levels off at the number of tolerant, meso-phytic species in the region, point (b). Right: Curve combining the exponential and depletion functions that simulates the field data from southeastern Wisconsin forest islands.   (a) = 2.3 ha   (b) = 3.8 ha

According to Levenson (1981), small woodlots are dominated by edge (shade-intolerant) species, but also support some interior (shade-tolerant species). With increasing woodlot size, species number increases up to the regional maximum. With a further increase in woodlot size, edge species are lost leaving only interior species. Levenson (1981) found that maximum woody species richness (= number of species) occurred in woodlots of about 2.3 ha in Wisconsin and that 3.8 ha was the critical woodlot size to maintain conditions favourable for only woody interior species. If these critical values of 2.3 and 3.8 ha also apply to deciduous woodlots in southern Ontario, it would simplify the task of setting size guidelines for the conservation and management of woody species in small woodlots.

Objectives

The objective of our study was to determine whether the critical values proposed by Levenson (1981) for Wisconsin applied to deciduous woodlots in southern Ontario. To achieve this objective we determined (1) whether maximum richness of woody species was evident in woodlots of 2.1-2.5 ha in size, (2) whether woody edge species were less frequent in the interior of woodlots larger than 2.1-2.5 ha, and (3) whether woody interior species were more frequent in the understory of woodlots 3.6-4.0 ha in size or larger.

Methodology

1. Study area and site selection procedure

The study was conducted in the southern portion of Wellington County, Ontario (Figure 2). Woodlots in five size classes ($\leq$ 2.0, 2.1-2.5, 2.6-3.5, 3.6-4.0, 4.1-7.5 ha) were located using topographic maps. Woodlots having the following characteristics were chosen for the study (five woodlots per size class) to be able to compare our findings with those of Levenson (1981). The woodlots were: (a) found on grey-brown podzolic loam, (b) had relatively uniform topography, (c) existed as discrete entities surrounded by agricultural land, (d) were mature Sugar Maple-beech forest rather than mixed coniferous-deciduous forest or planted forest, (e) had a well-defined understory and a complete canopy, of varying ages, (f) had similar ranges of soil moisture conditions, and (g) were free from recent major disturbance. Most of the woodlots showed signs of minor disturbance (both natural and human), therefore a disturbance index (Table 1) was constructed to quantify the actual extent of disturbance in the woodlots. Attributes included in the disturbance index were assessed during the vegetation census described below.

The extent of topographic variation present within a woodlot was also quantified during the vegetation census to provide a measure of the woodlot's habitat diversity. At each sample point (see below) the topography was classified subjectively as dry ridge, moist slope, or wet hollow, and the proportion of sample points (p_i) in each of the three topographic categories was used in the Shannon-Wiener diversity formula ($-\Sigma p_i \log p_i$) to calculate habitat diversity values. Values could range from 0 to 1, with higher values indicating greater diversity.

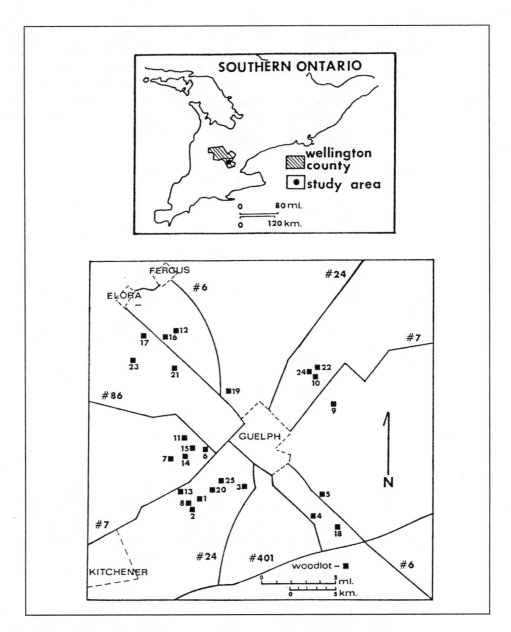

Figure 2: Locations of the twenty-five woodlots sampled in Wellington County, Ontario.

Table 1

Site attributes included in the disturbance index used to rate the twenty-five woodlots. Disturbance = A + B + C + D, with a maximum score of 4.0 indicating the most disturbance.

Site attribute		Criterion	Score
A	Presence of stumps	present	1.0
		absent	0.0
B	Cart tracks, paths, drainage ditches present	present	1.0
		absent	0.0
C	Time since woodlot last cut	> 30 years	0.0
		15-30 years	0.25
		5-15 years	0.50
		0-5 years	0.75
		continuous cutting for firewood	1.00
D	Number of gaps in canopy from cutting	0	0.00
		1-2	0.25
		3-4	0.50
		5-6	0.75
		> 7	1.00

2. Woody species survey

The twenty-five woodlots were censused between June and August 1985 to determine the woody species (shrubs, trees, vines) present in the canopy (stems >10 cm diameter at breast height) and (or) the understory (stems 2.5-10 cm diameter). Line transects were positioned at 30m intervals throughout the woodlot. Edge trees (i.e., trees with asymmetrical boles, with a considerable clear-length on the interior side (forest-grown side) and heavy branching to the outside (open-grown side)) were the end points of transects. These edge trees formed a continuous boundary around the physical edge of most woodlots sampled. To sample the interior portion of the woodlot, as Levenson (1981) did, the first sample point was located ten m inside edge trees. Other sample points were 30 m apart on transect lines. At each point the woody species present within a radius of ten m of the sampling point were recorded.

3. Data analysis procedures

To determine whether maximum woody species richness occurred in woodlots of 2.1-2.5 ha, species richness was compared for woodlots of the five size classes listed above. The statistical significance of differences in richness among size classes was tested with the Kruskal-Wallis test (Zar 1984).

To determine whether the frequency of occurrence of woody edge species decreased in woodlots larger than 2.1-2.5 ha in size, and conversely, whether interior species were more frequent in woodlots 3.6-4.0 ha in size or larger, the number of sample points at which a species was found within a particular woodlot was determined for each of five shade-tolerant (interior) woody species and five less-shade-tolerant woody (edge) species. The ten indicator species used for the analysis were chosen because they were common enough to permit statisticalevaluation (i.e., Kruskal-Wallis test) of their change in frequency with woodlot size.

The effect of woodlot size, habitat diversity, and minor disturbances on species richness or on the frequency of occurrence of indicator species was examined by calculating partial correlation coefficients, which removed the effects of potentially confounding variables.

Results

The number of woody species present in the twenty-five woodlots ranged from 16 to 38 (Table 2). Small woodlots (≤ 2.0 ha) were as rich, on average, as larger woodlots (up to 7.5 ha) (Figure 3). Species richness did not change significantly with a change in woodlot size (H = 2.1, P > 0.05, df = 4), so these results do not support Levenson's (1981) suggestion that richness should be greater in woodlots about 2.3 ha in size.

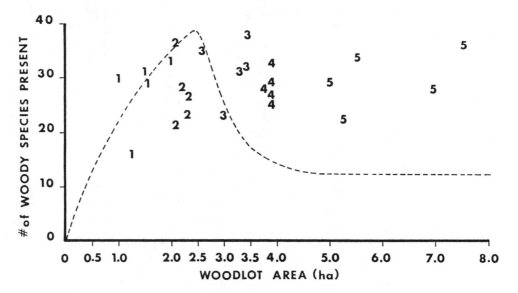

Figure 3: Woody species richness in woodlots of five different size classes (numbers 1 through 5). The dotted line shows the approximate relationship between species richness and woodlot area proposed by Levenson (1981) for Wisconsin.

The twenty-five woodlots differed in habitat diversity and in the degree of disturbance evident as well as in size (Table 2). Habitat diversity increased with woodlot size (partial r = 0.44, P < 0.05) but the degree of disturbance was not correlated with woodlot size (partial r = 0.20, P > 0.05). The effects of habitat diversity and disturbance on woody species richness are shown in Figures 4 and 5. Species richness did not increase significantly (partial r = 0.37, P > 0.05) with increased habitat diversity, nor did species richness show a consistent change with increased disturbance (partial r = -0.09, P > 0.05).

Table 2

Some characteristics of the twenty-five woodlots sampled in Wellington County, Ontario

Woodlot No.	Woodlot owner	Woodlot area(ha)	Woodlot habitat diversity	Woodlot disturbance index value	No. woody species present
1	Unknown	1.00	0	3.75	30
2	Haldeman	1.25	0	1.50	16
3	Scott	1.50	0	4.00	31
4	Morrison	1.55	0	0.5	29
5	Perrin	2.00	0.49	0.5	33
6	Braun	2.10	0	1.25	22
7	Maryhill	2.10	0.49	2.00	36
8	Burgetz	2.20	0	1.50	26
9	Alexander	2.30	0.12	0.25	30
10	Craige	2.30	0	1.00	23
11	Reinhart	2.60	0.30	0	35
12	Day	2.80	0	0	23
13	Walzneack	3.10	0.45	1.75	31
14	Cowborough	3.40	0.19	3.25	32
15	Harrop	3.45	0	1.75	38
16	Harrison	3.80	0.28	3.25	34
17	Harkens	3.90	0.37	2.00	29
18	Ord	3.80	0	3.00	28
19	Fletcher	3.90	0.14	2.25	30
20	Depesquier	3.80	0	0.50	25
21	Wedding	5.00	0.27	4.00	29
22	Swanston	5.25	0.49	4.00	21
23	Aitchison	5.50	0.38	2.75	34
24	Cairns	7.00	0.41	0	28
25	MaCartney	7.45	0.47	4.00	36

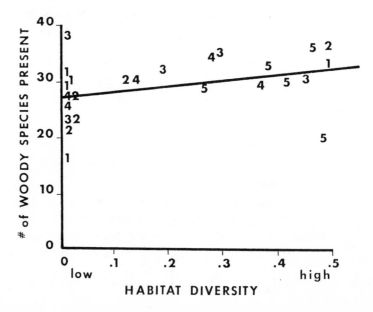

Figure 4: Effect of habitat diversity (X) on woody species richness (Y) in woodlots of five size classes (numbers 1 through 5). The straight line was fitted by linear regression and the equation is Y = 26.9 + 10.5X.

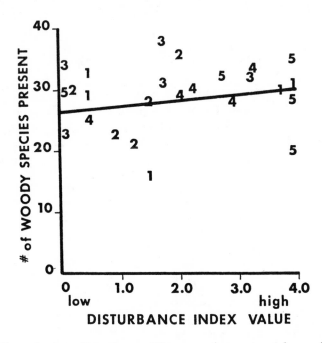

Figure 5: Effect of minor disturbance (X) on woody species richness (Y) in wood-lots of five size classes (numbers 1 through 5). The straight line was fitted by linear regression and the equation is Y = 25.9 + 0.96X.

Woody species composition of woodlots changed little with an increase in woodlot size. The same species (Table 3) dominated the canopy in all woodlots. These species were also dominant in the woodlots studied by Levenson (1981). Less dominant species (i.e., frequency of 1-2) were also found in woodlots of each size class, but the same species were not present in each woodlot. The species encountered most frequently in the understory (i.e., frequency 4-5) were present in woodlots in all five size classes (Table 4). For species that occurred less frequently (i.e., 1-2), there was no obvious association with woodlots of a particular size class.

A single species' frequency of occurrence *within* a woodlot also changed little with increased woodlot size, at least for the ten indicator species examined (Table 5). None of the five shade-tolerant woody species occurred more frequently in the understory of woodlots ≥ 3.8ha in size, which was considered by Levenson (1981) to be the minimum critical size to maintain conditions required by shade-tolerant (interior) woody species. Nor were any of the five less-shade-tolerant (edge) woody species less frequent in woodlots greater than 2.1-2.5 ha in size, as predicted by Levenson's model.

The canopy dominants (*Acer saccharum* and *Fagus grandifolia*) were found as frequently in the understory as in the canopy for each of the five woodlot size classes (Figures 6 and 7). This suggests that these two species are potentially self-sustaining in woodlots as small as 1.0 ha. These results do not support the hypothesis that only woodlots 3.8 ha or larger provide conditions required to maintain populations of mesophytic, interior woody species.

Table 3

Species composition of canopy trees in woodlots of five sizes in Wellington county, Ontario. Numbers in the table indicate the number of stands in which a species was found (maximum of five per size class).

Species	Woodlot size class				
	≤ 2.0	2.1-2.5	2.6-3.5	3.6-4.0	4.1-7.5
Acer saccharum	5	4	5	5	5
Fagus grandifolia	3	4	4	5	5
Tilia americana	4	4	5	5	5
Ostrya virginiana	4	3	5	3	5
Fraxinus americana & pennsylvanicum	4	4	4	4	5
Prunus serotina	5	3	4	5	5
Populus tremuloides	1	2	5	3	2
Acer nigrum	2	1	2	1	1
Acer saccharinum		3	4	2	5
Betula lutea		1	2	3	5
Quercus macrocarpa		3	1	3	2
Fraxinus nigra		2	1	2	3
Crataegus crus-galli	1			2	1
Ulmus rubra	1		4	3	3
Juglans nigra		1		2	1
Amelanchier arborea	2		1		
Juglans cinerea	1		1		
Pinus strobus	1				1
Pinus resinosa	1			1	
Carya cordiformis	1	1			
Malus coronaria		1		2	
Populus grandidentata		2			2
Tsuga canadensis				1	2
Quercus borealis	2				
Larix laricina	1				
Acer rubrum	1				
Acer negundo		2			
Salix nigra		1			
Betula papyrifera				1	
Quercus alba				1	
Thuja occidentalis					1

Table 4

Woody species composition of the understory in woodlots of five sizes in Wellington county, Ontario. Numbers in the table indicate the number of stands in which a species was found (maximum of five per size class).

Species	Woodlot size class (ha)				
	≤ 2.0	2.1-2.5	2.6-3.5	3.6-4.0	4.1-7.5
Prunus virginiana	5	5	5	5	5
Ulmus rubra	5	5	5	5	5
Acer saccharum	5	4	5	5	5
Rubus idaeus	5	4	5	5	5
Vitis riparia	5	4	5	5	5
Prunus serotina	5	4	5	5	5
Tilia americana	5	4	5	5	5
Parthenocissus quinquefolia	5	3	5	5	5
Fraxinus americana & pennsylvanicum	4	5	5	4	5
Fagus grandifolia	3	4	5	5	5
Rhamnus cathartica	4	2	5	5	5
Ostrya virginiana	4	3	5	4	5
Viburnum lentago	4	4	5	3	4
Solanum dulcamara	4	2	5	5	3
Ribes cynosbati	5	4	4	3	3
Ribes triste	5	3	3	5	2
Cornus rugosa	2	4	5	2	4
Carpinus caroliniana	1	3	4	4	5
Quercus macrocarpa	1	3	4	3	4
Ribes lacustre	3	2	4	3	3
Rubus occidentalis	4	2	3	4	1
Sambucus pubens	2	1	3	4	3
Cornus alternifolia	2	1	3	4	3
Crataegus crus-galli	2	1	4	3	3
Viburnum trilobum	2	2	3	4	2
Acer saccharinum		4	2	2	4
Rhus radicans	1	2	3	2	3
Lonicera tatarica	2	1	2	2	1
Euonymus obovatus	2	1	2	1	1
Fraxinus nigra		2	1	2	4
Betula lutea		1	1	1	3
Ribes americanum		3		1	3
Crataegus mollis				2	
Juglans nigra				2	1
Dirca palustris			1	1	1
Rhus typhina			1		1
Smilax hispida	1			1	1
Ribes hirtellum				1	
Populus tremuloides		1	4	3	2
Cornus obliqua			4	1	1
Tsuga canadensis		1		1	1
Prunus nigra	1				1
Quercus alba				1	
Thuja occidentalis				1	
Morus rubra				1	
Malus coronaria	1	1	2	2	1
Acer nigrum	2	1	2	2	1
Salix nigra		1	2	1	
Sorbus americana			2	1	1
Juglans cinerea	1		2		

Table 4 (continued)

Species	Woodlot size class (ha)				
	≤ 2.0	2.1-2.5	2.6-3.5	3.6-4.0	4.1-7.5
Crataegus succulenta			2		2
Rubus pubescens		2		1	1
Cornus stolonifera			2		
Corylus cornuta			1		1
Crataegus punctata			1		
Amelanchier arborea	3		2	1	1
Celastrus scandens	3			1	
Carya cordiformis	2	1	1		
Acer negundo	1	1			
Acer rubrum	1				
Pinus resinosa	1				
Quercus borealis	1				
Berberis vulgaris	1				
Prunus americana	1				
Viburnum rafinesquianum	1				
Rubus allegheniensis	1			1	
Crataegus monogyna	1				1
Rosa sp.	1		1		
Diervillea lonicera	1				
Lonicera dioica					

Table 5

Frequency of occurrence of some indicator species (x ± 1 SD percentage of sampling points per woodlot) in the understory of woodlots of five size classes in Wellington county, Ontario. Differences between size classes are not statistically sigtnificant (P > 0.05) for any species.

Species	Woodlot size class (ha)				
	≤ 2.0	2.1-2.5	2.6-3.5	3.6-4.0	4.1-7.5
Shade-tolerant species					
Acer saccharum	98 ± 4	73 ± 42	91 ± 13	74 ± 33	73 ± 22
Fagus grandifolia	18 ± 13	26 ± 22	53 ± 33	50 ± 36	23 ± 6
Ostrya virginiana	37 ± 23	27 ± 28	47 ± 29	25 ± 23	14 ± 9
Tilia americana	55 ± 28	39 ± 36	43 ± 23	56 ± 18	45 ± 22
Carpinus caroliniana	2 ± 5	15 ± 21	15 ± 18	17 ± 27	20 ± 17
Less-shade-tolerant species					
Prunus serotina	60 ± 16	44 ± 28	64 ± 13	43 ± 27	30 ± 12
Fraxinum americana & pennsylvanicum	74 ± 41	79 ± 40	75 ± 42	61 ± 42	92 ± 9
Quercus macrocarpa	3 ± 7	11 ± 8	13 ± 18	24 ± 42	11 ± 17
Rubus idaeus	58 ± 14	33 ± 17	61 ± 18	44 ± 23	47 ± 15
Ribes triste	14 ± 15	6 ± 7	8 ± 7	17 ± 22	5 ± 6

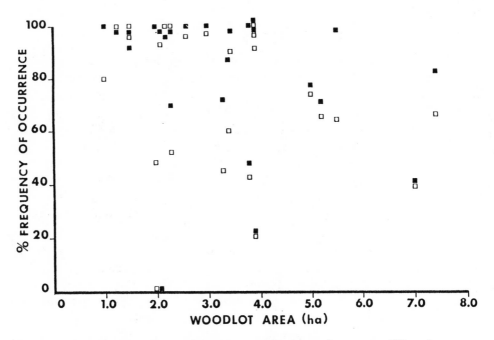

Figure 6: Frequency of occurrence of *Acer saccharum* in the canopy (□) and understory (■) of woodlots differing in size.

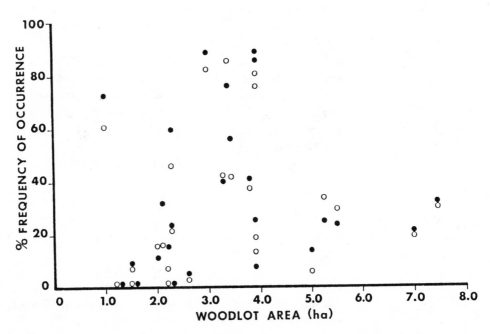

Figure 7: Frequency of occurrence of *Fagus grandifolia* in the canopy (○) and understory (●) of woodlots differing in size.

Significance of Results For Conservation

Results of the present study support neither Levensons's (1981) suggestion that woody species richness is greatest in woodlots of about 2.3 ha in size, nor his suggestion that a woodlot must be 3.8 ha or larger to support only self-sustaining populations of mesophytic woody species. In Wellington County, Ontario, woodlots between 1.0 and 7.5 ha in size have similar species richness, species composition, and frequency of occurrence of dominant woody species. If small woodlots (i.e., < 7.5 ha) were being considered for conservation of woody plants, woodlots less than 3.8 ha should also be examined since the assemblage of deciduous forest woody plants they contain is equivalent to that in woodlots between 3.8 and 7.5 ha in size. While our results suggest that even woodlots as small as 1.0 ha merit consideration for conserving woody plant assemblages, it should be emphasized that such small woodlots probably do not provide desirable habitat for all forest plants, birds, and mammals. In addition, the woodlots here had only experienced minor disturbance in the recent past. Vegetation in more heavily disturbed woodlots is likely to be quite different, regardless of woodlot size. Certainly some consideration should be given to protecting even small, but relatively undisturbed woodlots, since they can provide a dispersal corridor for both plants and animals.

Future Considerations

The size guidelines proposed by Levenson (1981) for Wisconsin forests are clearly not applicable to all woodlots in southern Ontario. Forest composition changes substantially from south to north in Ontario and results of the present study might only apply to deciduous woodlots in Wellington County. Results of two studies conducted in Great Lakes-St. Lawrence Forest further north in Ontario (Weaver and Kellman 1981, Middleton and Merriam 1983) generally support our findings, suggesting that our results have wider applicability than just Wellington County. Whether this includes Carolinian forests along the north shore of Lake Erie must still be determined.

While we have shown that Levenson's (1981) critical values (2.3 and 3.8 ha) probably do not apply to all woodlots in the vicinity of Wellington County, Ontario, we cannot provide alternative size guidelines that are more appropriate. The next step should be to examine entire plant assemblages in woodlots to see if patterns described by Levenson (1981) become apparent when a wider range of species is considered.

In the present study we only measured woody species richness and composition at one point in time. The woodlots sampled here might still be losing or gaining species and if they were resampled in the future the pattern predicted by Levenson (1981) could be more apparent. A longer term study monitoring species immigration and extinction rates would have to be set up to test this possibility.

References

Levenson, J.B. 1981. Woodlots as biogeographic islands in southeastern Wisconsin. pp.11-39 In: *Forest island dynamics in man-dominated landscapes.* R.L. Burgess and D.M. Sharpe, eds. Springer-Verlag, New York.

Middleton, J. and G. Merriam. 1983. Distribution of woodland species in farm woods. *J. Applied Ecology* 20:625-644.

Weaver, M. and M. Kellman. 1981. The effect of forest fragmentation on woodlot tree biotas in southern Ontario. *J. Biogeography* 8:199-210.

Zar, J.H. 1984. *Biostatistical analysis.* 2nd edition. Prentice-Hall, London.

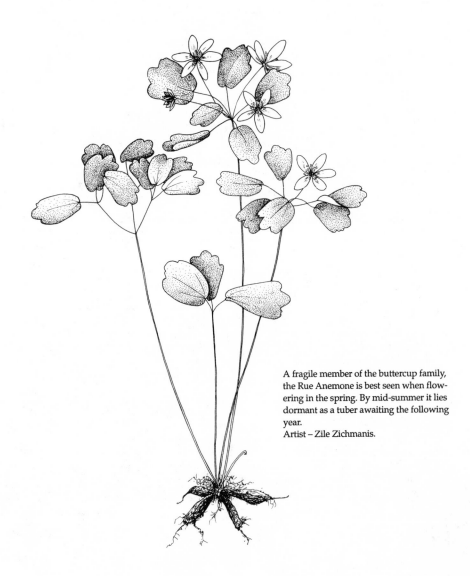

A fragile member of the buttercup family, the Rue Anemone is best seen when flowering in the spring. By mid-summer it lies dormant as a tuber awaiting the following year.
Artist – Zile Zichmanis.

A Comparison of the Population Ecology of *Liriodendron tulipifera* L. (Tuliptree) Among Allopatric Populations: Preliminary Recommendations for its Conservation in Ontario

Kevin Kavanagh

Department of Botany, University of Toronto
Toronto, Ontario M5S 2B3

Abstract. *A comparison of the population ecology of* Liriodendron tulipifera *L., a rare Carolinian tree, was made between the centre and northern edge of its range to determine those environmental factors which determine its distributional limits in Ontario. Fecundity, seedbank dynamics, and population structure of L. tulipifera forest stands were examined in the field in southwestern Ontario and the southern Appalachian mountains. In addition, seedlings from seven allopatric populations, stretching from the South Carolina coastal plain northward to Ontario, were grown under glasshouse conditions to determine population response to a range of simulated environmental conditions.*

Preliminary results indicate that measures of fecundity in Ontario populations (seed viability and production) are similar to values reported for more southern populations. Liriodendron tulipifera seed also remains viable in the forest seed bank at the edge of its range in Ontario. Seedling performance in the Ontario population was similar to all other populations except the coastal plain of South Carolina, which exhibited significantly greater growth. Preliminary results and field observations indicate that L. tulipifera is largely restricted in its Ontario distribution to wet-mesic sites on sandy soils, likely as a result of competition with shade-tolerant northern hardwoods on mesic sites. Recommendations are made for the conservation of L. tulipifera in Ontario.

Introduction

The following paper investigates potential differences in the population ecology of *Liriodendron tulipifera* among populations near the centre and northern edge of its range. The purpose of such a comparison is to provide insight into the performance and ecology of rare Carolinian species at the northern edge of their ranges in southwestern Ontario. Through such a comparative approach, it is hoped that management and conservation strategies for Carolinian trees may be refined to reflect the relative impacts of local environmental factors influencing their population ecology in southern Ontario.

Although this research is concerned specifically with *L. tulipifera,* I believe that many similarities can be drawn between the performance of this species and other rare or uncommon Carolinian tree species in southwestern Ontario. In particular, those species which exhibit such features as low shade tolerance, rapid height growth, and regionally low abundance levels, may be included.

1. Demographic and Ecological Characteristics of Rare Carolinian Tree Species: A Review

In order to investigate the population ecology of a Carolinian tree species with low frequencies of occurrence, there are a number of ecological and demographic characteristics which should be considered. They are as follows:

Population Isolation: Carolinian species classified as rare in Ontario often have populations that are geographically disjunct from main range areas to the south.

Abundance: Populations are often few and/or characterized by low numbers of individuals.

Fecundity: Reproductive rates may be low, possibly as a result of low cross pollination success due to low population densities.

Gene Ecology: Disjunct and/or isolated populations may have reduced genetic diversity.

Distribution: Ecological requirements may be highly site specific.

The above criteria can be applied to many of the Carolinian tree species in Ontario. Most are regionally disjunct from their more widespread populations to the south and are characterized by relatively low abundance in comparison to more southern localities (Fowells 1965, Hosie 1975). Reproductive output near the northern edge of a range may be lower in some species due to a shorter growing season in which to ripen seed. Some of the most isolated and rarest Carolinian tree populations in Ontario (e.g. *Magnolia acuminata* (Cucumber Magnolia), *Gymnocladus dioica* (Kentucky Coffee-tree)) may have lower genetic diversity as a result of having experienced bottlenecks (significant population reductions) or single founding events in the past. With regards to ecological requirements, there are several species which, due to a variety of possible environmental factors, exhibit greater site specificity in Ontario when compared to other geographic locations within their range (e.g. *Nyssa sylvatica* (Black Gum) or *L. tulipifera*) (McCaw 1985, Kavanagh in prep.).

2. Anthropogenic Factors Influencing Rare Species

In the contemporary landscape of southern Ontario there are several anthropogenic factors which may have had a negative impact on the population levels of Carolinian species. Among these factors are:

i)   Loss and fragmentation of natural habitat.

ii) Incompatible forest management practices in natural areas.

iii) Incompatible landuse.

An examination of the historical distribution of Carolinian tree species in Ontario indicates that the loss and fragmentation of natural habitat has played a significant role in reducing the number of extant populations (Argus *et al.* 1982-1987). In addition, the management and recreational uses of some natural areas has likely been incompatible with the ecological requirements for some rare species. The introduction of these anthropogenic influences in southern Ontario has undoubtedly resulted in significant population declines of what were already relatively rare species in the natural landscape.

3. Assessing the Performance of Carolinian Species: Life History Considerations

In order to address questions pertaining to the influence of the above factors on the demographic status of Carolinian trees species, an examination of their life history characteristics is required. Five critical life history stages can be identified as follows:

i)   Seed Production (Vegetative reproduction)
     – periodicity
     – viability
     – dispersal

ii) Seed Survival
     – predation
     – storage in the seed bank

iii) Seed Germination
     – timing in relation to competitors and season

iv) Juvenile Development
     – physical environment
     – relative growth rate (especially height)

v)   Maturity
     – longevity
     – long term growth rate

With respect to measures of reproductive potential, the most important factor is the production of viable seed. Not only does this help maintain genetic diversity, but for many species it is the principal mode of regeneration, although some Carolinian tree species successfully augment seedling establishment with vegetative propagation (e.g. *Sassafras albidum* (Sassafras), *Gymnocladus dioica*). In addition, the production of viable seed and/or vegetative propagation must be sufficiently frequent to ensure that enough new recruits establish to compensate mortality rates. The dispersal of seed to suitable seedbed conditions is also a critical factor, particularly within the current fragmented forest landscape of southwestern Ontario.

For those species whose seed must enter dormancy prior to germination, the seed must survive both predation and storage in the seed bank. Successful establishment following germination will be dependent on the site conditions and the timing of its germination in relation to potential competitors. For any Carolinian tree species requiring greater heating of the soil to promote germination in comparison to northern hardwoods, the delay may place them at a competitive disadvantage or result in an inability to harden off in time to survive winter temperatures.

Once established, a tree seedling must maximize its height growth in order to maintain a competitive advantage over its neighbours. This stage is critical for shade intolerant species which can rarely survive even moderate shading throughout their juvenile development. At maturity, such tree species must maintain a dominant position in the canopy in order to support optimum reproductive output.

Principal Objective of This Study

Liriodendron tulipifera is a relatively rare Carolinian tree which has been negatively impacted by the loss of forest habitat in Ontario (Kavanagh in prep.). The primary objective of this study is to compare the population ecology of *L. tulipifera* in Ontario with populations elsewhere in its range in an attempt to identify those environmental factors which appear to be principally responsible for limiting its distribution in Ontario. Results of this study will be used to develop conservation recommendations in regards to maintaining or promoting native populations of *L. tulipifera* in southwestern Ontario.

Life History Characteristics of *Liriodendron tulipifera* L.: An Overview

1. Range and Abundance
Liriodendron tulipifera is widely distributed over eastern North America (Fowells 1965). Abundance is highest in the centre of its range in the southern Appalachians and declines towards all geographic edges (Figure 1) (Hedlund and Knight 1969, Delcourt *et al.* 1983). In Ontario, *L. tulipifera* is restricted almost exclusively to sand plains (Figure 2). Despite its nearly complete absence from soils with a high clay content in Ontario, it can be found on a wide variety of soil textures, including those with a high clay content at the centre of its range (Kavanagh, unpublished data).

2. Growth Characteristics
Liriodendron tulipifera is a light demanding species that cannot survive long periods of suppression. It is considered to be one of the fastest growing tree species in eastern North America, often reaching heights of 30 to 35 m in 40 or 50 years on optimum sites (Beck and Della-Bianca 1981). *L. tulipifera* develops a tall, straight stem and narrow crown through its early life history. The combination of good form and fast growth makes it desirable as a commercial species (Fowells 1965). It can attain large sizes with diameters over 2.5 meters and heights over 50 m. Heights and diameters of trees near the northern edge of its range in Ontario appear to be somewhat less (Kavanagh, pers. obs.). *L. tulipifera* is long-lived with some trees attaining ages of more than 400 years (Lorimer 1980).

3. Reproductive Characteristics
Seed production in *L. tulipifera* begins by the age of 25 to 30 years and by 50 years dominant trees can be producing heavy seed crops. Seed set is characteristically low throughout the species range with only 5 to 25% of samaras containing viable seeds (Boyce and Kaeiser 1961). Seed dispersal occurs in late fall with the winged samaras being released during periods of warm, dry weather. Seed generally needs at least some cold treatment to break dormancy and may survive for three to seven years in the forest seed bank (Clark and Boyce 1964).

Methodological Approach

The following life history characters of *Liriodendron tulipifera* were examined in this study:

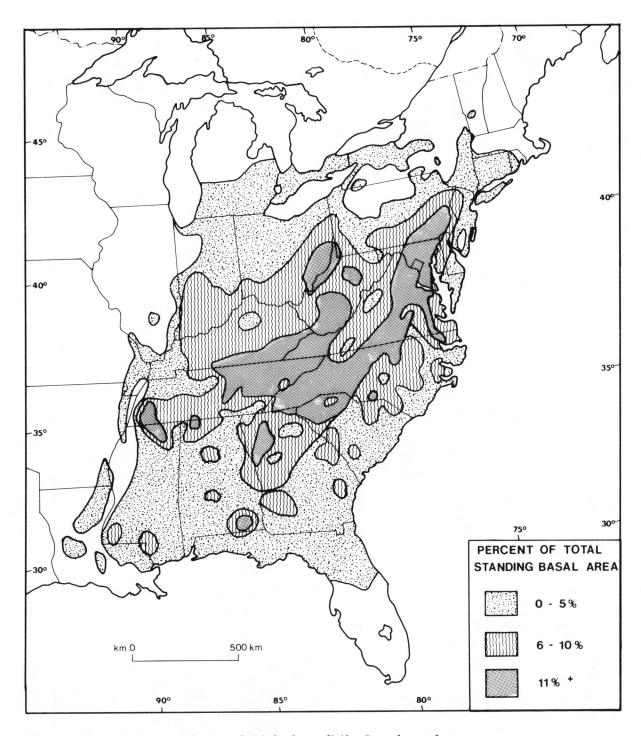

Figure 1: Mean relative contribution of *Liriodendron tulipifera* L. to the total standing basal area (after Delcourt & Delcourt 1983).

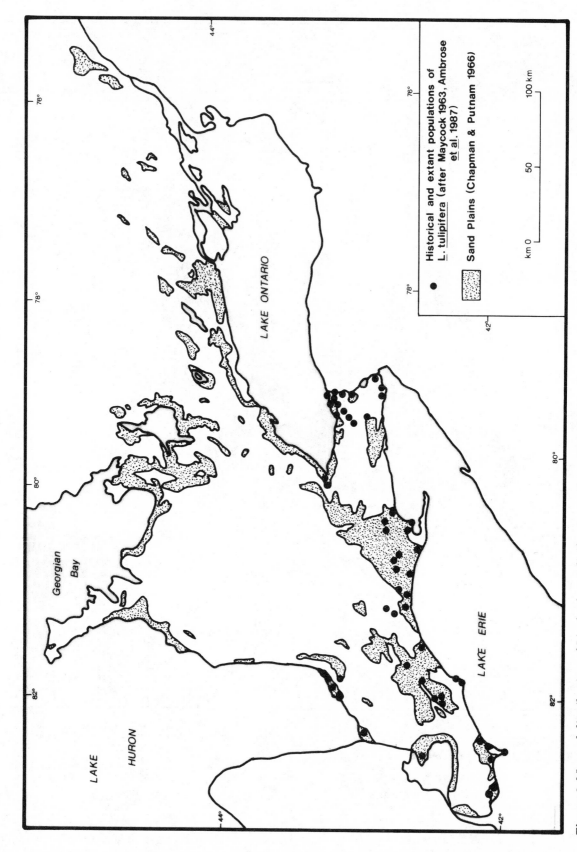

Figure 2: Natural distribution of *Lirodendron tulipifera* in southern Ontario in relation to sand plains.

1. Seed Productivity, Viability and Dispersal

Seed cones were counted on individual trees across size classes ranging from 10-75+ cm dbh in Ontario over a three year period from 1984-1986 to estimate seed productivity. Seed traps were placed radiating outward from under the canopies of four individual *L. tulipifera* trees of different dbh classes and in a regular grid network in two small stands of high *L. tulipifera* density in order to measure seed dispersal patterns between 1983-1985. Mensuration data for the stands are given in Table 1. Seeds collected in the traps were dissected to determine potential seed viability.

Table 1

Population characteristics of 6 seedfall study sites (Based on circular plots of 50 m radius).*

Site	Mean dbh (cm)	Density/ha (*L. tulipifera* stems)	Basal area (cm^2)/ha. (*L. tulipifera*)
Tree 1	35.5	15.3	16396.7
Tree 2	39.9	11.5	15863.3
Trees 3 and 4	64.7	3.8	13160.6
Landon's Woods	41.0	31.9	44642.3
Backus Woods	51.4	24.2	40950.4

* Includes only *Liriodendron tulipifera* > 15.0 cm dbh.

2. Seed Bank Ecology

To determine whether seed in Ontario can remain viable on the forest floor, two soil cores measuring 20 x 20 x 15 cm were extracted adjacent to each of 46 seed traps following a three year estimate of seed input and placed in a glasshouse to stimulate seed germination. Seedlings of all plant species germinating from the soil cores were recorded across a time sequence to determine the relative establishment of *L. tulipifera* in comparison to other plant species under conditions of simulated disturbance.

3. Comparative Seedling Ecology

Seed was collected from seven populations along a latitudinal gradient stretching northward from the coastal plain of South Carolina to southern Ontario (Table 2). Seeds were stratified and then placed in a combination of moist sand and peat for germination. Seedlings from each of the seven populations were transplanted into a series of simulated environmental treatments (approximately 8 replicates/treatment combination). Treatments consisted of a factorial design of 3 moisture X 2 nutrient X 5 soil types (Table 3). Comparisons were made at the population level to determine whether inherent population differences were present which could help account for the differences in species abundance and habitat preference documented across its range. Seedlings were harvested following a mean growing period of 120 days. Seedling performance was measured using a number of growth attributes including leaf, stem, and root dry weight, and developmental measures through time (e.g. height growth).

Table 2

Climatic characteristics and seed collection dates for the seven regions where seed was collected for population comparisons of seedling growth (after Fowells 1965).

Location	Lat. (N)	Long. (W)	Mean Temp.(°C) Jan.	July	Mean Annual Prec.(mm)	Seed Collection Dates (1983)
Southern Ontario, Canada	42	81	-4	21	950	Oct.21-Nov. 6
Northern Ohio	40	81	-2	23	950	Oct.30
Northern West Virginia	38	79	-1	22	1150	Oct.29-Oct.30
S. Appalachians (elev. > 800 m)	36	83	2	22	1500	Oct. 8-Oct.17
S. Appalachians (elev. < 800 m)	36	83	4	24	1400	Oct.14-Oct.16
South Carolina, Piedmont	34	81	7	27	1150	Oct.13-Oct.14
South Carolina, Coastal Plain	33	79	10	28	1250	Oct.11-Oct.12

Table 3

Nutrient, moisture and substrate treatments used in seedling growth study. Treatments consisted of a combination of one treatment level from each of the three categories. (Total treatment combinations = 30)

Nutrient	Moisture	Substrate
1. HIGH – 100 ppm N	1. WET – Pots standing in 1-2 cm of water.	1. Gravel/Coarse Sand
2. LOW – 5 ppm N	2. MESIC – watered daily, freely drained	2. Sand
Applied in solution once a week with watering schedule.	3. DRY – watered every second day, freely drained.	3. Garden Loam
		4. Clay rich mix
		5. Organic rich mix

4. Comparative Stand Dynamics

Old growth (trees estimated to be > 100 years) and second growth forest stands with *L. tulipifera* present as both a major and minor overstory component, were examined in the centre of the species range in the southern Appalachians and at the northern edge of the species range in southern Ontario, to assess competitive interactions with other tree species. Individual plots measured 25m x 50m and represented wet, mesic, and dry sites with variably open and closed forest canopies. Interactions among adjacent trees and between the forest overstory and understory are currently being investigated.

Preliminary Results

1. Seed Productivity, Viability and Dispersal

Both seed productivity and viability for *Liriodendron tulipifera* in southern Ontario appear to be comparable with southern populations (Beck and Della-Bianca 1981) where the species is more abundant and widespread. In Ontario, trees begin flowering when sizes of approximately 25 cm dbh are reached (estimated age at 30 to 40 years). Seed production continues to increase with crown expansion. Large trees with intact crowns are the heaviest seed producers. Seed cone counts indicate that annual seed production can reach 4000 cones/tree in Ontario, although 2000 cones/tree is the average (Figure 3).

Table 4 indicates that density of trees plays an important role in determining seed viability. Those trees which were relatively isolated or in stands of low *L. tulipifera* density (trees 1-4, Table 1) produced lower filled seed counts (approximately 10%) than trees growing in high density *L. tulipifera* stands (approximately 22%). Since individual cones in Ontario populations of *L. tulipifera* contain approximately 110 samaras, isolated trees or those in low density stands >75 cm dbh are estimated to have a potential reproductive output of 20,000 -30,000 viable seeds in favourable years. Similar trees in old-growth, high density stands may produce 40,000 – 60,000 viable seeds, while a few large-canopied trees may produce as many as 90,000 viable seeds.

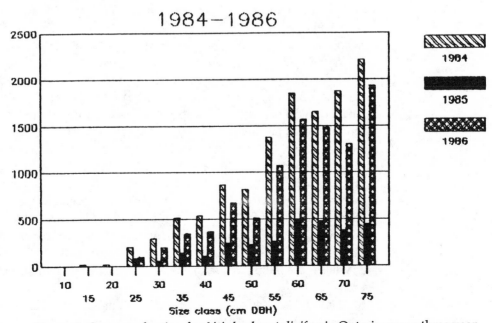

Figure 3. Cone production for *Liriodendron tulipifera* in Ontario over a three year period (1984-1986). Values represented are means for 5 cm dbh size classes (Total n=146 trees).

Table 4

Characteristics of seed production for *Liriodendron tulipifera* populations in
Ontario

Location	Year	Samaras/ filled seed	% Samaras with filled seed	% Samaras with 2 seeds
Tree 1	1983-1985	555/45	8.1%	
Tree 2	1983-1985	707/84	11.9%	
Tree 3	1983-1985	487/53	10.9%	
Tree 4	1983-1985	260/28	10.8%	
Total for trees 1-4	1983-1985	2009/209	10.4%	0.9%
Landon's Woods	1983	663/74	11.2%	
	1984	906/172	19.0%	
	1985	536/73	13.6%	
	1983-1985	2105/319	15.2%	2.0%
Backus Woods	1983	1164/252	21.7%	
	1984	1538/332	21.6%	
	1985	542/112	20.7%	
	1983-1985	3244/696	21.5%	3.6%
Rondeau Prov. Park	1984	890/151	17.0%	2.9%
All Ontario	1983-1985	8248/1375	16.7%	

All trees censused appear to produce moderate to heavy seed crops at least every second year with many showing relatively consistent annual production levels. Figure 3 indicates high seed production levels in 1984 and 1986 with an intervening low value in 1985. High seed production levels in 1984 appeared to be a response to an unusually hot and dry summer in 1983. Following the heavy seed crop of 1984, many trees were apparently unable to produce many seeds in 1985, with a resulting crash in seed output that year. Most trees returned to heavy flowering the following year and produced a heavy seed crop in 1986. This indicates that *L. tulipifera* may respond to stressful climatic situations (eg. hot/dry) by increasing seed production the following year. A subsequent reduction in seed output the next year (two years after aberrant climatic conditions) may then occur.

The dissemination of *L. tulipifera* seed in Ontario begins in late October and continues for a three to four week period, depending on weather conditions. By late November, approximately 90% of all seed has been dropped. The remaining 10% (including some viable seed) continues to fall throughout the winter months. This pattern of seedfall results in the seeds becoming variously incorporated into the litter layer. Those falling in late October are generally well covered by leaf litter, while those falling in mid to late November tend to remain exposed near the surface.

Although seed dispersal extended over long distances (seed traps located 30 to 40 m from individual trees received small amounts of seedfall), a majority of seed fell within 5-10 m of the canopy or directly beneath it. Seedfall densities indicate that over a three year period less than 100 viable seeds/m^2 were recorded beneath isolated trees. In comparison, densities exceeding 550 viable seeds/m^2 were recorded for an old-growth, high density stand of *L. tulipifera*. Figures 4a and 4b illustrate the pattern of seedfall around isolated trees while Figure 5 indicates the seedfall pattern in a small, high density stand of *L. tulipifera*.

2. Seed Bank Ecology

Seedling germination in the soil cores indicated that *L. tulipifera* seeds were able to remain viable in the seed bank at the northern edge of its range in relatively large numbers. When individual soil cores were classified according to the amount of organic matter present, it was noted that germination of stored seed was greatest when the relative amount of organic matter content was 8-15% (germination rate = 57.7%). According to estimated seed input over the previous three years, soils with either low or high organic matter content resulted in germination values closer to 40% (Table 5).

Table 5

Estimated germination rates of seed stored in soil of different organic matter content (for the period 1983-1985).

	Percent Organic Matter		
	< 8.0	**8.0 - 15.0**	**> 15.0**
estimated # of viable seeds/m^2	2828	4094	2749
# of seedlings/m^2	1044	2360	1077
% germination	36.9	57.7	39.2
# of seedtraps	14	23	8

There is some preliminary evidence to suggest that seeds in Ontario populations germinate most readily after two cold treatments, although seeds also germinate after a single cold season. Coefficients of determination (R^2) between number of seedlings germinating and estimated seed input over three years for 45 seed traps (of the original 46 seed traps, 1 was omitted) indicate that 1984 (2 years prior to germination trials) had the strongest relationship among single years with seedlings germinated while 1984-85 had the highest values for combined years (Table 6). Seedlings of *L. tulipifera* generally emerged between three and five weeks after being placed in the glasshouse (Table 7). This contrasts with other species which generally peaked in their germination after only two weeks.

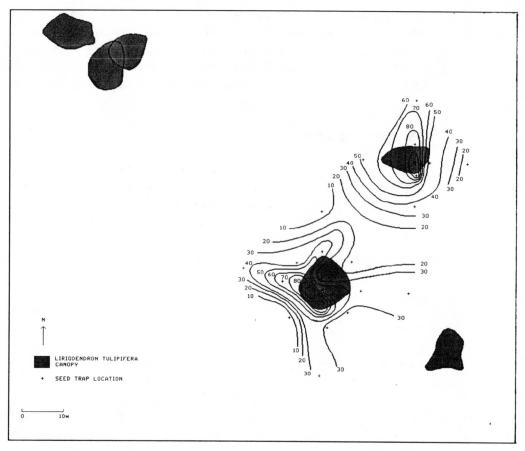

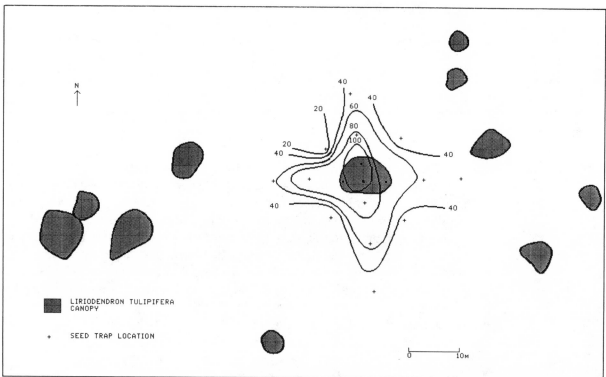

Figure 4. Dispersal patterns of filled seed for three relatively isolated *Liriodendron tulipifera* trees for the period 1983-1985. Figure 4a represents two mature trees (>150 years); figure 4b represents a 65 year old tree.

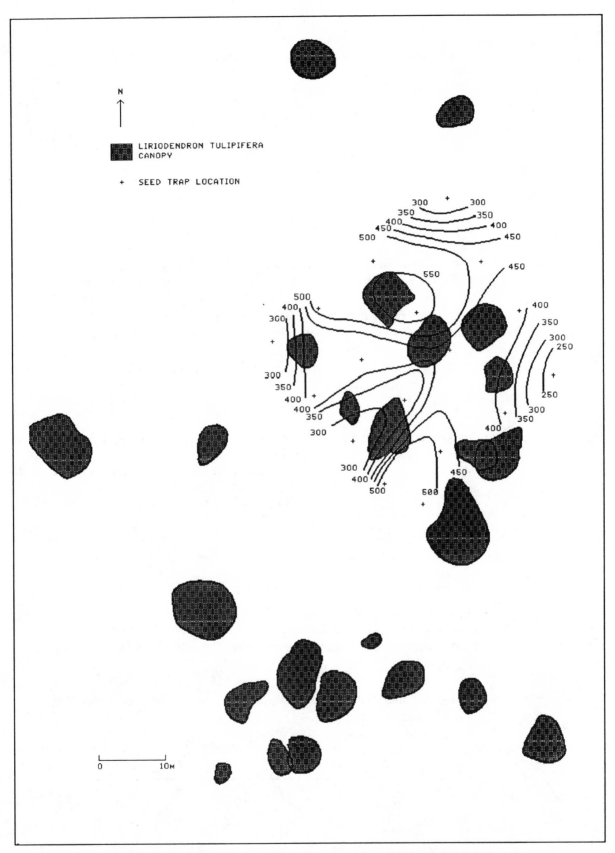

Figure 5. Dispersal patterns of filled seed in a mature (>150 year) high density *Liriodendron tulipifera* stand for the period 1983-1985. A peak value of 591 seed/m² was recorded at this site.

Table 6

Coefficients of Determination (R^2) between number of seedlings and viable seed input to seedfall traps for different time periods (n = 45).

	1983	1984	1985	1983-84	1984-85	1983-85
Total viable seeds	0.18**	0.38***	0.23***	0.39***	0.41***	0.39***

** $p < 0.01$
*** $p < 0.001$

Table 7

Number of seedlings germinating through time under glasshouse conditions for *Liriodendron tulipifera*, other dicots and graminoids. Seedlings were germinated after individual soil samples were brought in from the field and placed in the glasshouse. Following one simulated growing season, soil samples were placed in cold treatment for approximately 6 months after which they were returned to the glasshouse for a second growing season. Note that in both seasons, the peak germination time for *L. tulipifera* is between days 21 and 28, while other species generally peak around days 7 to 14.

7A. Germination totals for the first season. (Soil was turned over on day 63 for a second time).

					DAYS						
	7	14	21	28	35	42	49	56	63	98	TOTAL
L. tulipifera	6	23	63	85	55	13	5	5	2	4	261
Other dicots	3* /25	394	165	96	24	7	13	4	6	89	826
Graminoids	3	77	25	15	8	1	8	11	2	28	178
TOTAL	3* /34	494	253	196	87	21	26	20	10	121	1265

* represents *Acer rubrum* seedlings emerging from collection sites prior to excavation.

7B. Germination for the second season. (Soil was turned over on day 56 for a second time).

				DAYS				
	7	14	21	28	42	56	96	TOTAL
L. tulipifera	–	46	74	7	2	–	–	129
Other dicots	147	129	46	34	25	5	28	414
Graminoids	47	41	15	17	26	5	6	157
TOTAL	194	216	135	58	53	10	34	700

3. Comparison of Seedling Ecology

Moisture and nutrient levels had the most significant effect on growth for all seven populations. Soil type had little or no significant effect on seedling growth by the harvest date. Although the overall seedling response pattern to the different treatments was the same among populations, the magnitude of response varied significantly among some of the populations (Figure 6). In particular, the population from the coastal plain of South Carolina consistently demonstrated greater vigour over northern and central populations among all treatments. A north to south trend was evident in most of the growth measures, with northern populations (e.g. Ontario) showing the least growth and southern populations the most growth. Interestingly, however, there were few significant differences in seedling response among northern and central populations, despite the difference in population abundance in the field. The superior performance of seedlings from the coastal plain population suggests that *L. tulipifera* has the potential to be most widespread in that part of its range. In contrast, however, it is represented by relatively low population levels indicating that new competitive or environmental conditions are restricting its distribution in that region.

4. Comparative Stand Dynamics

The data for this portion of the study have yet to be statistically analyzed, however, some field observations are worth noting. In Ontario, *L. tulipifera* appears to be best represented on wet or wet-mesic sites. Rarely, is the species found either in great abundance or on any site dominating second-growth stands. This distribution pattern and stand structure is in sharp contrast to the southern Appalachians where *L. tulipifera* is widespread among different edaphic sites and often forms extensive pure stands on cut-over areas or on abandoned farmland. Seedlings and saplings of *L. tulipifera* in Ontario appear to be best represented in multiple tree blowdown gaps, particularly on wet-mesic sites.

Discussion

Preliminary results from this study have indicated that *Liriodendron tulipifera* in Ontario is not limited in its distribution by low seed production or viability. Seedfall distribution is sufficiently widespread to ensure potential recruitment of seedlings on newly disturbed sites within 30 to 50 m of mature trees. Some seed may be distributed to much greater distances allowing occasional long distance dispersal of the species.

Once seed has reached the forest floor it becomes incorporated into the seed bank where it was demonstrated to remain viable and germinate under simulated disturbance. Lower rates of germination on soils with low organic content may reflect desiccation of stored seeds in these surface soils. Most soils in this category could be classified as sandy loams or loamy sands which would be subject to rapid drying. Those soils with more than 15% organic matter content were typically saturated for part of the growing season and seeds may have been unable to survive these conditions. Hence, seed banks may develop best on well drained, mesic sites. It appears that seeds germinate best following two years of cold treatment in Ontario.

The relatively late germination of *L. tulipifera* in comparison to a wide selection of other weedy species in Ontario, however, may place it at a competitive disadvantage in the early phases of establishment. It was also noted that other Carolinian tree species which germinated in the seed bank experiment (e.g.

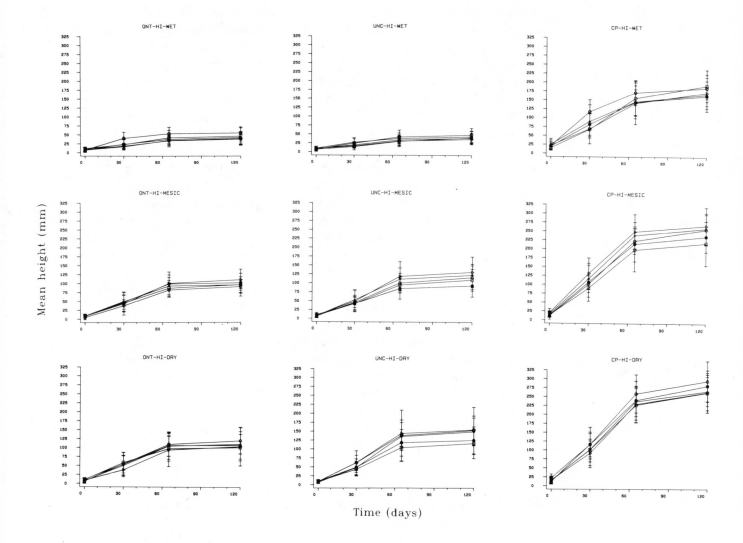

Figure 6 Mean height growth of *Liriodendron tulipifera* seedlings (+/- S.D.) over a 120 day mean growth period. Seedlings represent 3 populations: (1) Ontario (ONT) at the northern edge of *L. tulipifera's* range, (2) Upper elevations, southern Appalachians (UNC) at the range centre and (3) Coastal Plain, South Carolina (CP) at the southern edge of the range. All seedlings represented here were grown under a high nutrient regime and in one of three moisture treatments (WET, MESIC or DRY). Each of the five lines present in the individual line-graphs represents a different soil type. Note that soil has little effect on individual growth curves and overall high response of the South Carolina population to all treatments. Considerable similarity exists between the Ontario and southern Appalachian populations.

Sassafras albidum) had relatively late germination dates. This may reflect an intrinsic need for greater warming for initiation of seed germination among Carolinian species, relative to more northern species.

Although results from the glasshouse study on seedling development indicated that the Ontario population did not differ significantly from populations near the centre of its range, the clinal pattern of consistently lower measures of growth with increasing northern latitude may indicate that subtle changes in growth response are sufficient to place the species at a competitive disadvantage at the northern limits of its range. It is interesting, however, that the population from coastal South Carolina, which demonstrated the greatest seedling growth, is also relatively restricted in distribution and abundance in its natural habitat. This pattern may indicate that other environmental factors are operating at the southern edge of the species range to restrict its distribution, or that *L. tulipifera's* increased growth rates in South Carolina cannot compensate for increases in growth among a new suite of competing species.

The lack of influence of soil type (particularly with respect to clay rich soils) on the growth rates of *L. tulipifera* seedlings from Ontario populations indicates that there may be properties other than the textural characteristics of clay loams which restrict *L. tulipifera* from establishing on these sites. Slower warming of the soils in spring or a lack of suitable seed bank conditions may be additional factors worth investigating.

The apparent increase in *L. tulipifera* abundance on wet-mesic sites documented in this study agrees with earlier work conducted by Maycock (1963) in which *L. tulipifera* was noted to have a bimodal distribution around mesic sites, with highest importance values recorded for both dry-mesic and wet-mesic sites. Maycock interpreted this pattern as competitive exclusion by *Acer saccharum* (Sugar Maple) and *Fagus grandifolia* (American Beech). Both of these species are abundant in southern Ontario on rich, moist, and well-drained sites. The bimodal distribution of *L. tulipifera* in Ontario may be a response to the higher light levels characteristic of more open swamp and dry oak forests compared with dense forested stands on mesic sites. The higher incidence of seedlings and saplings of *L. tulipifera* found in such sites may indicate more frequent germination and establishment increasing the probability of continued population viability.

Aside from physical factors associated with clay rich soils in the field, *L. tulipifera* appears to be primarily restricted in its Ontario distribution by inter-competitive factors. It is probable that species characteristic of the northern hardwood forest association (e.g. *Acer saccharum*) play the greatest competitive role in restricting establishment of *L. tulipifera*.

Conservation Recommendations

Results and observations obtained to date can be incorporated into a series of conservation recommendations for *L. tulipifera* in southern Ontario. Aside from specific recommendations, it is apparent that loss of suitable forest habitat has been foremost in the population reduction of this species in Ontario. Some populations previously documented for southern Ontario could not be located during fieldwork, presumably due to habitat loss. Many other populations existing in small woodlots are represented by few individuals. Preservation of sizeable forest tracts remains the most important conservation measure for many Carolinian tree species, including *L. tulipifera*.

The following specific conservation recommendations are suggested for *Liriodendron tulipifera:*

1. Where sizeable tracts of old growth forest occur in southern Ontario, it is strongly recommended that they remain undisturbed. Evidence from both Rondeau Provincial Park and Backus Woods indicates that regeneration of shade intolerant species such as *L. tulipifera* occurs in the large gaps associated with multiple tree blowdowns (20 to 50 m across). Provided there are no extenuating circumstances, such as excessive deer browse (e.g. Rondeau Provincial Park), these species will continue to regenerate. Such old growth stands further serve as important research sites for investigating the ecology of the Carolinian forest and as benchmarks for comparisons with other anthropogenically disturbed or logged areas.

2. Where woodlot management is occurring for timber production, it is recommended that patch cuts be implemented as opposed to selective cutting. Small gaps created by the harvest of individual or small groups of trees are more often infilled by the canopies of adjacent trees and/or the small gaps provide the best sites for the establishment of more shade tolerant species such as *Acer saccharum*. Many woodlots inspected during the course of fieldwork, in which selective cutting had occurred, were found to contain substantial numbers of *L. tulipifera* seedlings and saplings, however most were highly suppressed and unlikely to reach the forest canopy. Although larger openings appear to be desirable, it is possible that severely disturbed patches larger than 200 m in diameter could encourage a dense weedy flora which might also suppress *L. tulipifera* seedlings. Open patches on the order of 50 to 200 m diameter may be optimal.

3. The seasonal timing of harvesting practices may be critical in determining the success of seed germination of *L. tulipifera*. A cut performed in late autumn (ie. November) or winter will encourage seed germination to occur in spring and allow a full growing season for seedlings to establish. A late spring or early summer cut may promote later germination of *L. tulipifera* seed, and seedlings may not harden off sufficiently to survive winter conditions. In addition, other species which may establish in a late spring or summer cut will be in a better position to outcompete any *L. tulipifera* seedlings subsequently germinating the following spring.

4. If promotion of *L. tulipifera* and other shade intolerant species is specifically desired, some scarification of the soil may be necessary to remove advance seedling regeneration of the more shade tolerant trees and shrubs in open patch cuts. This will also ensure that *L. tulipifera* seed is in contact with the mineral soil and less subject to competition with advanced regeneration of other species.

Acknowledgements

This research was supported by grants from World Wildlife Fund (Canada) to K. Kavanagh and a Natural Sciences and Engineering Research Council (NSERC) of Canada grant to Dr. T.J. Carleton. NSERC Postgraduate Scholarships and a Brody Award from The Nature Conservancy of Canada to K. Kavanagh are also gratefully acknowledged. I thank Gary Allen, Joyce Gould, and Steve Varga for helpful comments on the manuscript. Help received from numerous field assistants and friends over the past four years made fieldwork both pleasant and successful – to all of these people I extend a special thanks!

References

Ambrose, J.D., K. Kavanagh and C.J.Keddy. 1987. *Liriodendron tulipifera* L. 1 page *in:* G.W. Argus and D.J. White, eds. *Atlas of the rare vascular plants of Ontario*. National Museum of Natural Sciences, Ottawa.

Beck, D.E. and L. Della-Bianca. 1981. *Yellow Poplar: Characteristics and management*. Agriculture Handbook No. 583. USDA Forest Service, Southeastern Forest Experiment Station, Asheville, North Carolina. 91 pp.

Boyce, S.G. and M. Kaeiser. 1961. *Why yellow-poplar seeds have low viability*. USDA Forest Service, Central States Forest Experiment Station, Technical Paper 186, Columbus, Ohio. 16 pp.

Chapman, L.J. and D.F. Putnam. 1966. *The physiography of southern Ontario*. 2nd edition. University of Toronto Press. 386 pp.+ 3maps.

Clark, F.B. and S.G. Boyce. 1964. Yellow-poplar seed remains viable in the forest litter. *Journal of Forestry* 62:564-567.

Delcourt, P.A., H.R. Delcourt, and T. Webb III. 1983. *Atlas of mapped distributions of dominance and modern pollen percentages for important tree taxa of eastern North America*. 107 pp.

Fowells, H.A. 1965. *Silvics of forest trees of the United States*. Agriculture Handbook No. 271. USDA Forest Service. Washington. D.C. 762 pp.

Hedlund, A. and H.A. Knight. 1969. *Hardwood distribution maps for the south*. Bulletin SO-19, USDA Forest Service. 19 pp.

Hosie, R.C. 1975. *Native trees of Canada*. Canadian Forestry Service, Ottawa, Ontario. 380 pp.

Kavanagh, K. In preparation. *A comparison of the population ecology of* Liriodendron tulipifera L. *among allopatric populations*. Ph.D. Thesis, Department of Botany, University of Toronto, Toronto, Ontario.

Lorimer, C.G. 1980. Age structure and disturbance history of a southern Appalachian virgin forest. *Ecology* 61:1169-1184.

Maycock, P.F. 1963. The phytosociology of the deciduous forests of extreme southern Ontario. *Canadian Journal of Botany* 41:379-438.

McCaw, P.E. 1985. *The status of Black Gum* (Nyssa sylvatica *Marsh) in Backus Woods, southern Ontario*. M.Sc. Thesis. Dept. of Botany, University of Toronto, Toronto, Ontario. 136 pp.

Golden-seal is now threatened range-wide, due in large part to its medicinal qualities. Since the 1850s it has been harvested commercially for use in relieving ulcers, as a yellow dye, and as a general tonic. In Canada it is restricted to fewer than 20 populations in southwestern Ontario, where it inhabits rich deciduous woodlands.

Artist – Zile Zichmanis.

Provincially Rare Plants of the Carolinian Zone

Michael J. Oldham

Ontario Ministry of Natural Resources
Aylmer District Office
353 Talbot Street West
Aylmer, Ontario N5H 2S8

Abstract. *Forty percent of Ontario's 542 provincially rare plants are restricted to the Carolinian Zone. These plants are under increasing pressure from habitat modification and destruction, and already 36 species are possibly extirpated. Essex County has more restricted Carolinian rare plants (157) than any other county. Rare plant conservation in the Carolinian Zone is discussed, and recommendations are provided. An appendix of 231 rare plant species indicates the number of known sites for each, and lists counties of occurrence.*

Introduction

The Carolinian Zone (or Southern Deciduous Forest Region) in Ontario contains a greater rare plant diversity than any other similar sized region in Canada. Of the 542 provincially rare plants mapped in the recently completed *Atlas of the Rare Vascular Plants of Ontario* (Argus *et al.* 1982-1987), 351 (65%) occur in the Carolinian Zone, and 215 (40%) are restricted to the Carolinian Zone in Ontario, as mapped by Soper and Heimburger (1982). An additional 16 species (*Arisaema dracontium, Aster praealtus* var. *praealtus, Carex careyana, Carex hirsutella, Carex jamesii, Carex trichocarpa, Castanea dentata, Crataegus dodgei, Erigenia bulbosa, Euonymus atropurpureus, Liparis liliifolia, Lithospermum latifolium, Mertensia virginica, Morus rubra, Scirpus verecundus, Valeriana edulis* ssp. *ciliata*) whose ranges are virtually restricted to the Carolinian Zone, but have one or a few populations up to 50 km north of the boundary as delimited by Soper and Heimburger (1982), are included here as restricted Carolinian species.

As well as having the greatest rare plant diversity in the province, extreme southwestern Ontario is also the most heavily populated, industrialized, and agriculturalized part of Ontario. Rare plant species occurring in the Carolinian Zone are under many pressures, and populations are being lost at an alarming rate due to industrial and agricultural development, wetland drainage, clearcutting, shoreline development, and other man-caused habitat changes. We need to increase our vigilance over these species and their habitats, or many will disappear from the Canadian flora during the next few decades.

Some steps are already being taken to protect rare plant populations in Ontario. Six plant species are listed under the province's Endangered Species Act, all of which occur in the Carolinian Zone. COSEWIC (Committee on the Status of Endangered Wildlife in Canada) status reports have been prepared or are in preparation for 43 Ontario plant species, all of which occur in the Carolinian Zone. The Ontario Ministry of Natural Resources monitors populations of several plant species, including those covered under the Endangered Species Act. Lindsay

(1982) documented the rare vascular plants occurring in twelve provincial parks in the Carolinian Zone.

Methods

I have used information in the rare plant atlas, and more recent information, where available, to prepare the Appendix. This appendix lists those provincially rare species which are restricted or virtually restricted to the Carolinian Zone in Ontario. The appendix has been prepared from an Ontario perspective and there are plants included that have no populations north of the Carolinian Zone in Ontario, but are found in other provinces such as Quebec (e.g. *Arisaema dracontium*, *Carex lupuliformis*, *Justicia americana*, etc.) or Manitoba (e.g. *Carex gravida*, *Carex meadii*, etc.). For the purposes of this paper, the Carolinian Zone is considered to be anything southwest of a line joining Toronto and Grand Bend, which dips south towards central Lake Erie (see maps in Soper and Heimburger 1982 and Argus *et al.* 1982-1987). This zone includes the counties and regional municipalities of Essex (ES), Kent (KE), Lambton (LA), Elgin (EL), Haldimand-Norfolk (HN), Brant (BR), Hamilton-Wentworth (HW), and Niagara (NI), as well as most of Middlesex (MI) and Halton (HA), the southern portions of Peel (PE) and Oxford (OX), and extreme southern Huron (HU), Waterloo (WA), Wellington (WE), and York (YO). Several species extend slightly into Perth (PR) and Durham (DU).
In the Appendix, species status is indicated in four columns: those which may be extirpated (no post 1964 records), those known from a single recent (post 1964) site, those known from two recent sites, and those known from three to five recent sites. Species whose status is not indicated in one of these columns are known from more than five sites. Some species (and sites) have been considered extirpated if recent specific searches at known locations have been unsuccessful, even if the species was recorded since 1964. For the purposes of this compilation a site is considered distinct if it is separated from other sites by a kilometer or more of unoccupied territory. For each species, counties of occurrence have been listed using the above abbreviations. Counties whose abbreviations are in upper case letters have recent (post 1964) records, those in lower case have only historical records.

Results

Thirty-six (eleven percent) of the 231 species in the Appendix are possibly extirpated from the Carolinian Zone (and therefore from Ontario), 30 species are known from a single site, 31 species are known from two sites, and 40 species are known from between three and five sites. These 140 species currently known from five or fewer sites should be considered high priority for protection and further study. The county of Essex which has less than three percent forest cover, and is the most highly agriculturalized county in the province, has 157 provincially rare plants which are restricted to the Carolinian Zone. Of this total, 18 (eleven percent) are possibly extirpated. Essex is followed by Lambton with 90 species (11 extirpated), Kent with 76 (16 extirpated), Haldimand-Norfolk with 73 (10 extirpated), Niagara with 68 (31 extirpated), Middlesex with 55 (18 extirpated), and Elgin with 50 (9 extirpated).

Conservation Recommendations

1. Far more work is needed to ensure that these rare species continue to survive. Status reports are needed for many more species, and those found to be sufficiently imperiled should be added to the Ontario Endangered Species Act.

2. Only by periodic monitoring will we know if rare plant populations are declining.

3. Habitat manipulation may be needed to maintain suitable habitat for certain species.

4. Detailed mapping and further inventory work are needed to identify specific sites where rare plant populations are located. These detailed maps are needed by government agencies such as Ministry of Natural Resources district offices and Conservation Authority offices. In this way rare plant locations can be taken into account in assessing development proposals.

5. Landowner contact work has been very successful in protecting significant natural areas, and this technique could be extended to rare plant locations. Most rare plant locations in the Carolinian Zone are on private land, and in most cases landowners are not even aware of the presence of a rare species on their property. Local naturalist clubs could take a strong role in rare plant protection in their area.

6. The National Museum's rare plant atlas provides a sound foundation for rare plant protection efforts in Ontario. In particular, the detailed specimen data on which the atlas is based is very important for conservation agencies. We now know which plants are provincially rare, and where they occur. However, the Atlas is only a starting point, we now need to ensure that these species and their habitats are protected. The information contained in the Atlas needs to be continually updated. New native species are being found in Ontario almost annually, and these need to be added to the list (for example *Aster schreberi*, *Crataegus dilatata*, *Eragrostis capillàris*, and *Scleria pauciflora* are recent native additions to the flora not included in the Atlas). New locations for rare plants should be documented. The upcoming list of rare Canadian plants in preparation by the National Museum, which will rank rare plants both provincially and nationally, will be an extremely valuable publication.

7. Now that the National Museum is no longer cataloguing rare plant information at a provincial scale, there is the need for some agency to maintain data files on Ontario's rare plants. This function has been efficiently carried out in the United States by various state heritage programs initiated by the Nature Conservancy. Consideration should be given to implementing a similar program in Ontario.

Acknowledgements

The following individuals provided helpful comments on a draft of this article, or provided information used in the Appendix: Gary Allen, Wilf Botham, Mary Gartshore, Dave McLeod, Paul Prevett, Kathy Pryer, Tony Reznicek, John Riley, Bill Stewart, Don Sutherland, and Steve Varga.

References

Argus, G.W., K.M. Pryer, D.J. White, and C.J. Keddy, eds. 1982-1987. *Atlas of the rare vascular plants of Ontario.* Four parts. National Museum of Natural Sciences, Ottawa. (looseleaf).

Lindsay, K.M. 1982. Rare vascular plants of twelve provincial parks in the deciduous forest region of southern Ontario. *Ontario Field Biologist* 36(2):53-70.

Soper, J.H. and M.L. Heimburger. 1982. *Shrubs of Ontario.* Royal Ontario Museum, Toronto. 495 pp.

Appendix

Provincially Rare Plants Restricted To the Carolinian Zone in Ontario

Scientific Name	Common Name	Extir-pated	1 Site	2 Sites	3-5 Sites	Counties of Occurrence	Notes
Aesculus glabra	Ohio Buckeye			x		LA	Known from 2 sites on Walpole Is, where probably native, occasionally escaping elsewhere.
Agalinis gattingeri	Gattinger's Agalinis				x	LA,br	Locally common on Walpole and Squirrel. Is, formerly occurred near Galt. Recommended as Endangered in Canada.
Agalinis skinneriana	Skinner's Agalinis				x	ES,LA	Occurs at several prairies on Walpole and Squirrel Is, recently found at La Salle. Recommended as Endangered.
Agastache scrophulariaefolia	Purple Giant Hyssop	x				es,ke,ni	The three Ontario collections are all very old, the most recent being 1894.
Agrimonia parviflora	Small-flowered Agrimony					ES,KE,LA,EL, MI,ni,hw	Very common in ES, but rare elsewhere. A species of fields, scrubby areas, prairies, sometimes disturbed sites.
Aletris farinosa	Colicroot					ES,LA,HN,el	Locally common on Walpole Is and the Windsor-La Salle area. Recently recommended as Threatened in Canada.
Ammannia robusta	Scarlet Ammannia				x	ES	A wetland species known from Pelee Is. and 2 mainland sites in ES.
Amorpha fruticosa	Indigo Bush		x			ES	Perhaps native on Pelee Is, where collected as early as 1917. Planted and occasionally escaping elsewhere.
Arabis shortii	Short's Rock Cress					ES	Known from several of the Erie Islands and from Point Pelee. Fewer than 10 sites in Ontario.
Arisaema dracontium	Green Dragon					ES,KE,LA,MI, HU,EL,OX,HN, NI,wa	A few populations are just north of the Carolinian Zone. Locally common in some floodplain woods.

Scientific Name	Common Name	Extir-pated	1 Site	2 Sites	3-5 Sites	Counties of Occurrence	Notes
Aristida necopina	Three-awn				x	ES,KE,EL,MI HN	Known from Long Pt, the Bothwell area,the Dutton Swamp and La Salle. Inconspicuous and probably overlooked.
Aristida purpurascens	Arrow Feather Three-awn			x		ES	Occurs in southwest Windsor and at La Salle. A literature report from Squirrel Is. has never been confirmed.
Asclepias hirtella	Milkweed		x			ES	A single small populations exists at Ojibway Prairie Provincial Nature Reserve in Windsor.
Asclepias purpurascens	Purple Milkweed					ES,LA,HN,ke	Large populations at prairies in Windsor and Walpole Is, very rare and local elsewhere.
Asclepias sullivantii	Sullivant's Milkweed					ES,KE,LA,yo	Locally common at Windsor and Walpole Is., very rare elsewhere.
Asclepias variegata	Variegated Milkweed	x				hw	Only known from a single 1859 specimen, which may have come from cultivation.
Asimina triloba	Pawpaw					ES,KE,LA,MI, EL,HN,BR,NI, wa	Probably far less common than it once was. Occurs in rich woods. Many former populations eliminated.
Aster divaricatus	Aster				x	NI,YO,hw	A woodland species, similar to A. macrophyllus, and perhaps overlooked.
Aster praealtus var. praealtus	Willow Aster					ES,KE,LA,MI, PR	The PR population is slightly north of the Carolinian Zone. Often in prairie situations.
Aster shortii	Short's Aster					ES	Abundant on the Erie Islands and at Point Pelee, but very rare and local elsewhere.
Aster subulatus	Aster					ES,KE	ES sites are in disturbed, saline areas and appear non-native. The KE population is in an old, sandy field.
Aster undulatus	Wavy-leaved Aster	x				hn	Searches at the only known site have been unsucessful, and it is suspected that the collection is mis-labeled.
Aureolaria pedicularia	Fern-leaved False-foxglove					ES,LA,HN,hu, br,yo,wa,ni,hw	A species of open, dry, often oak-hickory, woods. Probably still extant in a number of counties.
Aureolaria virginica	Downy False-foxglove				x	HN,WA,HA,hw, ni	A post-1964 collection by A. Reznicek from WA is not mapped (specimen at WLU). Collected in HN and HA in 1988, WA in 1989.

Scientific Name	Common Name	Extirpated	1 Site	2 Sites	3-5 Sites	Counties of Occurrence	Notes
Baptisia tinctoria	Wild Indigo				x	ES,LA,HN,ke,ni	Local in prairies at Walpole Is and Windsor, and one small area near Turkey Point.
Betula lenta	Cherry Birch		x			NI	A second NI site (specimen at BUF) at Niagara Gorge, Ontario, has not beenverified.
Blephilia ciliata	Downy Wood Mint		x			ES	Locally common on Stone Road Alvar, Pelee Is, unconfirmed elsewhere.
Blephilia hirsuta	Hairy Wood Mint	x				la	Historic records (1958 and 1959) from a single site on the Ausable River.
Buchnera americana	Blue-hearts				x	LA	Only known from the Pinery-Ipperwash-Port Franks area. Rare or extirpated in much northern part of range.
Camassia scilloides	Wild Hyacinth					ES	Currently restricted to 6 Erie Islands sites. Formerly collected on Bois Blanc. Is in the Detroit R.
Campsis radicans	Trumpet Creeper					ES	Quite rare (fewer than 10 sites) as a native, some populations may be escapes from cultivation.
Carex aggregata	Clustered Sedge		x			ES	Recently (1982) discovered on Middle Is.
Carex alata	Sedge		x			HN	Known in Canada from a single clump on Long Point.
Carex careyana	Carey's Sedge					KE,LA,MI,EL,PR,OX,HN,HAwe	A few populations just north of the Carolinian Zone. Recently discovered in at least 6 sites not in Atlas.
Carex crus-corvi	Crow-spur Sedge			x		ES,LA	Known from low woods. Rare in several US states.
Carex davisii	Sedge					ES,LA	Rare and local in low woods and floodplains, usually on clay soil. 10 to 12 sites known.
Carex emmonsii	Sedge		x			NI	Easily confused with C. artitecta, but preferring acid soils. Wainfleet Bog.
Carex frankii	Sedge					ES,EL	Rare and local in wet areas. Known from less than 10 sites.
Carex glaucodea	Glaucescent Sedge			x		ES,HN	Recently discovered in ES and HN during natural area inventory fieldwork.
Carex gravida	Sedge	x				es	Known from a single old Windsor collection. Recently discovered in Manitoba.

114

Scientific Name	Common Name	Extir-pated	1 Site	2 Sites	3-5 Sites	Counties of Occurrence	Notes
Carex hirsutella	Hirsute Sedge					ES,KE,HN,NI, HU	A population on the Bayfield River, HU, is just north of the Carolinian Zone. Recently found at 6 HN sites.
Carex hyalinolepis	Sedge					ES,KE,LA	Abundant and widespread in ditches and wet woods in ES. Found in several new ites in western KE and LA.
Carex inops ssp. heliophila	Sun-loving Sedge	x				hn	Could not be relocated despite searches at its only known site. Last collected in 1982.
Carex jamesii	James's Sedge					ES,LA,EL,MI, PR,HN,NI,BR, ox,wa	A few sites are slightly north of the Carolinian Zone. Recently discovered at more than 10 sites not in Atlas.
Carex leavenworthii	Sedge		x			ES	Known only from thickets at the Stone Road Alvar, where it is rare and local.
Carex lupuliformis	Sedge		x			ES,wa	Known from a floodplain woods near Amherstburg. Formerly known from near Galt. Also occurs in Quebec.
Carex meadii	Sedge					ES,KE,LA,EL, MI	Usually in dry, open, often prairie sites. Easily confused with C. tetanica. Recently discovered in Manitoba.
Carex muskingumensis	Sedge					ES,KE,LA	Locally common in low woods in ES and on Walpole Island, rare in KE.
Carex nigromarginata	Sedge		x			HN	Known only from Long Point.
Carex retroflexa	Reflexed Sedge			x		ES	Recently discovered in woodland edges and openings at 2 sites in ES.
Carex seorsa	Sedge					HN,NI	An easily overlooked species of swamps and wet woods, recently found at 10 sites in HN.
Carex shortiana	Sedge		x			ES	Occurs in floodplain woods near Amherstburg.
Carex squarrosa	Sedge					ES,KE,ni	Locally common in woodlands in ES, rare in KE.
Carex suberecta	Sedge				x	ES,LA	A species of wet prairies, ditches, and swamps. Common at Oxley Swamp, ES, rare and local elsewhere.
Carex torta	Sedge	x				mi,pe	Known from old collections only.
Carex virescens	Sedge					ES,EL,HN	Recently found at 11 new sites in HN. A species of sandy, open woods.

Scientific Name	Common Name	Extir- pated	1 Site	2 Sites	3-5 Sites	Counties of Occurrence	Notes
Carex willdenowii	Willenow's Sedge	x				HN,ni	Recently discovered in eastern HN, also known from a single historic NI collection.
Carya glabra	Pignut Hickory					ES,HN,NI,WA, BR,HW,HA	Recorded at 22 sites in HN during a recent inventory. Less common in other counties.
Carya laciniosa	Big Shellbark Hickory					ES,KE,LA,HN, NI,el	Locally common in ES and on Walpole Island, but scarce elsewhere.
Cassia hebecarpa	Wild Senna				x	ES,KE,ni	Rare and local, often in somewhat disturbed sites.
Castanea dentata	Chestnut					ES,KE,LA,MI, EL,HN,NI,BR, WA,WE,HA,ox	A historic site in OX is just north of the Carolinian Zone. Much reduced from former numbers.
Celtis tenuifolia	Dwarf Hackberry				x	ES,LA	Locally common in the Grand Bend area, much rarer at Point Pelee and Pelee Is. Recom- mended as Rare in Canada.
Cerastium velutinum	Mouse-ear Chickweed					ES,LA	Locally common on Pelee Is, rare elsewhere.
Cercis canadensis	Redbud	x				es	A single tree seen on Pelee Is in 1892 was probably native, other Ontario records are introductions.
Chaerophyllum procumbens	Creeping Chervil					ES,LA	Known from the Erie Islands, a single site in LA, and old records from Amherstburg and Bois Blanc Island.
Chamaelirium luteum	Devil's-bit	x				hn,ni	Collected as recently as 1979 at Turkey Point, but not seen on several subsequent searches.
Chenopodium standleyanum	Goosefoot					ES,KE	Recent records from the Erie Islands and Wheatley, historic record from Point Pelee.
Cimicifuga racemosa	Black Cohosh					HN,NI,HW	Recently found at 3 sites in HN, and at a site in HW. Toronto dot in Rare Plant Atlas is an introduction.
Collinsia verna	Blue-eyed Mary	x				el,mi,ox	Only collected once in Ontario since 1896. Not found during investigations for a recent COSEWIC status report.
Coreopsis tripteris	Tall Coreopsis					ES,LA,MI	Locally common at Walpole Is an Windsor. Two small populations recently found in MI.
Cornus drummondii	Rough-leaved Dogwood					ES,KE,EL,HN	Common and widespread in ES, but apparently rare and local elsewhere. Possibly somewhat overlooked.

Scientific Name	Common Name	Extir-pated	1 Site	2 Sites	3-5 Sites	Counties of Occurrence	Notes
Corydalis flavula	Yellow Harlequin				x	ES,ni,hn	Known from the Erie Islands and Pt. Pelee, and from single early records in NI and HN.
Crataegus beata	Hawthorn	x				hn,ni	Known from 2 collections: 1952 in HN and pre-1925 in NI.
Crataegus conspecta	Hawthorn				x	NI,HA,yo	A large and distinctive hawthorn.
Crataegus dissona	Hawthorn					ES,LA,EL,MI, NI,HW,HA,wa	Found in ES since the Rare Plant Atlas.
Crataegus dodgei	Hawthorn					LA,MI,HU,EL, HN,WA,HW,ni, pe,yo	The HU and WA sites are slightly north of the Carolinian Zone. Recently found at 4 HN sites.
Crataegus foetida	Hawthorn	x				ni	Known only from a single pre 1925 collection.
Crataegus formosa	Hawthorn			x		NI,HW	Extremely restricted world range.
Crataegus lumaria	Hawthorn					KE,EL,LA,MI	Locally common. Formerly included in Crataegus dodgei.
Crataegus margaretta	Hawthorn				x	LA,MI,HN	Recently found at 2 sites in HN. The London population is threatened by site modification.
Crataegus mollis var. gigantea	Hawthorn			x		ES	Known from 2 Pelee Island sites.
Crataegus nitidula	Hawthorn		x			LA	Known from a single site and on the verge of extirpation in Ontario.
Crataegus perjucunda	Hawthorn			x		MI	Locally frequent at its 2 MI sites.
Crataegus prunifolia	Hawthorn			x		ES,NI	The large NI population has been severely reduced by agricultural clearance. Only a single shrub at ES site.
Cuscuta coryli	Dodder					ES,LA	Known from prairie areas of Windsor and Walpole Is.
Cuscuta polygonorum	Dodder	x				es	Known from a historic Point Pelee record.
Cyperus flavescens	Umbrella-sedge					KE,LA,EL,HN	First found in Canada at Long Point, now known from 5 sites in HN, and single sites in KE, EL, and LA.
Cystopteris protrusa	Creeping Fragile Fern					ES,LA,MI,EL, HN	Occurs in rich, lowland woods, but apparently quite local. Can be difficult to distinguish from C. tenuis.
Desmodium canescens	Tick-trefoil				x	ES,KE	Locally common at Point Pelee, rare at 2 sites on Pelee Is. Apparently extirpated at several former sites.

Scientific Name	Common Name	Extir-pated	1 Site	2 Sites	3-5 Sites	Counties of Occurrence	Notes
Desmodium ciliare	Tick-trefoil	x				ni	Occurrence based on 2 very old NI collections.
Desmodium illinoense	Tick-trefoil	x				mi	A single 1888 Ontario collection.
Desmodium marilandicum	Tick-trefoil	x				es,la,wa	Occurrence based on 3 very old Ontario collections.
Desmodium sessilifolium	Tick-trefoil	x				es	Collected in Windsor in 1901.
Dichanthelium clandestinum	Broadleaf Panic Grass					ES,LA,HN	Grows at 7 sites along Big Creek in HN, as well as Walpole and Squirrel Is, and 1 site in ES. Also in Quebec.
Dichanthelium commonsianum	Panic Grass	x				es,mi	Var. euchlamydeum occurs in Ontario. A difficult taxon requiring further research, some records may be hybrids.
Dichanthelium meridionale	Panic Grass			x		LA	Grows in open sandy soil on Walpole Is. Historic record from Squirrel Island.
Disporum lanuginosum	Yellow Mandarin					EL,MI,HN,WE, HA,HW,ke,ni	Locally abundant in HN, where recently documented at 41 sites. Perhaps a candidate for delisting.
Eleocharis caribaea	Spikerush		x			HN,ke	Locally common near tip of Long Point, on moist sand. Not relocated at Rondeau, where it was once collected.
Eleocharis engelmannii	Engelmann's Spike-rush				x	ES,HN	Found in moist, open, sandy sites. Easily confused with similar species, particularly E. obtusa.
Eleocharis equisetoides	Spike-rush		x			HN	Rediscovered at Long Point in 1988, where it occurs as a small population at one site.
Eleocharis quadrangulata	Four-angled Spike-rush		x			HN,ke,la	Known from Long Point, but not recently collected at several former sites. A wetland species.
Eragrostis spectabilis	Purple Love Grass					ES,KE,LA,EL, MI,OX	Occurs in dry, open, often sandy areas. Records from HN,HW,NI are introductions.
Erigenia bulbosa	Harbinger-of-spring					ES,LA,MI,EL, hu,pr,wa,pe,yo	Formerly occurred just north of Carolinian Zone in HU, PR, and WA, but recent records all Carolinian.
Euonymus atropurpureus	Burning Bush					ES,EL,HN,NI, HW,HA,WE, DU,mi,wa,yo	A few populations are just north of the Carolinian Zone. Sometimes confused with the introduced E. europaeus.
Eupatorium coelestinum	Mistflower			x		ES,KE	The Point Pelee plants originated from a former garden, which may also be the case at Rondeau.

Scientific Name	Common Name	Extir-pated	1 Site	2 Sites	3-5 Sites	Counties of Occurrence	Notes
Euphorbia obtusata	Blunt-leaved Spurge			x		ES	A wetland edge species.
Fimbristylis spadicea	Fimbristylis		x			LA	Known from several nearby prairies on Walpole and Squirrel Islands.
Frasera caroliniensis	American Columbo				x	HN,WA,NI,HA, BR,hw,la	Rare and local, and possibly extirpated from some former sites.
Fraxinus quadrangulata	Blue Ash					ES,KE,LA,EL, MI	Occurs on floodplains, particularly on the Thames R, and also on Point Pelee and several of the Erie Islands.
Fuirena pumila	Umbrella-grass	x				ni	Known only from a single, very old collection from the Port Colborne area.
Gaura biennis	Biennial Gaura					ES,NI,hn,yo	Known from at least 10 sites in western ES, very rare elsewhere.
Gentiana puberulenta	Downy Gentian	x				la,yo	Old records from Walpole Is and Toronto.
Geum vernum	Spring Avens					ES,KE,LA,MI, hn	Very common in low clay woods and floodplains in ES, rare elsewhere. Not relocated in HN during recent work.
Gleditsia triacanthos	Honey Locust					ES,KE,NI	Frequently planted, but uncommon and local as a native species.
Gnaphalium purpureum	Purplish Cudweed	x				es,ni	Known from 1885 and 1901 Macoun collections.
Gymnocladus dioica	Kentucky Coffee-tree					ES,KE,LA,mi, ox,hn	Local and uncommon. Most populations are single-sex clones. Recently designated as Threatened in Canada.
Hemicarpha micrantha	Hemicarpha		x			ES	Occurs on a sand beach in southern ES. Very small and easily overlooked. Also in Quebec and British Columbia.
Heuchera americana	Alum-root				x	ES	Recorded from woodlands and alvars on Pelee Is and mainland ES.
Hibiscus laevis	Halberd-leaved Rose Mallow	x				es	Known only from a 1904 Pelee Island specimen. Recent searches have been unsucessful.
Hibiscus moscheutos	Swamp Rose Mallow					ES,KE,LA,HN, NI,EL	Recently designated Rare in Canada by COSEWIC. A wetland species occurring along Great Lakes shores.
Hieracium longipilum	Long-bearded Hawkweed	x				la,hn	A distinctive species not seen in Ontario since 1918.

Scientific Name	Common Name	Extir-pated	1 Site	2 Sites	3-5 Sites	Counties of Occurrence	Notes
Hydrophyllum appendiculatum	Appendaged Waterleaf					ES,KE,EL,mi, ox	Locally common at Point Pelee and on the Erie Islands.
Hypericum gentianoides	Orange-grass			x		ES	Rare and local in the Windsor-La Salle area. Small and easily overlooked. Occurs in open, sandy sites.
Ipomoea pandurata	Wild Potato-vine			x		ES,ni	Known from Point Pelee and Pelee Is, and from an old NI specimen. Possibly extirpated on Pelee Is.
Iris brevicaulis	Leafy Blue Flag				x	ES	Known from low woods at Sturgeon Creek near Point Pelee and several Pelee Is. sites.
Isopyrum biternatum	False Rue-anemone				x	EL,MI,la	A species of wooded floodplains and slopes.
Isotria medioloides	Small Whorled Pogonia		x			EL	Known from a single site in Canada and rare throughout its range. Protected under the Ontario Endangered Species Act.
Isotria verticillata	Large Whorled Pogonia				x	MI,HN,OX	Very rare in Canada, and recommended for Endangered status. Most populations small.
Juncus biflorus	Two-flowered Rush				x	ES,HN	Grows in several prairie sites near Windsor, and one dry field near Turkey Point.
Juncus brachycarpus	Short-fruited Rush			x		ES	Restricted to prairie sites in Windsor.
Juncus marginatus	Grass-leaved Rush					ES,MI,HN,NI	Recently found at 11 new sites in HN, and perhaps overlooked elsewhere.
Justicia americana	Water Willow					ES,KE,EL,HN, NI	Seven Carolinian Zone sites, also a St. Lawrence River site is either in Ontario or New York. Also in Quebec.
Krigia biflora	Two-flowered Cynthia					ES,LA,ke	Apparently absent from a number of historic sites. Easily overlooked when not in flower.
Lactuca floridana	Blue Lettuce					ES	Locally common at Point Pelee and on the Erie Islands, but rare at its only other site at Kingsville.
Lechea minor	Lesser Pinweed	x				es	Single historic (1901) record from Windsor. A recent Windsor collection is unverified.
Lechea pulchella	Pinweed				x	ES,LA	Known from several sites in the Windsor-La Salle area, and from Walpole Is.

Scientific Name	Common Name	Extir-pated	1 Site	2 Sites	3-5 Sites	Counties of Occurrence	Notes
Lechea villosa	Hairy Pinweed					ES,KE,LA,HN, mi	Recently found at 17 sites in HN. Fairly widespread in the Carolinian Zone, in open, dry sandy situations.
Leptoloma cognatum	Fall Witch Grass					ES,KE,LA,MI	Occurs in prairie area at Windsor, Walpole Is, and Bothwell, and probably native. Other records adventive.
Lespedeza violacea	Bush Clover			x		ES,NI	Rare and local at its only site in ES.
Lespedeza virginica	Bush Clover		x			ES	Known from 2 nearby sites in Windsor. Probably extirpated at Leamington. COSEWIC report recommends Endangered.
Leucospora multifida	Conobea				x	ES	On Pelee Is. on limestone out crops and sandy shores. A site near a railway in MI is probably adventive.
Liatris aspera var. intermedia	Rough Blazing Star					ES,LA,ke,hu	Locally common on Walpole Is and Windsor, but less so than L. spicata. Apparently extirpated at some sites.
Liatris spicata	Dense Blazing Star					ES,KE,LA,EL, YO	Abundant in the Windsor-La Salle and Walpole Is areas, rare else-where. Recently designated Rare in Canada.
Linaria canadensis	Toadflax		x			NI,el	Ontario collections are from disturbed sites and may represent introductions.
Linum medium var. texanum	Stiff Yellow Flax				x	MI,HN,la	Locally common at Long Point, and recently collected in south west MI. Not seen at Sarnia since before 1925.
Linum virginianum	Virginia Yellow Flax					ES,KE,HN,HA, la,ni,wa,yo	Widespread in dry, open woods. Many records are old, but perhaps under-collected.
Liparis liliifolia	Lily-leaved Twayblade					ES,KE,EL,YO, ni,mi	Most populations small. YO site just north of Carolinian Zone. Recently designated Endangered in Canada.
Liriodendron tulipifera	Tulip Tree					ES,KE,LA,MI, EL,HN,NI,hw	Widespread and locally common in theCarolinian Zone. Recently recorded at 18 sites in HN.
Lithospermum incisum	Fringed Puccoon				x	ES,LA,HW,ha	Occurs in sandy, open ground. Uncommon on Pelee Is and at Sarnia.
Lithospermum latifolium	American Gromwell					EL,MI,HU,WA, HA,es,ke,la, yo	A few populations just north of Carolinian Zone in HU and WA. Fewer than 10 known sites.

Scientific Name	Common Name	Extir-pated	1 Site	2 Sites	3-5 Sites	Counties of Occurrence	Notes
Ludwigia alternifolia	False Loosestrife			x		ES	Occurs in the Windsor-La Salle area.
Ludwigia polycarpa	Many-fruited False Loosestrife					ES,KE,LA,HN, ni	Uncommon and local in low, wet areas, most common in ES.
Lycopus rubellus	Stalked Water Horehound					ES,KE,LA,HN	A species of wet woods and swamps, similar to other Lycopus, and probably overlooked. 11 sites in HN.
Lycopus virginicus	Virginia Bugleweed				x	ES,KE	Known from Pelee Is, Big Creek, and Sinclair's Bush. Hybridizes with L. uniflorus, and easily overlooked.
Magnolia acuminata	Cucumber Tree				x	HN,NI	Recently added to Ontario's Endangered Species Act. 3 viable populations, others small or non-reproducing.
Mertensia virginica	Virginia Cowslip					ES,LA,MI,EL, HN,NI,HA,PE, YO	Occurs just north of the Carolinian Zone in YO. A species of rich floodplain woods.
Mimulus alatus	Winged Monkey-flower					ES,KE,EL,HN, ni	Recently found at several new sites, and now known from 6 sites. May be overlooked elsewhere.
Monarda punctata	Spotted Horsemint		x			HN	Probably native only near Turkey Point, other Ontario populations being clearly adventive.
Morus rubra	Red Mulberry					ES,KE,NI,HW, HA,mi,yo,du	A historic DU record is just east of the Carolinian Zone. Fewer than 10 populations. Hybridizes with M. alba.
Myosotis macrosperma	Large-seeded Forget-me-not				x	ES,KE	Known from several sites on Pelee Is, and from the Kent-Elgin Shoreline ANSI.
Myrica pensylvanica	Bayberry				x	HN	Only known from the Turkey Point vicinity, where it is locally common.
Nuphar advena	Yellow Pond-lily					ES,HN,el,mi, br,hw,ni	Locally common in ES. Very under-collected, possibly due to confusion with N. variegata.
Nyssa sylvatica	Black Gum					ES,KE,LA,MI, EL,HN,NI	A species of deciduous swamps, locally common in the Carolinian Zone. Recorded at 21 recent sites in HN.
Oenothera clelandii	Cleland's Evening Primrose			x		EL,PE	Occurs in a prairie remnant in Mississauga and in an old field at Springwater Forest. Rare at both sites.

Scientific Name	Common Name	Extir-pated	1 Site	2 Sites	3-5 Sites	Counties of Occurrence	Notes
Oenothera fruticosa ssp. glauca	Sundrops	x				ni	Only known from an old collection near Fort Erie. Commonly cultivated.
Opuntia humifusa	Eastern Prickly Pear			x		ES,ke	Locally common at Pt Pelee NP, rare at Fish Pt, Pelee Is. Historic specimen from southwest KE.
Oxypolis rigidior	Cowbane				·	ES	Locally common in swamps and moist woods in ES.
Paronychia canadensis	Smooth Forked Chickweed				x	ES	Known from 3 sites in ES, rare at each.
Paronychia fastigiata	Hairy Forked Chickweed			x		HN,NI	Rare at each site.
Paspalum setaceum	Paspalum					ES,KE,LA,MI, HN	Var. muhlenbergii occurs in Ontario. Recently discovered at 3 sites in HN. A species of sandy open areas.
Phacelia purshii	Miami Mist				x	ES	Restricted to the Lake Erie Islands, where known from Pelee, East Sister, Middle Sister, and Middle Islands.
Phlox pilosa ssp. pilosa	Downy Phlox	x				es	Known in Canada only from an 1882 specimen from Amherstburg.
Phyla lanceolata	Fog-fruit					ES,KE,LA	Typically on moist, clay edges of creeks and rivers. Easily over-looked. Fewer than 10 known sites in Ontario.
Plantago cordata	Heart-leaved Plantain			x		MI,LA,es	Several hundred plants at each site. On Ontario Endangered Species Act, and rare in many US states.
Platanthera ciliaris	Orange-fringed Orchid	x				es	Not seen in Canada since 1901 when collected near Leamington.
Poa sylvestris	Sylvan Blue Grass				x	ES,KE	Known from 2 ES and 2 KE sites. Uncommon and local at all sites, but perhaps more common at Rondeau.
Polygala cruciata	Cross-leaved Milkwort	x				es	Known from an 1894 Windsor collection.
Polygala incarnata	Pink Milkwort				x	LA	Only known from prairies on Walpole and Squirrel Islands. Rare in adjacent US states.
Polygonum erectum	Erect Knotweed			x		ES,mi,el,ni, hw,yo	Two small populations in ES. Appears to have declined markedly from much of the northern part of its range.

Scientific Name	Common Name	Extir- pated	1 Site	2 Sites	3-5 Sites	Counties of Occurrence	Notes
Polygonum tenue	Slender Knotweed					ES,LA,HN,mi	A species of dry, open sandy sites. Fewer than 10 poulations in Canada.
Potamogeton pulcher	Pondweed	x				ke	A 1948 record from Rondeau is the only one in Canada.
Ptelea trifoliata	Hop Tree					ES,KE,LA,EL, HN,NI	Largely occurs on sandy shore-lines and threatened by shoreline development.
Pycnanthemum incanum	Hoary Mountain-mint			x		HA,hw	Recently designated Endangered in Canada by COSEWIC.
Pycnanthemum pilosum	Hairy Mountain-mint			x		ES,KE	Known from Cedar Creek, Rondeau Provincial Park, and historically from Leamington.
Quercus palustris	Pin Oak					ES,KE,LA,NI	A species of wet woods and prairie areas, locally common in ES and NI.
Quercus prinoides	Dwarf Chinquapin Oak				x	ES,LA	Known only from the Grand Bend and St. Williams areas, but locally common at both.
Quercus shumardii	Shumard Oak					ES,KE,LA,NI	Locally common in ES. Long confused with other oaks and often difficult to identify.
Ratibida pinnata	Gray-headed Coneflower					ES,KE,LA,EL	A prairie species common on Walpole Is, Windsor, and Stone Road Alvar. Other populations small.
Rotala ramosior	Branched Toothcup		x			HN	Recently discovered in moist areas in a sandy field near Turkey Point.
Sabatia angularis	Rose-pink	x				hw	Only known from an 1865 Hamilton specimen.
Sanicula canadensis var. grandis	Long-styled Canadian Sanicle	x				mi,el,br,wa	Known from 5 historic sites. Typical variety not provincially rare.
Scirpus verecundus	Bashful Bulrush		x			HW,YO	The YO population is slightly east of the Carolinian Zone. COSEWIC status Threatened in Canada.
Scleria triglomerata	Tall Nut-rush					ES,LA,mi,yo	Locally common at Windsor and on Walpole Is. in prairies.
Scutellaria nervosa	Veined Skullcap				x	ES	Known from several sites along Cedar Creek and the Canard River.
Senecio glabellus	Butterweed	x				es	Repeated searches at the single known site have been unsuccess-ful, and habitat at the site has been disturbed.

Scientific Name	Common Name	Extir-pated	1 Site	2 Sites	3-5 Sites	Counties of Occurrence	Notes
Silene virginica	Fire Pink	x				es	A single historic (1873) record from "islands in the Detroit River".
Silphium perfoliatum	Cup-plant					KE,EL,MI	Scattered populations along the Thames River in Kent County.
Silphium terebinthinaceum	Prairie Dock					ES,LA	Locally common in Windsor and on Walpole Is., several smaller native populations in ES.
Sisyrinchium albidum	Blue-eyed Grass				x	ES,LA	Locally common in prairies at Windsor, also on Walpole Is.
Smilax rotundifolia	Common Greenbrier					ES,NI	Recently found in several ES and NI woodlots, but populations small.
Solidago riddellii	Riddell's Goldenrod					ES,LA,EL,ke	Locally common in prairies on Walpole Is and the Windsor area, rare elsewhere.
Solidago sempervirens	Seaside Goldenrod					ES	All Ontario populations are probably non-native. Locally abundant at Canard River mouth and parts of Windsor.
Solidago speciosa	Showy Goldenrod			x		LA	Only known from prairies on Walpole Island, where it is uncommon and local.
Solidago ulmifolia	Elm-leaved Goldenrod	x				mi	May be confused with S. rugosa or S. arguta.
Sphenopholis nitida	Wedge Grass			x		HN,HA,ni	Apparently rare at its 2 sites. A species of rich deciduous woods.
Sphenopholis obtusata	Wedge Grass				x	ES,LA,EL,ke	Currently known from 3 sites, but not relocated on Walpole or Pelee Is during recent fieldwork.
Spiranthes lacera var. gracilis	S. Slender Ladies'-tresses			x		LA,NI,ke,el,yo	Small, inconspicuous, and easily confused with var. lacera. Extirpated at several historic sites.
Spiranthes ochroleuca	Yellow Ladies'-tresses					KE,LA,EL,MI,HN,NI,hu	New sites recently found on Walpole Is and HN. Several historic sites destroyed. Fewer than 10 extant sites.
Spiranthes ovalis	Oval Ladies'-tresses			x		LA	Recently discovered on Walpole Is, where it is known from 2 small populations. Var. erostellata in Ontario.
Stipa avenacea	Black Oat-grass	x				la	Collected in Pinery Provincial Park in 1965, but recent searches there have failed to relocate it.
Stylophorum diphyllum	Wood Poppy		x			MI	Recently discovered along the Thames River near London. This population numbers several hundred plants.

Scientific Name	Common Name	Extir-pated	1 Site	2 Sites	3-5 Sites	Counties of Occurrence	Notes
Tephrosia virginiana	Goat's-rue				x	HA	Occurs at 3 nearby sites in the Turkey Point area, in open, sandy woods and edges.
Thalictrum revolutum	Waxy Meadow-rue					ES,HN,ke,la,ni	Recently found at 4 sites in HN. Manitoulin Is records mapped in the Atlas are in error. Easily overlooked.
Thaspium barbinode	Hairy-jointed Meadow Parsnip			x		ES,KE,ni	Recent collections from Pelee Is and Rondeau. A 1906 WE record is not mapped in the Atlas, or included here.
Thaspium trifoliatum	Meadow Parsnip					ES,KE	Known from about 7 sites in ES, and 1 in KE.
Tradescantia ohiensis	Ohio Spiderwort					ES,LA,hn	Locally abundant in prairie areas of Windsor and Walpole Is. Not seen at Courtland, HN, since 1901.
Trichostema dichotomum	Forked Blue Curls		x			HN	Occurs in open sandy soil in the St Williams Forestry Station.
Trillium flexipes	Bent Trillium	x				es,mi,ni	Known from 5 pre-1925 and 1 1950-1964 collections. Populations of T. cernuum should be carefully checked.
Triosteum angustifolium	Yellow Horse-gentian		x			ES	Only known from the Stone Road Alvar on Pelee Is. At least 20 to 30 clumps present.
Triphora trianthophora	Nodding Pogonia			x		ES,KE	Recommended as Threatened in Canada. Occurs at Rondeau Park and 1 woodlot in southeast ES.
Uvularia perfoliata	Perfoliate Bellwort				x	NI,HA,hw,hn	Several historic NI records. Not seen in HN since 1938, despite searches.
Valeriana edulis ssp. ciliata	Hairy Valerian		x			HU,mi,br,wa	The only recent record, at Goderich, HU, is slightly north of the Carolinian Zone.
Valerianella umbilicata	Corn-salad		x			ES	Occurs in Canada only at the Stone Road Alvar on Pelee Is, where it is locally common.
Verbesina alternifolia	Wingstem					ES,KE,LA,EL	Abundant and widespread along the Thames R in KE, also grows along the Sydenham R in LA.
Vernonia gigantea	Tall Ironweed					ES,KE,LA,HN,EL,ni	Widespread and locally abundant in ES, and on Walpole Is, less common elsewhere. Sometimes along roadsides.
Veronicastrum virginicum	Culver's-root					ES,KE,LA	Locally common in prairies at Windsor and Walpole Is, rare elsewhere.

Scientific Name	Common Name	Extir-pated	1 Site	2 Sites	3-5 Sites	Counties of Occurrence	Notes
Viola palmata	Early Blue Violet					ES,KE,MI,HN, el	Var. dilatata (=Viola triloba) restricted to Norfolk Sand Plain, var. palmata, more widespread, and on clay.
Viola pedata	Bird's-foot Violet			x		HN,BR,ni	Restricted to Turkey Point and Brantford Savannah. Extirpated at several former sites. Needs open, sandy sites. COSEWIC report recommends endangered.
Viola rafinesquii	Rafinesque's Violet				x	ES,NI	Grows at several spots on Pelee Is, and near Fort Erie (recent specimen at BUF, not included in Atlas).
Viola striata	Cream Violet					ES,LA,MI,PR, WE,ke,el	A species of rich, usually clay, floodplains and slopes, often quite local, but sometimes abundant.
Vitis vulpina	Chicken Grape			x		ES	Occurs at 2 nearby wooded areas along the Canard River. Similar to the common and widespread V. riparia.

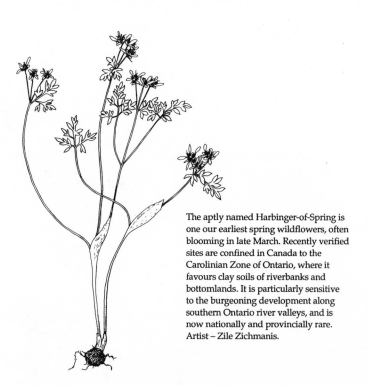

The aptly named Harbinger-of-Spring is one our earliest spring wildflowers, often blooming in late March. Recently verified sites are confined in Canada to the Carolinian Zone of Ontario, where it favours clay soils of riverbanks and bottomlands. It is particularly sensitive to the burgeoning development along southern Ontario river valleys, and is now nationally and provincially rare. Artist – Zile Zichmanis.

County/Regional Municipality Vascular Plant Floras for the Carolinian Zone of Canada

Steve Varga
Gary M. Allen

Ministry of Natural Resources, Central Region
820 Yonge St. S.
Aurora, Ontario L4G 3G8

Abstract. *Summaries are given on vascular floras in progress for each of the 16 counties and regional municipalities (RMs) which occur in the Carolinian Zone of Canada. Botanists known to be undertaking floras in these areas were asked to summarize their studies, and provide a list of botanical highlights (post-1980) and significant botanical sites. Findings indicate that floras of 14 counties/RMs are being investigated by 18 field botanists. Since 1980 these efforts have produced checklists for eight counties/RMs with checklists in progress for an additional four. Seven of these lists are computerized. Fifty-nine provincially rare species cited represent 72 first county or RM records, and 16 of these are additions to the Ontario flora. One hundred and seventy-four botanical sites are listed, many of which have not been noted in previous studies.*

Introduction

A considerable amount of systematic research has focused on the vascular floras of the 16 counties and regional municipalities (RMs) which occur wholly or partially within the Carolinian Zone in southern Ontario. At present, the floras of 14 counties/RMs are being investigated by 18 field botanists; only Oxford and Huron are not currently being studied at the county level. For the most part, these compilers have begun their fieldwork over the past 25 years. The noteworthy exception is Bill Stewart who began his work in 1935. All are working on a volunteer basis. These efforts have produced checklists for eight counties/RMs since 1980, with checklists in progress for an additional four. In contrast, four county checklists were produced between 1960 and 1980, and only three between 1920 and 1959.

The recent advent of a network of volunteers and professionals working on floras in southern Ontario has greatly enhanced our knowledge of significant botanical areas, and plant distributions and status. This has paralleled a renewed interest in botanical exploration in Ontario and a rise in general skill levels. Collectively, this wealth of information has proved invaluable in a number of recent conservation efforts, including the Rare Plant Atlas Project, the identification of the top 36 unprotected Carolinian Canada sites, the selection and evaluation of wetlands and ANSIs, the preparation of 39 post-1980 COSEWIC reports on Carolinian plants, the legislative protection accorded by the Endangered Species Act to six plant species during this decade, and several ESA studies such as the recent Haldimand-Norfolk Natural Areas Inventory. The incorporation of good floristic data has come to be expected in regional and municipal planning and environmental impact assessments. The demand for and usefulness of such information to species and natural areas conservation has never been more evident.

This survey contacted individuals compiling county/RM checklists in the Carolinian Zone of southern Ontario. Each of the compilers was asked to answer the following: 1) format of the flora (e.g. is it computerized or annotated), 2) where specimens are housed (herbarium acronyms are given in the text, full names are listed at the end of the paper), 3) availability of the flora or work in progress, 4) future work required (i.e. poorly covered geographical areas, herbarium searches, etc.), 5) the botanical highlights (native species) since 1980, and 6) the top botanical sites in the county or RM. The latter are the sites considered by the regional compilers to be the most significant from a species perspective, essentially their favourite botanical haunts. No criterion other than this was applied. With the exception of Middlesex County and York RM, the sites are not priority ranked in any manner.

Seven of the county/RM lists are computerized, using seven different programs (WordPerfect, Microsoft Works, Symphony, Volkswriter, SCRIPT, TAXA-COM, and WATFILE). A total of 174 significant botanical sites[1] were listed, many of which were not previously identified as Environmentally Significant/Sensitive Areas, Areas of Natural and Scientific Interest (ANSIs), or International Biological Programme (IBP) sites.

The compilers noted 81 provincially rare species as botanical highlights. Fifty-nine of these represent 72 first county or RM records. Sixteen of these taxa are first records for Ontario; all but two of which are additions to the Canadian flora. Nine of these species have been discovered since the last report on additions to the Ontario flora by Reznicek *et al.* in 1985, and at about the same average rate of discovery of two 'new' Ontario species per year from the Carolinian Zone, noted for the 1965 to 1985 period. Our compilation adds further evidence to the importance of the Carolinian Zone in Canada and the need for further documentation of its flora.

Another ten provincially rare species noted represent the first Ontario records for the taxa since 1925. Nine of these records are the only extant stations for the province (Stations are defined as separate if they are a kilometre or more apart).

Fifty-seven (70%) of the provincially rare species cited by the compilers are Carolinian[2] species (denoted in the botanical highlights section by an asterisk). The remaining 24 provincially rare species are an assortment of Great Lakes endemics, western, southern, northern, Appalachian, or Atlantic Coastal Plain taxa. The most noteworthy are:

1) *Polygonum careyi* and *Panicum rigidulum* var. *rigidulum*, two Atlantic Coastal Plain species previously known in Ontario only from the Canadian Shield.

2) *Carex typhina*, an Appalachian species, previously known in Ontario only from the Ottawa Valley.

3) *Calamovilfa longifolia* var. *magna* and *Alisma gramineum*, two lakeshore species new to the north shore of Lake Erie.

4) *Carex bicknellii* and *Quercus prinoides*, two mid-western species which are extremely rare in Ontario, discovered for the first time at an 'inland' site.

---

[1] Many of these sites are privately owned and the rights of the landowners must be respected. Permission should be sought before visiting them.

[2] A Carolinian species is restricted in Ontario to the Carolinian Zone as defined by Soper (1955), with at most a few stations up to 50 kms beyond the Zone boundary.

Updates for each of the 16 Carolinian counties and RMs (Figure 1) follow. In addition, there is an update for Perth County. Although not in the Carolinian Zone as delineated by Soper (1955), it is surrounded by counties that occur within this zone, and for the sake of completeness, was added. The records for Perth are not included, however, in the totals cited above for the Carolinian Zone.

The format for the botanical highlights section is as follows: species, discoverer, year of discovery, general location, significance of record, and bibliographic citation if the record has been published. All records are listed chronologically.

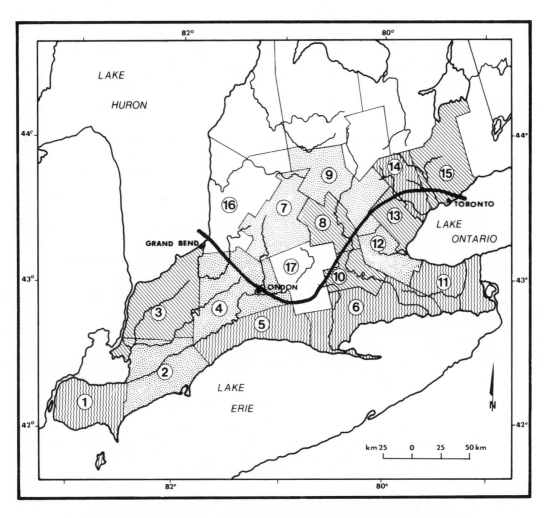

COUNTY/REGIONAL FLORAS IN THE CAROLINIAN LIFE ZONE

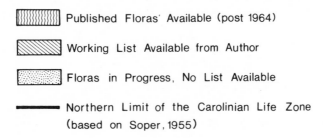

Published Floras Available (post 1964)

Working List Available from Author

Floras in Progress, No List Available

Northern Limit of the Carolinian Life Zone
(based on Soper, 1955)

Figure 1: County/Regional Floras in the Carolinian Life Zone.

1. Essex County

Compiler – Michael J. Oldham
                Ministry of Natural Resources
                Aylmer District Office
                353 Talbot Street West
                Aylmer, Ontario N5H 2S8

Wilf Botham produced the "Plants of Essex County, a preliminary list" in 1981. This provides documentation of collections and sight records of 1350 taxa for 20 sub-areas of the County and relies heavily on Wilf's own records dating back to 1937. Also incorporated are the records from previously published work in the County such as Dodge's 1914 flora of Point Pelee and vicinity, Core's 1948 flora of the Erie Islands, and inventories of Point Pelee (Maycock *et al.* 1976), Ojibway Prairie (Pratt 1979), and Essex County biologically significant areas (Johnson and Wannick 1977). Wilf's vouchers are mainly housed at DAO, CAN, and in his personal herbarium, which is currently being prepared for deposition at CAN and MICH.

Wilf was working on a revision of the flora when he died suddenly in October 1989. More than 135 taxa which have been added to the Essex list since 1981 were to be included. Wilf's revision will be continued by Mike Oldham who is in the process of computerizing Wilf's collection records in Dbase, with assistance from Gary Allen and Shannon Managhan. Mike welcomes sight and collection records and would appreciate being informed of any revisions to Essex County collections noted by those searching various herbaria.

Despite a relatively small percentage of natural land and substantial work by several individuals, Wilf states that most areas of the County need more work. In particular, many private woodlots have been poorly inventoried or not visited at all by a botanist.

Wilf's flora is available at a cost of $5.00 from the Essex Region Conservation Authority, 360 Fairview Ave. West, Essex, Ontario N8M 1Y6.

Essex has probably yielded more additions to the Ontario flora in this decade than any other County. Some examples are:

Reflexed Sedge *(Carex retroflexa)** (reported by J.W. Johnson in 1977, confirmed by M.J. Oldham – 1981, Harrow and Cedar Creek). New to Canada (Oldham and Crins 1988).

Clustered Sedge *(Carex aggregata)** (A.A. Reznicek and M.J. Oldham – 1982, Middle Island). New to Canada (Oldham and Crins 1988).

Glaucescent Sedge *(Carex glaucodea)** (M.J. Oldham – 1982, Canard River). New to Canada (Oldham and Crins 1988).

Crow-spur Sedge *(Carex crus-corvi)** (W. Botham – 1985, Tilbury West Township). New to Canada (Botham 1985).

Slender Nut-rush *(Scleria pauciflora)** (M.J. Oldham – 1988, LaSalle). New to Canada.

Hawthorn *(Crataegus dilitata)** (M.J. Oldham – 1988, Pelee Island). New to Canada.

Other botanical highlights in Essex are:

Milkweed *(Asclepias hirtella)** (W. Botham – 1983, Ojibway Prairie). Rediscovery from the 1890s and the only Canadian station.

Leavenworth's Sedge *(Carex leavenworthii)** (M.J. Oldham – 1984, Stone Road Alvar). First provincial record since 1882 and only known Ontario station (Oldham and Crins 1988).

Hemicarpha *(Hemicarpha micrantha)** (M.J. Oldham – 1984, Holiday Beach). First provincial record since 1901 (Oldham and Crins 1988).

Hop-like Sedge *(Carex lupuliformis)** (A.A. Reznicek, M.J. Oldham and W. Botham – 1985, near Amherstburg). First Ontario record since 1902 and only known Ontario station (Oldham and Crins 1988).

Cattail Sedge *(Carex typhina)* (M.J. Oldham – 1985, Tilbury West Township). First County record and first Ontario record south of the Ottawa Valley.

Skinner's Agalinis *(Agalinis skinneriana)** (M.J. Oldham – 1987, LaSalle). First Canadian station outside of Walpole.

The top botanical sites for Essex County are:

1. Ojibway Prairie (including Provincial Nature Reserve and nearby sites such as Springarden Road Prairie and Sandwich West Woodlot) (40J/6 290800, 307807; 40J/3 313782)
2. Point Pelee National Park (40G/15 740470)
3. Stone Road Alvar (40G/15 643239)
4. Oxley Poison Sumac Swamp (40J/2 450520)
5. Cedar Creek (40J/2 500535)
6. Fish Point Nature Reserve (40G/10 610210)
7. Big Creek Marsh (40J/3 300560)
8. Middle Island (40G/10 600157)
9. Upper Big Creek Woods (40J/3 280650)
10. Canard River Kentucky Coffee Tree Woods (40J/2 357660)
11. LaSalle Prairie (40J/3 283782)

2. Kent County

Compiler – Jane Bowles
RR #3, Thorndale, Ontario N0M 2P0

Rose and Brian Klinkenberg began fieldwork in 1976 and decided, in 1982, to produce a checklist for the plants of Kent County. By the end of 1986, when they moved to Vancouver, B.C., a partially annotated working list existed in draft. In addition, during 1986 as part of the Natural Areas Survey of Kent County, all known records of potentially significant species were mapped. The total species list for Kent County is still incomplete, but the present compiled flora stands at a little over 1000 species. Jane Bowles is continuing work on the project.

The entire flora has been computerized in WordPerfect and Volkswriter. The published version will contain a checklist of plants with voucher records and dot distribution maps will be added for selected species. Many vouchers are at present housed in the personal herbaria of the Klinkenbergs and Jane Bowles. Some vouchers (mainly sedges) have been deposited at TRTE and MICH. Eventually, most specimens will be sent to TRTE with some duplicates to UWO.

More fieldwork needs to be done in Kent County and there are several areas which have been inadequately explored. These include larger wooded areas south and east of Moraviantown Indian Reserve and some woodlots between Thamesville and Kent Bridge. A systematic search of RPP is also required and searches have yet to be made at TRT, and UWO for non-graminoids. Some searching was done at MICH, mainly for sedges, grasses, lilies, and grasses. Any new information or voucher records for Kent County should be sent to Jane Bowles.

Several significant species have been discovered in Kent County during this decade:

Tussock Sedge *(Carex emoryi)* (A.A. and S.A. Reznicek – 1982, Prairie Siding). First County record (Oldham and Crins 1988).

Purple Twayblade *(Liparis liliifolia)** (J.R. Brown – 1982, Deyo's Woods). First County record.

Long-leaved Reed Grass *(Calamovilfa longifolia* var. *magna)* (Y. Dalp* and C. Babcock – 1983, Rondeau Provincial Park). First County record and first for Lake Erie (Darbyshire *et al.* 1984)

Shumard Oak *(Quercus shumardii)** (G.E. Waldron – 1983, Wilson Conservation Area). First County record (Waldron *et al.* 1987).

Water-willow *(Justicia americana)** (M.J. Oldham and M.B. Delisle -1984, Rondeau Provincial Park). First County record (Oldham 1984).

Virginia Water-horehound *(Lycopus virginicus)** (G.M. Allen – 1984, Sinclair's Bush). First County record.

Carey's Sedge *(Carex careyana)** (M.J. Oldham – 1986, Sinclair's Bush). First County record.

Six-weeks Fescue *(Vulpia octoflora)* (P.M. Catling and V.R. Brownell - 1986, Wheatley Provincial Park). First County record.

Muhly Grass *(Muhlenbergia tenuiflora)* (D.A. Sutherland and S.L. House – 1989, Rondeau Provincial Park). First County record.

The top botanical sites in Kent County are as follows:

1. Rondeau Bay Marshes and Rondeau Provincial Park (40I/5 270820)
2. Wheatley Provincial Park (40J/1 805605)
3. Kent-Elgin Shoreline (40I/5 420000)
4. Sinclair's Bush (40I/5 229855)
5. St. Clair Marshes (40J/8 845915)
6. Skunk's Misery (40I/12 305195)
7. Moravian Indian Reserve (40I/12 275130)
8. Deyo's Woods (40J/9 999149)
9. Jeanette's Creek (40J/8 916865)
10. Thamesville Sandhills (40I/12 180085)

3. Lambton County

Compilers –   John and Dorothy Tiedje
        1060 Bruce St., Sarnia, Ontario N7V 3B1

"A Survey of the vascular plants of Lambton County, Ontario" was published by the Plant Research Institute (now the Biosystematics Research Centre, Agriculture Canada) in 1966. This list, compiled by Raymond J. Moore, was based on collections of the late Lulu Gaiser's survey of the County between 1957 and 1964. This publication includes a comparison of Gaiser's findings with those of the Michigan botanist C.K. Dodge, whose reports are not necessarily substantiated by specimens (Dodge 1914b).

In 1987-88 John and Dorothy Tiedje compiled all available vascular plant records for Lambton County, input these on a Macintosh computer using

Microsoft Works, and produced a list of 1697 species. The species are listed alphabetically within the families which are numbered and ordered according to Gray's Manual (Fernald 1950). The source for each record is indicated, and where possible, the township in which the species was found. Copies of the list are available from the Tiedje's for the cost of xeroxing and mailing.

The Tiedje's began fieldwork about 1966 and have vouchers in their personal herbarium for nearly half of the Lambton species. They hope that their collection will remain in Lambton County and be accessible to the public. In addition, they have deposited many duplicates at UWO and plan to continue to do so.

The Tiedjes are interested in receiving sight or collection records, would appreciate any corrections to their list, and have not yet conducted herbarium searches. The list is being updated as new information comes to light. Several areas of Lambton are poorly covered including the Bear Creek and Plum Creek ANSIs, the west and east branches of the Sydenham River, the Sarnia Indian Reserve, and the Ipperwash Military Reserve.

Fieldwork in Lambton has yielded a number of significant discoveries in the last few years.

Ohio Buckeye (*Aesculus glabra*)* (M.J. Oldham and S.J. Darbyshire -1981, Walpole Island). New to Canada (Darbyshire and Oldham 1985).

White Gentian (*Gentiana alba*) (D.F. Rupert and J.R. Brown – 1984, Walpole Island). The third Canadian record of this species and the first since 1891. First County record.

Heart-leaved Plantain (*Plantago cordata*)* (M.J. Oldham – 1984, Ipperwash). Had not been observed in Canada since 1967 (Allen and Oldham 1985).

Oval Ladies'-tresses (*Spiranthes ovalis*)* (J.R. Brown – 1985, Walpole Island). New to Canada (Brown 1986) and one of only three stations in the Great Lakes Region (Case 1987).

Lace Grass (*Eragrostis capillaris*)* (M.J. Oldham – 1985, Walpole Island). New to Canada.

Panicum (*Dichanthelium meridionale*)* (A.A. Reznicek – 1985, Walpole Island). Rediscovery from the early 1900s and the only extant station in Canada.

Fimbristylis (*Fimbristylis spadicea*)* (G.M. Allen – 1985, Walpole Island). Not confirmed in Canada since 1914.

Crow-spur Sedge (*Carex crus-corvi*)* (M.J. Oldham and A.A. Reznicek - 1985, southern Lambton). Second Canadian record and first County record.

Shumard Oak (*Quercus shumardii*)* (G.E. Waldron – 1985, Sombra Township). First County record (Waldron *et al.* 1987).

Southern Slender Ladies'-tresses (*Spiranthes lacera* var. *gracilis*)* (J.R. Brown – 1985, Walpole Island). First County record since early 1900s and one of only two extant stations in Canada.

The top ten botanical sites in Lambton are:

1. Walpole Island Indian Reserve (40J/9 768167)
2. Pinery Provincial Park (40P/4 285872, 287878)
3. Ausable River Valley (40P/4 345740)
4. Port Franks (including the Ipperwash Military Reserve) (40P/4 265855, 240845)
5. Ipperwash Dunes Woodlot and Provincial Park (40P/4 215835)
6. County Line Woods (Lambton section of Skunks Misery) (40I/12 315310)
7. Sydenham River Corridor (40I/13 312347)
8. Kentucky Coffee Tree Grove (40/12 217281)

9. Clearwater Nature Trail (Blackwell Prairie) (40O/1 915636)
10. Bear Creek Woodlot #4 (40J/16 902350)

4. Middlesex County

Compiler – Dave McLeod
                92 Stroud Cres. Unit 48
                London, Ont. N6E 1Y8

Dave has been keeping records on plants in Middlesex since 1971 and has a working checklist based on his own collections, those of Frank Cook and other Middlesex County collectors (Mike Oldham *et al.*), and a cursory search of UWO. Vouchers are housed mainly at UWO and duplicates have been sent to DAO (grasses) and TRTE (sedges). Since 1981, a partial checklist (up to Ranunculaceae) was published in six instalments of "The Cardinal", the newsletter of the McIlwraith Field Naturalists (Cook and McLeod 1981, 1983, 1984; McLeod and Cook 1981, 1982a, 1982b). These are now badly dated by the many recent additions made to the flora, and there is no intention to continue the series. Instead, Dave has been computerizing all records toward the eventual goal of publishing a complete flora. This will be in the form of an annotated checklist with species information on levels of abundance, collectors, and distribution (dot maps based on townships).

    Additional fieldwork still needs to be done on a township and habitat basis. The north-central areas of the County have relatively low coverage. Dave intends to do a thorough search of UWO and searches also have to be made of TRTE, OAC, DAO, CAN, and MICH.

    There have been several botanical highlights in Middlesex over the past few years.

Tussock Sedge *(Carex emoryi)* (A.A. Reznicek – 1983, Thames River). First County record (Oldham and Crins 1988).
Large Whorled Pogonia *(Isotria verticillata)** (D. McLeod – 1984, Skunk's Misery). First County record since 1879 and second extant Canadian station. Since been found at a third station in Ontario.
Grass-leaved Rush *(Juncus marginatus)** (D. McLeod – 1984 and 1985, Strathroy and Dorchester Swamp). First two records for Middlesex County.
Long Manna Grass *(Glyceria melicaria)* (D. McLeod – 1985, Dorchester Swamp). First County record and second record for southwestern Ontario.
Wood Poppy *(Stylophorum diphyllum)** (D. Stephenson – 1987, Westminster Twp.). Last collected in Ontario in 1889. It remains the only extant station in Canada.
Heart-leaved Plantain *(Plantago cordata)** (M.J. Oldham – 1987, McGillivray Twp.). The first County record since 1893 and the second extant Canadian station.
Smith's Club-rush *(Scirpus smithii)* (M.J. Oldham – 1988, Sifton Botanical Bog). First County record.
Three-awn *(Aristida longispica)** (D. McLeod M.J. Oldham – 1989, 5 km northeast of Parkhill). First County record.
Three-awn *(Aristida necopina)** (M.J. Oldham and D. McLeod – 1989, Skunk's Misery). First County record.

The top ten botanical sites in Middlesex County are as follows (in priority ranking):

1. Skunk's Misery ANSI (40I/12 340230)
2. Ausable River ANSI (40P/4 345740)
3. Dorchester Swamp ANSI (40I/14 980570)
4. Westminster Ponds/Pond Mills (40I/14 820055)
5. Sifton Botanical Bog (Byron Bog) (40I/14 735575)
6. Komoka Provincial Park (40I/14 670550)
7. Fanshawe Conservation Area and Thorndale River Valley (40P/3 860710).
8. Meadowlily Woods (40I/14 860570)
9. Parkhill Conservation Area (Creek Woods) (40P/4 480790)
10. Longwoods Conservation Area (40I/14 610475)

5. Elgin County

Compiler – William G. Stewart
     6 Yarwood St., St. Thomas, Ontario N5P 2Y3

Lorne James began collecting in Elgin County in 1911 while Bill Stewart's County experience dates back to 1935. Upon meeting in 1951 they collaborated on the flora until Lorne's death in 1964. Their cooperative efforts were realized in 1969 with the publication of "A guide to the flora of Elgin County, Ontario". This is an annotated flora which cites vouchers and is available in short supply from the Catfish Creek Conservation Authority, RR #8, St. Thomas, Ontario N5P 3T3 at a cost of $2.50.

Since publication, fieldwork has been continued by the author, and in recent years numerous contributions have been made by other botanists as various environmental studies and assessments have been carried out on specific areas. Annual updates have been published in "The Cardinal", the publication of The McIlwraith Field Naturalists of London Inc. (Stewart 1971-1989). Three hundred and fifty-two taxa have been added to the flora since 1969 bringing the total to 1298 at the end of the 1988 field season. Bill is now working on a supplement to the flora which will list all revisions and additions from 1969 to 1988.

Vouchers are housed at UWO, CAN, DAO and OAC. Specimens from the Kent-Elgin Natural Areas Survey are in the personal herbaria of Jane Bowles and Rose Klinkenberg but will eventually be housed at TRTE and UWO.

Elgin County has been quite evenly covered. As a director of the Kent-Elgin Natural Areas Survey, Bill instructed the field workers on the most productive areas and the areas which he and James had not personally investigated; nevertheless, only a handful of new County records were added via the Survey.

Elgin botanical highlights during this decade have been:

Creeping Fragile Fern (Cystopteris protrusa)* (W.G. Stewart – 1981, St. Thomas). First Canadian record (Britton et al. 1985).

Tall Ironweed (Vernonia gigantea)* (V. Brownell – 1983, Aldborough Twp., 6 km NE of Clearville). First County record.

Frank's Sedge (Carex frankii)* (D. McLeod – 1984, Dunwich Tp., Lot 23, Conc.II). First County record (Oldham and Crins 1988).

Panic Grass (Panicum rigidulum var. rigidulum) (G.M. Allen – 1985, Dunwich Swamp). First County record and one of two recent stations south of the shield.

Cup-plant *(Silphium perfoliatum)** (W.G. Stewart – 1985, Aldborough Twp., Lot 1, Broken Front Conc.). First County record.

Pale Coneflower *(Echinacea pallida)* (W. Lamond – 1986, Dunwich Twp., Lot 9, Conc. A). First County record and appears to be the second native Canadian record.

Gray-headed Coneflower *(Ratibida pinnata)** (W. Lamond – 1986, Dunwich Twp., Lot 9, Conc. A). First County record.

Tussock Sedge *(Carex emoryi)* (M.J. Oldham – 1987, Catfish Creek at Port Bruce). First County record (Oldham and Crins).

Nodding Trillium *(Trillium cernuum)* (W.G. Stewart – 1987, Dunwich Twp., Lot 12, Conc. A). First County record.

Three-awn *(Aristida necopina)** (M.J. Oldham – 1988, Dutton Swamp). First County record.

The top botanical sites in the County are:

1. Springwater Conservation Area (40I/11 980320)
2. Stewart's Swamp Forest (40I/10 085296)
3. Patterson Conservation Area (40I/14 880415)
4. Port Burwell Provincial Park (40I/10 145215)
5. St. Thomas Waterworks Park (40I/14 850380)
6. Thames River Siding (40I/14 615347)
7. Dunwich Swamp and Prairie (40I/12 545195)
8. Lily Field (40I/12 547112)
9. Port Glasgow Natural Area Complex (40I/12 491062)

6. Haldimand-Norfolk Regional Municipality

Compiler – Donald A. Sutherland
P.O. Box 278, Port Rowan, Ontario N0E 1M0

The first checklist of the flora of Norfolk County, "Vascular Plants of Norfolk County, Ontario" (Norfolk is the western half of Haldimand-Norfolk RM) by Monroe Landon, was published by the Big Creek Region Conservation Authority in 1960. Later, James E. Cruise (1969) published a second annotated version which includes 1029 species and 111 varieties of vascular plants. Copies of this publication are available from TRT. Dr. Cruise's specimens are housed at CU; duplicates are at TRT and other major herbaria.

The most recent flora was produced by Donald Sutherland in 1987 and is included in Volume II of "The Natural Areas Inventory of the Regional Municipality of Haldimand-Norfolk". This effort added several hundred species to the flora since 1985. The current flora is a fully annotated list of 1401 species with vouchers cited and is stored on floppy disks in Symphony. All vouchers are housed at TRTE. The flora is not available separately but must be purchased as part of the 547-page two-volume Natural Areas Inventory report available for $44 from: Natural Areas Inventory, P.O. Box 424, Waterford, Ontario N0E 1Y0. Since publication of the flora the total for the RM has increased to 1427 species.

The eastern part of the RM is less well known than the rest and could use further work. Some historical data, in particular Monroe Landon sight records, could also use checking. Donald is interested in receiving records of new and/or rare species.

Botanical highlights in Haldimand-Norfolk over the past decade include:

Black-edged Sedge *(Carex nigromarginata)** (A.A. Reznicek and P.M. Catling – 1980, Long Point). New to Canada (Reznicek and Catling 1982).

Broad-winged Sedge *(Carex alata)** (A.A. Reznicek, P.M. Catling and P. Keddy – 1980, Long Point). New to Canada (Reznicek and Catling 1982).

Rotala *(Rotala ramosior)** (M.J. Oldham – 1984, Lot 11, Conc. III, Charlotteville Tp.). New to Ontario. This site has since been converted to agriculture. Rediscovered at a nearby site in 1986, this entire habitat was also lost to agriculture in 1989.

Spotted Horsemint *(Monarda punctata)** (D.A. Kirk – 1984, Northeast of Turkey Point Provincial Park, Charlotteville Twp). First native station in Canada.

Willdenow's Sedge *Carex willdenowii** (M.E. Gartshore – 1985, Caistor-Canborough Slough Forest). First RM record and second Canadian record. First recent record for Canada.

Glaucescent Sedge *(Carex glaucodea)** (M.E. Gartshore – 1985, Caistor-Canborough Slough Forest). First RM record and second Canadian collection (Oldham and Crins 1988).

Two-flowered Rush *(Juncus biflorus)** (D.A. Sutherland and M.J. Oldham – 1986, Lot 11, Conc. III, Charlotteville Tp.). First RM record and second Canadian record. Site has since been converted to agriculture.

Side Oats Gramma *(Bouteloua curtipendula)* (D.A. Kirk – 1986, Turkey Point Provincial Park). Rediscovery from 1957.

Purple Milkweed *(Asclepias purpurascens)** (D.A Sutherland and D. Bradley – 1986, Turkey Point). First RM collection.

Colic-root *(Aletris farinosa)** (D. Bradley – 1986, Northwest of Turkey Point Provincial Park, Charlotteville Twp.). First RM record since 1954.

Yellow Bartonia *(Bartonia virginica)* (D.A. Sutherland – 1987, St. Williams Forestry Station). First RM record since 1937.

Wild Indigo *(Baptisia tinctoria)** (D.A. Sutherland – 1987, Northeast of Turkey Point Provincial Park, Charlotteville Twp.). First RM record since 1972.

Spike-rush *(Eleocharis equisetoides)** (A.A. Reznicek – 1988, Long Point). Only Canadian station; not observed since 1960.

Downy Foxglove *(Aureolaria virginica)** (D.A. Sutherland – 1988, Normandale). First RM record since the 1930s.

Carey's Smartweed *(Polygonum careyi)* (S. Varga – 1989, Backus Woods). First RM record and second Ontario station south of the shield.

The top botanical sites in Haldimand-Norfolk (based on Gartshore, *et al.,* 1987) are:

1. Long Point (40I/9 600120)
2. Turkey Point (40I/9 540280)
3. Backus Woods (40I/9 420235)
4. St. Williams Forest and Savannah (40I/9 440280)
5. Spooky Hollow (40I/9 560305)
6. Deer Creek Valley (40I/10 361275)
7. South Walsingham Sand Ridges and Big Creek Floodplain (40I/10 360200)
8. Delhi-Big Creek Valley (40I/15 401404)
9. Oriskany Sandstone and Woodlands (30L/13 865560)
10. Caistor – Canborough Slough Forest (30M/4 070640)
11. Delhi Kettle Bog (40/15 394417)
12. Waterford Ponds (40I/16 558524)

13. Salem – Rockford Rocklands (40I/16 682568)
14. Sandusk Creek Floodplain Woods (40I/16 772465)
15. Cultus Forest (40I/10 300230)
16. Fairground Forest (40I/10 243223)
17. Langton Woods (40I/15 350340)
18. Courtland Swamp (40I/15 310395)
19. Big Creek Bend (40I/10 395280)
20. Attercliffe Station Slough Forest (30L/13 110587)
21. North Cayuga Slough Forest (30L/13 940590)

7. Perth County

Compilers – Dr. Arnold Wellwood
15 Churchill St.
Kentville, Nova Scotia B4N 2H7

Dr. Terry McIntosh
Biology Department
Wilfrid Laurier University
Waterloo, Ontario N2L 3C5

Perth County is not within the Carolinian Zone as defined by Soper (1955) but is included here because the surrounding Counties are partially within the Zone.

Dr. Wellwood began collecting information on the flora of Perth County in 1971 and continued until his retirement from Wilfrid Laurier in 1980. His records of over 1025 species have been computerized in two files, one a list of all County species, the other a list of all species by station. The principal collection of vouchers is at WLU with duplicates at QK, LKHD, and CAN.

Terry McIntosh worked with Dr. Wellwood on inventories for the Perth flora in the 1970s, and is now on faculty at WLU and is herbarium curator. He is acting as co-compiler of the flora and recently produced a preliminary checklist in WordPerfect from all Perth collections at WLU (All Perth accessions had been confirmed by Wellwood prior to his departure). This is available from Terry and he and Dr. Wellwood will continue to work toward either an annotated treatment or a checklist indicating vouchers. They are interested in additions to the flora and would appreciate a voucher sent to WLU.

The most noteworthy addition to the flora over the past decade is:

Willow Aster (Aster praealtus var. praealtus)* (J.G. Chmielewski - 1983, Ellice Tp. Conc. 4,5). First County record (Chmielewski and Semple 1986).

Based on information in the Perth County Preliminary Environmentally Sensitive Areas Survey (Hoffman and Lamb 1982) the top botanical sites in the county as selected by Lamb (pers. comm. 1989) are:

1. Ellice Huckleberry Marsh (40P/7 040140)
2. Gad's Hill Agreement Forest (40P/7 070090)
3. Molesworth Woods (40P/14 990462)
4. Little Lakes (40P/7 065020)
5. Twinleaf Woods (40P/6 847943)
6. Wallace Woods (40P/15 125447)
7. Whirl Creek Woods (40P/6 870070)
8. Avonbank Woods (40P/6 885965)

8. Regional Municipality of Waterloo

Compilers – Craig Campbell
294 Albert St., Waterloo, Ontario N2L 3T8

Larry Lamb
Department of Environmental Studies
University of Waterloo, Waterloo, Ontario N2L 3G1

William Herriott made the first known extensive collection in this Region in the area of Galt circa 1900. F.H. Montgomery then authored the first flora in 1945. In 1970 Craig Campbell and Larry Lamb began to update Montgomery's flora and in 1984 compiled a preliminary flora of Waterloo. This is an annotated list of about 1400 taxa indicating status and distribution where known, and is available from Larry Lamb for the price of a computer printout. The entire list is computerized on SCRIPT and vouchers are housed at WAT, WLU, CAN, TRTE, OAC (Pteridophytes), and WES. Craig and Larry are intending to produce a comprehensive flora, complete with biographical sketches of local botanists such as Herriott, Montgomery, and John Goldie.

The compilers are interested in receiving records of 'new' species or additional distributional information.

Botanical highlights in Waterloo during this decade have included:

Ternate Grape Fern *(Botrychium rugulosum)* – (D.M. Britton and C.A. Campbell – 1981, Sunfish Lake). First confirmed Regional record.

Watershield *(Brasenia schreberi)* – (D.P. Coulson – 1985, Grass Lake and Dean's Lake). First Regional collections since 1939.

Adder's-tongue Fern *(Ophioglossum vulgatum)* – (D.M. Britton and C.A. Campbell – 1985, 1989 and 1989, Roseville Swamp, Kossuth Bog, and Kitchener). Not recorded in the Region since 1940 and thought to be extirpated.

Hairy-fruited Sedge *(Carex trichocarpa)* – (M.J. Oldham – 1987, Shep's Subdivision). First Regional collection since the early 1900s.

Giant Hyssop *(Agastache foeniculum)* – (L.E. Lamb – 1987, Shep's Subdivision). First Regional record.

Flowering Spurge *(Euphorbia corollata)* – (L.E. Lamb – 1988, Cambridge). First Regional record since the early 1900s.

Tussock Sedge *(Carex emoryi)* – (G.M. Allen – 1988, 1 km S of Cambridge; and M.J. Oldham – 1988, 5 km SSW of Elmira on Conestogo River). First Regional records since the early 1900s.

Rigid Sedge *(Carex tetanica)* – (G.M. Allen – 1989, 3 km S of Cambridge). First Regional record.

The top botanical sites for the Waterloo Regional Municipality are:

1. Branchton Railway Prairie (40P/8 560956)
2. Sudden Bog (40P/8 534955)
3. Schaefer's Woods (40P/7 313138)
4. Cruickston Park (40P/8 527033)
5. F.H. Montgomery Sanctuary (40P/7 295988)
6. Grass Lake (Cranberry Bog) (40P/8 527935)
7. St. Jacobs Floodplain (40P/10 330215)
8. Altrieve Lake (including Orr's and Barrie's Lakes) (40P/8 511009, 515003, 523007)
9. Roseville Swamp (40P/8 462005)

10. Oliver's Bog (40P/8 580974)
11. McCrone Lake (40P/8 470932)
12. Dean's Lake (40P/8 540943)
13. Taylor Lake (40P/8 535965)

9. Wellington County

Compiler – Allan Anderson
                  Department of Botany and Genetics
                  University of Guelph, Guelph, Ontario N1G 2W1

John Stroud compiled a list of plants of this County in 1941. Most of Stroud's collecting was done in the southern part of the County.

Allan Anderson began compiling records of the flora of this County in 1975. In addition to some discoveries by Don Britton and the Guelph Field Naturalists, Allan's work brings the County total to about 1400 species and hybrids. Data are recorded on file cards which include all the specimens at OAC and additional or rare species housed at TRT, TRTE, and WAT. Allan is working towards a checklist with annotations by township.

Allan welcomes any sight or collection records, especially from Maryborough and Peel townships. He has yet to complete a checklist for distribution.

There have been several notable botanical finds in recent years.

Broad-lipped Twayblade *(Listera convallarioides)* (A. Sandilands -1980, Luther Marsh). First County record.

Hairy-fruited Sedge *(Carex trichocarpa)* (A. Anderson – 1981, Wallenstein Forest). First County record.

Shining Ladies'-tresses *(Spiranthes lucida)* (D.P. Coulson – 1984, Edge of Hwy. 401, Puslinch Twp.). First County record (Coulson 1984).

Spicebush *(Lindera benzoin)* (A. Anderson – 1984, Puslinch Twp., UTM 744081). First County record.

Sweet Chestnut *(Castanea dentata)** (J. Irwin – 1985, Galt Creek and Forest). The species was noted by Herriot but apparently no voucher was made. This station is the only known County record.

Heart-leaved Twayblade *(Listera cordata)* (A. Anderson – 1987, Alton Branch of Credit River). First County record.

Smooth Scouring-rush *(Equisetum laevigatum)* (A. Anderson – 1987, Guelph Township Park, Marden). First County record.

Case's Ladies'-tresses *(Spiranthes casei)* (A. Anderson – 1988, Mount Forest Bog). First County record.

Many of the historical records have been searched for successfully in the field. Such species, however, as Calypso Orchid *(Calypso bulbosa)* (from Elora – no date), Leaf Cup *(Polymnia canadensis)* (Arkell – 1937), Pickerelweed *(Pontederia cordata)* (Puslinch Lake – 1906), and Stout Goldenrod *(Solidago squarrosa)* (Rockwood – 1919, Killean – 1904), have not been refound and may have been extirpated from the County.

The top botanical sites in Wellington County are:

1. Mount Forest Bog (40P/15 175655)
2. Crieff Bog (40P/8 710075)
3. Luther Marsh (40P/16 460650)

4. Elora Gorge (40P/9 445355)
5. Rockwood Conservation Area (40P/9 688285)
6. Drew Bog and Swamp (40P/15 110685)
7. Wallenstein Forest (40P/10 285295)
8. Eramosa River Valley (40P/9 700420)
9. Galt Creek and Forest Area (40P/8 620060)
10. Alton Branch of Credit River (40P/16 705545)
11. Puslinch Lake Swamp and Bog (40P/8 589063)

10. Brant County

Compiler – Dr. Paul Eagles
Department of Recreation and Leisure Studies
University of Waterloo, Waterloo, Ontario N2L 3G1

Although collections had been made in Brant by botanists such as William Herriott, R. Cain, E. Medhurst, R. Adams, M. Eddy, and F.H. Montgomery, the first compilation of records was made recently by Paul Eagles. Paul initiated the flora database in 1978 as a result of his supervision of the Brant County ESA Study (Eagles *et al.* 1980). More records were added from a search of WAT, the inventory of Six Nations Indian Reserve in 1986 (Chamberlain *et al.* 1985), the Rare Plants Atlas database (to 1986), and consulting reports which Paul has been involved with. The flora is computerized in WATFILE and contains 7412 records of 1139 species. For each record information is provided on such things as UTM, habitat, and voucher location. Paul estimates that about 25% of the flora is vouchered, including the majority of the significant species. No vouchers are kept specifically for the study; however most of Paul's specimens are deposited at WAT.

Paul welcomes information on collections, sight records, or published references from the County. The majority of the major herbaria in Ontario have not been searched and collection information from any of these would be much appreciated. A copy of the flora can be provided upon request.

Areas with potential to add 'new' species to the flora are the southern half of the County on the clay plain and the Six Nations Indian Reserve.

Botanical highlights in the last several years have been:

Bird's-foot Violet *(Viola pedata)** (B.A. Ford and W.D. Bakowsky – 1986, Brantford Savannah). The first County record since 1900 and the only extant Canadian station outside of the Turkey Point area (Kavanagh *et al.* 1989).

Rigid Sedge *(Carex tetanica)* (A.A. Reznicek and M.J. Oldham – 1987, Grand River). First County record.

Tussock Sedge *(Carex emoryi)* (M.J. Oldham – 1987, Glen Morris). First County record.

Hairy-fruited Sedge *(Carex trichocarpa)* (M.J. Oldham – 1987, Glen Morris). First County record.

James' Sedge *(Carex jamesii)** (G.M. Allen and S. Varga – 1988, Glen Morris). First County record.

Handsome Sedge *(Carex formosa)** (G.M. Allen and S. Varga – 1988, Glen Morris). First County record.

Oswego Tea *(Monarda didyma)* (L.E. Lamb and G.M. Allen – 1988, Glen Morris). First post-1950 County record.

Side Oats Grama *(Bouteloua curtipendula)* (A. Sandilands and W.D. Bakowsky – 1989, Brantford). Second and third County records, only known extant

County populations, and only extant Carolinian populations outside of the Turkey Point area.

Muhly Grass *(Muhlenbergia tenuiflora)* (G.M. Allen – 1989, Glen Morris). First County record.

Slender Sedge *(Carex gracilescens)* (W.D. Bakowsky – 1989, New Credit Indian Reserve). First County record.

Bicknell's Sedge *(Carex bicknellii)** (W.D. Bakowsky and A. Sandilands – 1989, Brantford). First County record and first Ontario populations outside of Walpole Island and the Windsor area.

Dwarf Chinquapin Oak *(Quercus prinoides)** (W.D. Bakowsky and A. Sandilands – 1989, Brantford). First County record and only Canadian population outside the St. Williams and Pinery Provincial Park areas.

Stiff-leaved Goldenrod *(Solidago rigida)* (A. Sandilands and W.D. Bakowsky – 1989, Brantford). First and second County records.

The top botanical sites in Brant County are as follows:

1. Grand River Valley (40P/8 520900)
2. Spottiswood Lakes (40P/8 500900)
3. Eastern Edge of Six Nations Reserve (abutting the Grand River) (40P/1 798715)
4. McKenzie Creek Watershed within Six Nations (40P/1 695665)
5. Oakland Swamp (40P/1 510690)
6. Blue Lake and nearby County Forests (40P/1 543868, 543857)
7. Whiteman's Creek Valley (40P/1 510760)
8. Brantford Savannah (40P/1 558760)
9. St. George Prairie (40P/1 615877)
10. Turnbull Lake (40P/8 473905)

11. Niagara Regional Municipality

Compilers –   Patricia M. Eckel
              Buffalo Museum of Science
              Buffalo, New York, USA 14211.

              Gustave Yaki
              127A Princess Street, Kingston, Ontario K7A 1A8

The flora of this area has been studied by botanists from both sides of the Canada - US border. In 1934, C.A. Zenkert's "The flora of the Niagara Frontier Region" (an 80 km radius around Buffalo, New York, which includes the entire RM of Niagara) was published in the Bulletin of the Buffalo Society of Natural Sciences. This flora was updated by Zenkert and Zander (1975) and Zander and Pierce (1979). Copies of Zenkert's 1934 flora and the two supplements are available from the Gift Shop, Buffalo Museum of Science, Buffalo, NY 14211.

The flora of the Niagara Frontier Region is an ongoing project of workers in the botany division of the Buffalo Museum of Science. Most of the vouchers noted in the botanical publications reside in the Clinton Herbarium (BUF) at the Buffalo Museum of Science. Other vouchers consulted to date are at the State Museum (NYSM) in Albany and the New York Botanical Garden (NY). The publications generally do not include sight records, except as notes.

Since the last checklist was published in 1979, the flora has been expanded to include about 20 new taxa. These will be noted in a new updated list scheduled for electronic publication on TAXACOM.

The floral work undertaken by the Buffalo Museum of Science in the RM of Niagara include the systematic surveys of Wainfleet Township (e.g. the Wainfleet Bog), Fort Erie, the Niagara River, and the Niagara Gorge. As part of the Museum's activities the flora of Niagara Falls and vicinity is currently being systematically surveyed by Patricia Eckel. It is based on extensive collections made by Eckel over the past two years along the Ontario side of the Niagara River and on the specimens housed at the Niagara Park School of Horticulture Herbarium (NFO). The museum would be interested in any botanical information on the RM of Niagara, particularly specimens in Ontario herbaria that pertain to the Niagara Falls vicinity (including bryophytes).

On the Canadian side of the border, Gustave Yaki culminated his efforts with an annotated checklist of 1368 species, largely based on sight records (Yaki 1970). Seven grass species new to Ontario (five of them new to Canada) were reported from Niagara by Catling *et al.* (1977). New records of 33 species from the Niagara Peninsula were published by McIntosh and Catling (1979). Floras of the Niagara Parks Commission lands (stretching along the length of the Niagara River) have been published by Roderick Cameron (1896) and George H. Hamilton (1943). Their specimens are housed at NFO and CAN. Bert Miller also collected extensively in Niagara during the 1950s, with specimens at HAM, TRT, DAO, and a few at OAC, CAN, and QFA. The Miller records are summarized in an unpublished manuscript prepared by Margaret Heimburger (1955). The manuscript also includes information from various herbaria on historical collections in Niagara RM.

Recent botanical highlights in Niagara are:

Divided Sedge *(Carex seorsa)** (D. Faber-Langendoen – 1981, Turner's Corners). New to Canada (Reznicek and Catling 1984).
Sedge *(Carex emmonsii)** (A.A. Reznicek and P.M. Catling – 1981, Wainfleet Bog). First and only authentic Ontario record (Reznicek and Catling 1984).
Carey's Smartweed *(Polygonum careyi)* (A.A. Reznicek and P.M. Catling – 1981, Wainfleet Bog). First RM record and only Ontario record south of the shield.
Shumard Oak *(Quercus shumardii)** (S.W. Aboud – 1983, St. David's). First RM record (Waldron *et al.* 1987).
Biennial Gaura *(Gaura biennis)** (P.M. Eckel and R.H. Zander – 1987, Niagara Gorge, Niagara Falls). Last observed in the Region at Fort Erie in 1964 and new to the Niagara Falls area.
Narrow-leaved Water-plantain *(Alisma gramineum)* (M.J. Oldham – 1988, Point Abino). First RM record and first Lake Erie record.

Based on information in various natural area reports (Macdonald 1980; Cuddy *et al.* 1976) and Yaki (pers. comm. 1989) the most significant botanical sites in Niagara are:

1. Niagara Gorge (30M/3 570760)
2. Wainfleet Bog (30L/14 400535)
3. Point Abino Peninsula Sandland Forest (30L/14 550460)
4. Niagara Section Escarpment (30M/4 130830)
5. Caistor-Canborough Slough Forest (30M/4 120620)
6. Fifteen-Sixteen Mile Creek Valleys (30M/3 360800)

7. Jordan Valley (30M/3 325780)
8. South St. Ann's Slough Forest (30M/3 235680)
9. Beamsville Escarpment (30M/3 270785)
10. Navy Island (30M/3 615690)
11. Two Mile – Four Mile Creek Plain (30M/6 535910)
12. Short Hills Provincial Park (30M/3 395730)
13. Fonthill Sandhill Valley (30M/3 405687)
14. Lyon's Creek Floodplain and Wetlands (30L/14 505620)
15. Empire Beach Backshore Forest Basin (30L/14 515485)
16. Willoughy Clay Plain Forest (30L/14 550620)
17. Humberstone Muck Basin Swamp Forest (30L/14 490530)
18. Northwest Fenwick Forest (30M/3 320660)
19. Short Hills Wildlife Refuge (30M/3 362691)
20. St. John's Conservation Area (30M/3 395695)
21. Banks of Niagara River, Paradise Grove, Niagara-on-the-Lake (30M/3 and 30M/6 575895)
22. Dufferin Islands, Niagara Falls (30M/3 and 30M/6 570700)
23. Niagara Dry Gorge, Mountain and Drummond Rd., Niagara Falls (30M/3 and 30M/6 530790)
24. Queenston Escarpment (30M/3 and 30M/6 575798)

12. Halton Regional Municipality

Compilers – William J. Crins
            Biological Survey, New York State Museum
            C.E.C. 3132
            Albany, New York 12230

            Brenda K. Axon
            Halton Region Conservation Authority
            P.O. Box 1097, Stn. B
            Burlington, Ontario L7P 3S9

Bill Crins began working on the flora of Halton County in 1974. Since 1978, extensive field work by Bill, and by the Halton Region Conservation Authority, have contributed to the species total of 1174 plus 28 recognizable hybrids. Virtually all taxa are supported by vouchers and the great majority of them are housed at TRTE. A number of herbaria have been searched for additional records, including HAM, OAC, parts of WAT, TRTE, TRT, and CAN. The area that is least well collected is the mid-eastern part of the Region, east of Oakville Creek, between Highway 5 and Highway 401.

Bill has produced a preliminary annotated checklist which notes for each species its level of abundance (rare: 1-5 stations, uncommon: 6-15 stations, and common: more than 15 stations) and its distribution within the region (e.g. north or south of the Niagara Escarpment, or confined to the southwest corner of the region). He would be pleased to send his checklist to those who are interested.

Recent botanical highlights are:

Hoary Mountain Mint *(Pycnanthemum incanum)** (W. Crins – 1981 and D.J. Bradley – 1988, Burlington). Two stations in close proximity. These are the only known stations in Canada and are the first records since the 1900s (Crins 1985).

Striped Coralroot *(Corallorhiza striata)* (D.P. Coulson – 1981, Halton Forest South). First RM record.

Green Milkweed *(Asclepias viridiflora)* (L.E. Lamb – 1987, Christie). First RM record.

Red Mulberry *(Morus rubra)** (D.J. Bradley – 1988, Waterdown Woods). First RM record.

Winged Pigweed *(Cycloloma atriplicifolium)* (B.K. Axon – 1988, Burlington Beach). First RM record.

Schreber's Aster *(Aster schreberi)** (D.J. Bradley – 1988, Grindstone Creek Valley). First RM record.

Downy Foxglove *(Aureolaria virginica)** (D.J. Bradley – 1988, Cappison Woods). First RM record and second collection in Ontario since 1945.

The top botanical sites for Halton Region are:

1. Sassafras Woods (30M/5 919971)
2. Guelph Junction Woods (30M/5 820120)
3. Halton Forest North and South (Hilton Falls Complex) (30M/12 840230,820190)
4. Ballinafad Pond (40P/9 805365)
5. Crawford Lake – Milton Outlier Valley (including Rattlesnake Point) (30M/5 855135)
6. Waterdown Escarpment Woods (30M/5 916985)
7. Grindstone Creek (30M/5 902970)
8. Clappison Escarpment Woods (30M/5 895965)
9. Medad Valley (30M/5 895030)
10. Mount Nemo Escarpment (30M/5 915080)
11. Calcium Pits (30M/5 850120)
12. Bronte Creek Provincial Park (30M/5 005070)
13. Silver Creek Valley (30M/12 835390)
14. 16 Mile (Oakville) Creek Valley (30M/5 000126)

13. Peel Regional Municipality

Compiler – Jocelyn Webber
2744 Hollington Cres.
Mississauga, Ontario L5K 1E7

Jocelyn Webber began collecting vascular plants in Peel County in 1973. By 1977 efforts to produce a checklist were well underway. Voucher specimens are mainly at TRTE; some duplicates are in CAN and DAO.

An annotated checklist of the 1334 vascular plant taxa known from the Region has been prepared. Geographic distribution by township and abundance codes for these plants are included. An introduction discusses the vegetation and the history of plant collecting in Peel. The publication "The Vascular Plant Flora of Peel County, Ontario" is available from the author's address for $10.00, which includes postage and mailing.

Since the publication 21 additional species, weedy ones for the most part, have been found in Peel. The most noteworthy addition is:

Cleland's Evening-primrose *(Oenothera clelandii)** (D. Brunton – 1985, Lorne Park Prairie). The second Canadian record and the first RM record. The site has since been degraded.

The top botanical sites in Peel Region are:

1. Credit Forks (30M/13 820500)
2. Caledon Mountain Slope Forest (30M/12 845440)
3. Caledon Lake Forests (40P/16 710590)
4. Dufferin Lake (40P/16 790500)
5. Lorne Park Prairie (30M/12 124208)
6. Creditview Bog (30M/12 060264)
7. Tea Pot Lake Bog (Heart Lake Conservation Area) (30M/12 967442)
8. Gibson Lake (30M/13 945673)
9. Palgrave Conservation Area and vicinity (30M/13 920670)
10. Cawthra Woods (30M/12 146262)
11. Credit River at Erindale (30M/12 080230)

14. York Regional Municipality

Compiler – Steve Varga
         5900 Yonge Street, Apt. 618
         Willowdale, Ontario M2M 3T8

In 1974, a herbarium search of TRT by Paul Catling, Tony Reznicek, Sheila McKay-Kuja, and Karen McIntosh, resulted in a preliminary list of herbarium specimens from York County. Steve Varga began researching the flora of York in 1978.
By searching for uncommon plant communities, many additions to the flora and new stations for rare plants were found. Specimens are mainly housed at TRT with some also at TRTE.

In 1987 a handwritten draft of "Vascular Plants of the Regional Municipalities of York and Metropolitan Toronto (York County), Ontario", was completed.
The authors are S. Varga, P.M. Catling, A.A. Reznicek, S.M. McKay-Kuja, and K.L. McIntosh. They are currently revising the manuscript, and hope to have the partially annotated checklist available by 1990. The 1987 draft can be obtained by writing to Steve Varga.

The flora contains 1446 taxa (1393 species, 22 varieties, three forms, six subspecies, and 22 hybrids). Four hundred and forty-nine species (459 taxa) are introduced and 942 species (988 taxa) are native. Forty-three percent of the native flora or 409 species (412 taxa) are considered rare to the Region, defined as occurring at five or fewer, post 1925 stations in York Region. The authors would appreciate any additional botanical records from York.

A working list of 1010 vascular plant species has also been compiled for Metropolitan Toronto by Diana Banville. This list is based on sight record material from the Toronto Field Naturalists (TFN) library (e.g. park checklists, outings reports, etc.). Annotations are provided for each of the species on location by watershed and level of abundance (C-Common, U-Uncommon, R-Rare (3 or less stations), E-Extirpated).

A revised version of this working list will be published by the TFN. Until then, a xerox of the working list is available by sending $10.00 to TFN, 20 College St., Suite 4, Toronto, Ont. M5G 1K2.

Some of the noteworthy discoveries in the Region include:

Radiate Sedge (*Carex appalachica*) (S. Taylor – 1980, Highland Creek). First RM record.

Hairy-fruited Sedge *(Carex trichocarpa)* (S. Varga – 1980, Don River). First RM
  record.
Sharp-leaved Goldenrod *(Solidago arguta)* (S. Varga – 1980, Wilcox Lake). First RM
  record.
Prairie White-fringed Orchid *(Platanthera leucophaea)* (S. Varga, S.M. McKay – 1981,
  Holland River Mouth Fen). First RM record.
Grass-leaved Arrowhead *(Sagittaria graminea* var. *cristata)* (S. Varga and G.M. Allen
  – 1988, Rouge River Marshes). First RM record.

Within York Region, the top 20 natural areas in terms of their rarities include (in
priority ranking):

1. Holland Landing Prairie and Fen (31D/3 218975) (63 regionally rare species
    (R), with 15 of them unique to the site within the Region (U), 3 provincially rare
    species (P))
2. Toronto Islands (30M/11 298305) (38R, 15U, 3P)
3. Rouge River (30M/14 490520) (59R, 13U, 4P)
4. High Park (30M/11 240335) (41R, 9U, 4P)
5. Keswick (Holland) Marsh (31D/4 180940) (43R, 7U, 1P)
6. Duclos Point Wetlands (31D/6 400100) (26R, 6U)
7. Happy Valley Forests (30M/13 115685) (21R, 2U, 2P)
8. Wilcox Lake Bog and Upland Forest (30M/14 270670) (9R, 2U, 1P)
9. Bond Lake and Bog (30M/14 244599) (7R, 3U)
10. Zephyr Creek Swamp (31D/6 395015) (9R, 2U)
11. Lambton Park Prairie (30M/12 201354) (14R)
12. Pefferlaw Brook Swamp (31D/6 430050) (11R, 1U)
13. Musselman Lake Fen and Upland Forest (31D/3 375755) (8R, 1U)
14. Snively Road Wetlands and Upland Forest (30M/14 244684) (10R)
15. Pottageville Swamp and Upland Forest (31D/4 100740) (9R)
16. Vandorf Bog (31D/3 325735) (5R, 1U)
17. Glenville Hills (Thornton Bales Conservation Area) (31D/4185770) (5R)
18. Cold Creek Conservation Area (30M/13 042623) (7R,1U,1P)
19. Brown Hill Swamp (31D/3 320980) (6R)
20. Pogonia Fen (30M/13 054648) (2R, 1U)

15. Hamilton-Wentworth Regional Municipality

Compiler – Christine Bishop
       203 - 50 Main St.
       Dundas, Ontario L9H 6P8

Dr. James Pringle published a checklist of the Royal Botanical Gardens flora in
1969 based on his own fieldwork since arriving at RBG in 1963 and on fieldwork
between 1954 and 1959 by Alexander Tamsalu and others. The specimens are at
the Garden's herbarium (HAM). Although there is no intention to formally revise
this list, Dr. Pringle would be interested in receiving 'new' records. The 1969 list is
now out of print, but those interested can contact Dr. Pringle for a xerox copy.

       Although the RBG list is useful as a reference point for Hamilton-Wentworth,
there has surprisingly been no concerted effort to document the Region's flora.
However, as a result of various Biological Inventories initiated in 1988 by the
Hamilton Naturalists' Club, the expertise and technical support is in place to begin

to compile botanical records. Christine Bishop is keenly interested in receiving any sight and collection records for the Region.

16. Huron County

We are not aware of anyone compiling botanical records for this County.

17. Oxford County

Similarly, no one has come forward to act as a compiler for Oxford County. The only plant list for the County was a preliminary one produced in 1978 (Hilts and MacFabe 1978).

Acknowledgements

We are grateful to the 20 regional compilers who provided the information which forms the basis of this paper. The following people were also very helpful in reviewing individual sections of the paper or in drawing our attention to new information on specific floras: W.D. Bakowsky, J.M. Bowles, J.R. Brown, C.A. Campbell, D.P. Coulson, D.A. Kirk, R. Klinkenberg, L.E. Lamb, and J.S. Pringle. The final manuscript was graciously reviewed by M.J. Oldham, A.A. Reznicek, J.L. Riley and D.A. Sutherland.

Herbaria

BUF	Clinton Herbarium, Buffalo Museum of Science, Buffalo.
CAN	National Herbarium, Ottawa.
CU	Cornell University, Ithaca, New York.
DAO	Department of Agriculture Herbarium, Ottawa.
HAM	Royal Botanical Gardens Herbarium, Hamilton.
LKHD	Claude Garton Herbarium, Lakehead University, Thunder Bay.
MICH	University of Michigan Herbarium, Ann Arbor, Michigan.
NFO	Niagara Park School of Horticulture Herbarium, Niagara Falls, New York.
NY	New York Botanical Garden, Bronx, New York.
NYSM	New York State Museum, Albany, New York.
OAC	University of Guelph Herbarium, Guelph.
QFA	Herbier Louis-Marie, Québec, Québec.
QK	Fowler Herbarium, Queen's University, Kingston.
RPP	Rondeau Provincial Park Herbarium, Morpeth.
TRT	University of Toronto Herbarium, Toronto.
TRTE	Erindale College Herbarium, Mississauga.
UWO	University of Western Ontario Herbarium, London.
WAT	University of Waterloo Herbarium, Waterloo.
WES	Environmental Studies Herbarium, University of Waterloo, Waterloo.
WLU	Sir Wilfred Laurier University Herbarium, Waterloo.

References

Allen, G.M. and M.J. Oldham. 1985. *Plantago cordata* Lam. (Heart-leaved plantain) still survives in Canada. *The Plant Press* 3(3):94-97.

Banville, D. 1987. *A working list of vascular plants of Metropolitan Toronto*. Toronto Field Naturalists. 64 pp. (xerox draft version).

Botham, W. 1981. *Plants of Essex County: a preliminary list*. Essex Region Conservation Authority, Essex, Ontario. 210 pp.

Botham, W. 1985. *Carex crus-corvi* Shuttlew.: A sedge new to Canada from Essex County. *The Plant Press* 3(4):125.

Britton, D.M., W.G. Stewart, and W.J. Cody. 1985. *Cystopteris protrusa*, Creeping Fragile Fern, an addition to the flora of Canada. *Canadian Field-Naturalist* 99(3):380-382.

Brown, J.R. 1986. *Spiranthes ovalis* Lindley var. *erostellata* Catling (Oval Ladies'-tresses): A new orchid for Canada from Lambton County, Ontario. *The Plant Press* 4(3):84-86.

Cameron, R. 1896. *Catalogue of plants which have been found growing without cultivation in the park and its outlying territories*. Annual Report of Commissioners for the Queen Victoria Niagara Falls Park. pp. 351-394.

Campbell, C.A. and Lamb, L.E. 1984. *A preliminary annotated list of the plants of the Regional Municipality of Waterloo, Ontario*. Unpublished. 109 pp.

Case, F. 1987. *Orchids of the Western Great Lakes Region*. Revised edition. Cranbrook Institute of Science Bulletin 48. 251 pp.

Catling, P.M., A.A. Reznicek, and J.L. Riley. 1977. Some new and interesting grass records from southern Ontario. *The Canadian Field-Naturalist* 91(4):350-358.

Chamberlain, D.A., R. Diebolt, and P.F.J. Eagles. 1985. *A biological inventory of the natural environment of the Six Nations Indian Reserve*. Department of Recreation and Leisure Studies, University of Waterloo. 196 pp. + appendices.

Chmielewski, J.G. and J.C. Semple. 1986. Significant range extension series: *Aster praealtus* var. *praealtus* new to Perth County. *Ontario Field Biologist* 38:37.

Cook, F. and D. McLeod. 1981. The vascular plants of Middlesex County, Ontario. Part 1: Horsetails, Clubmosses, Spikemosses and Ferns. *The Cardinal* 104:20-23.

Cook, F. and D. McLeod. 1983. The vascular plants of Middlesex County, Ontario. Part 5: Araceae to Orchidaceae. *Supplement to The Cardinal* 111:1-5.

Cook, F. and D. McLeod. 1984. The vascular plants of Middlesex County, Ontario. Part 6 : Saururaceae to Amaranthaceae. *Supplement to The Cardinal* 116:1-4.

Core, E.L. 1948. *The flora of the Erie Islands, an annotated list of vascular plants*. Ohio State University, Franz Theodore Stone Laboratory Contribution No. 9. 106 pp.

Coulson, D.P. 1984. *Spiranthes lucida* new to Wellington County. *Ontario Field Biologist* 38:43.

Crins, W.J. 1985. *Status report on Hoary Mountain Mint* Pycnanthemum incanum *(L.) Michx. an endangered species in Canada*. Prepared for the Committee on the Status of Endangered Wildlife in Canada. 18 pp.

Crins, W. 1986. *Vascular Plants of the Regional Municipality of Halton, Ontario*. Unpublished. 27 pp.

Cruise, J.E. 1969. A Floristic Study of Norfolk County, Ontario. *Transactions of the Royal Canadian Institute* 35:3-116.

Cuddy, D.G., K.M. Lindsay, and I.D. MacDonald. 1976. *Significant Natural Areas Along the Niagara Escarpment*. A Report on Nature Reserve Candidates and other Significant Natural Areas in the Niagara Escarpment Planning Area. Park Planning Branch, Division of Parks, Ontario Ministry of Natural Resources. 426 pp.

Darbyshire, S.J., S.G. Aiken, and Y. Dalpé. 1984. A new significant collection of *Calamovilfa longifolia* var. *magna* from Rondeau Provincial Park, Kent Co., Ontario. *The Plant Press* 2(3):77.

Darbyshire, S.J. and M.J. Oldham. 1985. Ohio Buckeye, *Aesculus glabra,* on Walpole Island, Lambton County, Ontario. *Canadian Field-Naturalist* 99(3):370-372.

Dodge, C.K. 1914a. *Annotated list of flowering plants and ferns of Point Pelee, Ontario, and neighbouring districts.* Canada Department of Mines, Geology Survey Memoir 54, No. 2, Biological Series. 131 pp.

Dodge, C.K. 1914b. *The Flowering Plants, Ferns and Fern Allies Growing without Cultivation in Lambton County, Ontario.* Sixteenth Report. Michigan Academy of Science, Lansing, Michigan, 1914. pp. 132-200.

Eagles, P.F.J. 1980. *Environmentally Sensitive Areas of Brant County.* Second Edition. Dept. of Man-Environment Studies, Faculty of Environmental Studies, University of Waterloo. 285 pp.

Fernald, M.L. 1950. *Gray's Manual of Botany.* Eighth Edition. American Book Company, New York. 1632 pp.

Gaiser, L. D. 1966. *A Survey of the Vascular Plants of Lambton County, Ontario.* Compiled by Raymond J. Moore. Ottawa: Plant Research Institute, Research Branch, Canada Department of Agriculture. 122 pp.

Gartshore, M.E., D.A. Sutherland and J.D. McCracken. 1987. *The Natural Areas Inventory of the Regional Municipality of Haldimand-Norfolk.* The Norfolk Field Naturalists, Simcoe. 2 vols. 547 pp.

Hamilton, G.H. 1943. *Plants of the Niagara Parks System of Ontario.* The Ryerson Press, Toronto. 233 pp.

Heimburger, M.L. 1955. *Report on the flora of Lincoln, Welland, Haldimand and Norfolk Counties, based on the Miller and Landon collections, 1948-1952.* (Unpaginated, handwritten and typed manuscript. Original at the Royal Botanical Gardens).

Hilts, S.G. and S. MacFabe. 1978. *A working list of the flora of Oxford and Middlesex Counties, Ontario.* Preliminary edition. Studies of the Ontario Landscape. No. 2. Conservation Committee, McIlwraith Field Naturalists Inc. and Department of Geography, University of Western Ontario, London, Ontario.

Hoffman, D. and L. Lamb. 1982. *Perth County: Preliminary Environmentally Sensitive Areas Survey.* Ontario Ministry of the Environment Experience '81/'82 and University of Waterloo. 128 pp.

Johnson, J.W. and W. Wannick. 1977. *A study of biologically significant natural areas of the Essex Region.* Essex Region Conservation Authority, Essex. 563 pp.

Kavanagh, K.C., L. Hutchison, and S. Varga. 1989. *Status report on Bird's-foot Violet* Viola pedata *L. in Canada.* Prepared for the Committee on the Status of Endangered Wildlife in Canada (COSEWIC). 30 pp.

Klinkenberg, B. and R. Klinkenberg. 1986. *Preliminary unpublished checklist of the plants of Kent County.* 130 pp.

Landon, M. 1960. *Vascular Plants of Norfolk County, Ontario.* The Big Creek Region Conservation Authority, Simcoe, Ontario. 66 pp.

MacDonald, I.D. 1980. *Life Science Features of the Haldimand Clay Plain Physiographic Region.* Ontario Ministry of Natural Resources, Parks and Recreation Section, Central Region, Richmond Hill. 266 pp.

Maycock, P.F., A.A. Reznicek and D.R. Gregory. 1976. *Point Pelee dryland vegetation analysis.* Unpublished report, Parks Canada.

McIntosh, K.L. and P.M. Catling. 1979. Notes on the flora of the Canadian portion of the Niagara Frontier. *Ontario Field Biologist* 33(1):1-11.

McLeod, D. and F. Cook. 1981. The vascular plants of Middlesex County, Ontario. Part 2: Taxaceae to Hydrocharitaceae. *The Cardinal* 105:14-15.

McLeod, D. and F. Cook. 1982a. The vascular plants of Middlesex County, Ontario. Part 3: Cyperaceae. *The Cardinal* 106:10-13.

McLeod, D. and F. Cook. 1982b. The vascular plants of Middlesex County, Ontario. Part 4: Graminae (Poaceae). *Supplement to the Cardinal* 109:5-9.

Montgomery, F.H. 1945. *A botanical survey of Waterloo County, Ontario.* Transactions of the Royal Canadian Institute. XXV: 217-265.

Montgomery, F.H. 1944. *A botanical survey of Waterloo County, Ontario.* M.A. thesis, McMaster University, Hamilton. 168 pp.

Oldham, M.J. 1984. *Justicia americana* new to Kent County. *Ontario Field Biologist* 38:39.

Oldham, M.J. and W.J. Crins. 1988. New and significant records on Ontario sedges (Cyperaceae). *Canadian Field-Naturalist* 102(3):500-507.

Pratt, P.D. 1979. *A preliminary life science inventory of the Ojibway Prairie Complex and surrounding area.* City of Windsor and Ontario Ministry of Natural Resources, Chatham. 163 pp.

Pringle, J.S. 1969. Checklist of the Spontaneous Vascular Flora of the Royal Botanical Gardens, Hamilton, Ontario, Canada. *Royal Botanical Gardens Technical Bulletin* No. 4. 47 pp.

Reznicek, A.A. and P.M. Catling. 1982. Cyperaceae new to Canada from Long Point, Norfolk County, Ontario. *Canadian Field-Naturalist* 96:184-188.

Reznicek, A.A. and P.M. Catling. 1984. Notes on Canadian Sedges, Cyperaceae. *Canadian Field-Naturalist* 98(2):209-214.

Reznicek, A.A., P.M. Catling and J.L. Riley. 1985. Additions to the native flora of Ontario since 1965: another view of plant collecting. *The Plant Press* 3(2):51-56.

Soper, J.H. 1955. Some families of restricted range in the Carolinian flora of Ontario. *Transactions of the Royal Canadian Institute* 31(1):69-90.

Stewart, W.G. 1971-1989. Additions to "A guide to the flora of Elgin County". *The Cardinal* 70:26-27 (1971); 73:20-23 (1972); 77:15-16 (1973); 79:16-17 (1974); 83:20-22 (1975); 85:9-10 (1976); 88:13-14 (1977); 91:12-15 (1978); 95:10 (1979); 98:19-21 (1980); 102:18-19 (1981); 106:8-9 (1982); 110:20-21 (1983); 114:8-9 (1984); 119:14 (1985); 122:10-13 (1986); NONE: (1987); 130:13-14 (1988); 135b:8-10 (1989).

Stewart, W.G. and L.E. James. 1969. *A Guide to the Flora of Elgin County, Ontario.* Catfish Creek Conservation Authority. 118 pp.

Stroud, J.J. 1941. A Study of the flora of Wellington County, Ontario. *Canadian Field Naturalist* 55:56-62, 73-76, 85-88, 104-107.

Sutherland, D.A. 1987. Annotated checklist of the plants of Haldimand-Norfolk. pp. 1-160, Vol II, In: Gartshore, M.E., D.A. Sutherland, and J.D. McCracken. *The Natural Areas Inventory of the Regional Municipality of Haldimand- Norfolk.* Norfolk Field Naturalists, Simcoe. 2 vols. 547 pp.

Tiedje, J. and D. 1989. *Vascular plants of Lambton County.* Third edition. Unpublished. 43 pp.

Varga, S., P.M. Catling, A.A. Reznicek, S.M. McKay-Kuja, and K.L. McIntosh. 1987. *Draft Vascular Plant Checklist of York County, Ontario.* Regional Municipalities of York and Metropolitan Toronto. (Unpublished, handwritten). 67 pp.

Waldron, G.E., S.W. Aboud, J.D. Ambrose, and G.E. Meyers. 1987. Shumard Oak, *Quercus shumardii,* in Canada. *Canadian Field- Naturalist* 101(4):532-538.

Webber, J.M. 1984. *The Vascular Plant Flora of Peel County, Ontario.* Botany Press, Toronto. 94 pp.

Yaki, G.J. 1970. *Plants of the Niagara Peninsula.* Niagara Falls Nature Club. Special Publication No. 2. 42 pp.

Zander, R.A. and G.J. Pierce. 1979. *Flora of the Niagara Frontier Region, second supplement and checklist.* Bulletin Buffalo Society of Natural Sciences 16 (supplement 2).

Zenkert, C.A. 1934. *The flora of the Niagara Frontier Region, ferns and flowering plants of Buffalo, N.Y., and vicinity.* Bulletin of the Buffalo Society of Natural Sciences. Buffalo, New York. 328 pp.

Zenkert, C.A. and R.A. Zander. 1975. *Flora of the Niagara Frontier Region, Supplement.* Bulletin Buffalo Society Natural Sciences 16 (supplement 1).

Birds and Mammals

Rarely observed in the wild, the Southern
Flying Squirrel depends on cavities in
trees for winter and summer homes.
Largely Carolinian in distribution, this
tiny, fascinating squirrel is now rare in
Canada, a function of forest clearing and
the removal of its nest sites – dead,
diseased, or large, mature trees.
Artist – Suzanne L. House.

The Ontario Rare Breeding Bird Program

Michael Cadman

Federation of Ontario Naturalists
355 Lesmill Road
Don Mills, Ontario

Abstract. *The Ontario Rare Breeding Bird Program (ORBBP) is a 5-year endeavour to clarify and report on the current status of the rarest breeding birds in Ontario. Status Reports resulting from the program's activities can be used to establish priorities in the conservation of Ontario's rarest birds. Additionally, the program will gather information as to the locations of present breeding sites of rare species, greatly facilitating direct conservation activities and providing useful information for research on those birds.*

Introduction

The Ontario Breeding Bird Atlas was a 5-year program of the Federation of Ontario Naturalists (FON) and the Long Point Bird Observatory (LPBO), undertaken in cooperation with the Federal and Provincial governments. More than 1300 volunteer naturalists contributed over 180,000 hours of field work and 400,000 records in helping the atlas provide an up-to-date picture of the distribution of Ontario's birds: the atlas was essentially an overall inventory of Ontario's avian resources.

The atlas data provide an unprecedented opportunity to evaluate the relative abundance of Ontario's birds and thus determine which are the rarest species. The atlas has also shown the data collection capabilities of a well organized corps of volunteer naturalists. As such the atlas project has made feasible a logical next step in the conservation of Ontario's birds – a more detailed evaluation of the status of the province's rare breeding birds, with fieldwork to be undertaken by volunteers under professional supervision.

The Ontario Rare Breeding Bird Program (ORBBP) is a 5-year program sponsored by the FON, and co-sponsored by the LPBO, the Nature Conservancy of Canada and the Ontario Field Ornithologists. It is a follow-up to the atlas project, modelled on its predecessor. The ORBBP will assess the current Ontario status of those species shown to be rare by the atlas project, and those species already designated as Rare, Threatened or Endangered by the Ontario Ministry of Natural Resources (MNR) and the Committee on the Status of Endangered Wildlife in Canada (COSEWIC). It will also make available, for research and conservation purposes, a large volume of information on the locations of nesting sites of rare species.

The ORBBP is the first large-scale follow-up to the atlas project. It is the result of the activities of a committee formed at the termination of the atlas project. The committee is made up of representatives of the Federation of Ontario Naturalists, the Long Point Bird Observatory, the Royal Ontario Museum and the academic community, and was established to further the development of volunteer-based natural history data collection projects in Ontario. It is intended that the ORBBP will be one of a series of programs which involve naturalist clubs and their members in the collection of such data.

The participation of volunteer naturalists will mean that this work can be undertaken very cost-effectively throughout well-populated areas of the province. Logistical difficulties preclude such work with volunteers in remote areas of Ontario.

Objectives

The major objectives of the ORBBP are:

1. To establish a list of bird species of concern for Ontario based upon the atlas and other sources.

2. To mobilize the province's naturalists to compile existing information as to the locations of nesting sites of those species of concern, and the known history of the use of those sites by those species.

3. To use volunteer naturalists to monitor those sites to determine if the site is still being used and if so, how many pairs of birds are present.

4. To use volunteer naturalists to survey suitable habitat to find additional breeding sites of selected species of concern.

5. To use the data to assess the current status of species of concern, and in the conservation of those species shown to require assistance.

Those objectives will be met through 2 work phases made possible as a result of the following preparatory work. Field testing of methods took place in 1987 and 1988. Data from these activities were used to help design a computer system to store and process program information. The system presently serves minimum requirements and is still under development. A proposed list of species of concern has been devised using atlas data and COSEWIC and MNR designations. That list has been circulated for comment to government agencies and conservation groups.

In order to compile existing information on species of concern, the area of the province to be covered under the ORBBP has been divided into regions based upon the boundaries of counties, regional municipalities and districts. The study area includes the entire area south of North Bay and Sault Ste. Marie, Thunder Bay District and the Lake of the Woods area. There are too few naturalists with the necessary skills outside of these areas to obtain extensive coverage. Coverage is anticipated to be comprehensive south and east of the Canadian Shield, and fairly comprehensive and even throughout the remainder of the study area.

Naturalist clubs have been assigned a region for which they are responsible, and have been provided with the proposed list of species of concern. They have been asked to form regional committees of expert naturalists who will complete standardized data forms, known as Site History Forms, on known breeding sites of proposed species of concern in their region. The information they gather was input to the ORBBP computer in 1989.

The ORBBP's data base is on a microcomputer and uses *Paradox*, a DOS-based relational data base. Paradox is a flexible and easy to use program. Data input is simplified by an applications program written for the ORBBP in 1988. Report production capability is high and data from the *Paradox* system are easily transferred into other DOS-based database packages. The data base will be housed at the Federation of Ontario Naturalists office in Don Mills.

Phase 1. Surveying and Monitoring Species of Concern.

Phase 1 begins April 1989 and ends in August 1991.

Regions will remain as those established during preparatory work, but the membership of regional committees will be adjusted to suit their new role in coordinating fieldwork. Each committee will be responsible for ensuring that all sites reported during preparatory work are monitored over the three years of phase one. Monitoring will consist of visiting the site during the breeding season, determining whether species of concern are present, and if so, determining how many pairs of birds are using the site. Information will be recorded on standardized data forms.

Committees will also be responsible for ensuring that thorough surveys of their region are undertaken for selected species of concern. Twenty-four species have been selected from the proposed list of species of concern. That is the maximum number for which it is felt thorough surveys can be undertaken. The goal of the surveys will be to search for those species away from known breeding sites, and thus to provide a more thorough accounting of their population size and nesting sites. The breeding sites of any other species of concern found during these surveys will be documented, providing for a useful but less rigorous assessment of the status of species other than the selected 24.

Fieldwork each year will extend throughout the breeding season (April through August). Data will be compiled by regional committees and provided to the ORBBP office for entry to the computer.

Surveying and monitoring techniques will be standardized to ensure consistency throughout the study area. As was true in the atlas, most volunteers will take responsibility for covering one or more 10 x 10 km UTM squares. They will monitor known sites in each square, spending a specified minimum time at each site to ensure whether or not the birds are present and, for some species, determining how many pairs of birds are using the site. Results will be reported on standardized data forms.

Volunteers will be provided with information on the breeding season, breeding behaviour and nesting habitat of each species so that surveying and monitoring can be appropriately timed and situated. Using atlas data, preliminary information from the ORBBP, and other sources, regional committees and volunteer field workers will decide which species should be surveyed for in each square. The volunteer's task will be to survey all available habitat for rare species which might breed in the square. Survey effort, both in time and distance travelled, as well as survey results will be recorded on standardized data forms.

Communicating with volunteers

A key aspect of involving, motivating and coordinating volunteers is communicating with them. A provincial newsletter will be used, as it was during the atlas project, to inform and encourage participants. In addition, regional committees will produce their own regional summaries providing more detailed local information on results and activities.

As a means of informing naturalists and developing their interest in natural history data collection programs, the provincial newsletter will inform participants of the activities of other volunteer-based programs such as the Forest Bird Monitoring Program, the Ontario Herpetofaunal Summary and the Ontario Lakes Loon Survey.

The newsletter will be produced three times annually: once at the end of the breeding season to encourage people to send in their results; once in mid-winter to summarize results of the previous year, to keep people thinking about the program, and to let them know of off-season activities such as workshops, etc.; and once just before the breeding season to help motivate and ensure maximum efficiency in the use of participants' time in the field.

Phase 2. Using the ORBBP data in the conservation of species of concern

Following the preparatory work, considerable data will have been collected and will be available for the purposes outlined below. The majority of the work required to complete the program's end products will be undertaken in the final year of the program (fiscal 1992) when all program data have been compiled and summarized, but some of the work will be feasible before that time.

1. Data collected for the ORBBP will pinpoint breeding sites of Ontario's species of concern. This information has never been gathered together before, and has never been nearly as extensive or current as it will be at the end of the program. It has several useful applications:
   - it can be made available to scientists wishing to research the cause of a species' scarcity or decline or to undertake other work useful in the conservation of the species. For example, information could be used in CWS' plans to survey significant species on the Great Lakes, or the information could be used in Environment Canada's Endangered Species data base.
   - it can be made available to resource managers, such as MNR foresters, so that habitat management plans can take into consideration breeding sites and the requirements of species of concern;
   - it can be used in the determination of the significance of a site for environmental assessment or for protection purposes. In this regard, the data are most effective when used in conjunction with information on other significant species and habitats. To facilitate this process, the ORBBP data will be made available to the Nature Conservancy of Canada for use in its Conservation Data Centre.

2. The known history of the usage of each site, including the number of pairs of birds known to be present in different years will also be contained in the ORBBP data base. This information can be used to look at changes in distribution of species, and in assessing the significance of specific sites. When combined with data from on-going, long-term monitoring programs such as the Forest Bird Monitoring Program and the Breeding Bird Survey, it will facilitate an assessment of the current status of each species.

3. Site ownership will be determined, and will indicate whether or not a site is protected. This information will be useful in assessing the effectiveness of the current system of protected areas in protecting species of concern. Because the program will include data on site tenacity, it will also permit an evaluation of whether a system of protected areas is an effective means of conserving all rare birds, or whether alternative means might be more effective for some species.

4. ORBBP data will also indicate the number, the proportion and the location of known sites which have been destroyed by human activity. These data will be available to some extent for historical sites, but also for recent sites, providing

useful data for assessing direct human impact on the habitat of species of concern. Monitoring sites between 1989 and 1991 will give up-to-date information on human impact on the habitat of species of concern in that period.

5. The ORBBP data will establish a baseline against which future changes in rare bird distribution and abundance can be compared. That baseline will be well suited to follow-up monitoring work on an individual species or for a repetition of the whole program at some time in the future.

Products

The program will produce a network of regional, naturalist club-based, data collection operations. This network will be nurtured as a permanent fixture, so that the systematic collection of information on significant habitats and species becomes an integral part of the activities of naturalist clubs. This should greatly facilitate the success of future endeavours in this field. At the same time, naturalists involved in the program will become more aware of, and likely more involved with environmental concerns in their area.

A series of status reports will be produced on the species of concern, summarizing the findings of the ORBBP and relating those findings to previous information. Existing status reports will be updated and new reports will be produced for species of concern whose status have not previously been assessed. Status reports will be relevant to Ontario only. A number of Canadian species of concern are found only in Ontario, so reports on those species will be of significance nationally.

The production of those status reports will be undertaken in cooperation with COSEWIC and the MNR, both of which are represented on the program's steering committees.

It is likely that the information gathered will be of considerable value in the production of Recovery Plans for some species, although that cannot really be determined until data collection is well under way. It is hoped that information will be applied to that purpose and that one or more Recovery Plans can be produced in cooperation with the new federal RENEW program, and the MNR.

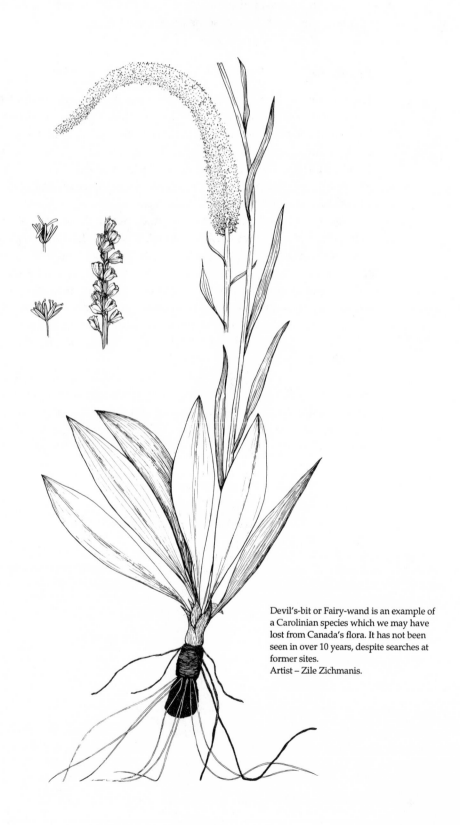

Devil's-bit or Fairy-wand is an example of a Carolinian species which we may have lost from Canada's flora. It has not been seen in over 10 years, despite searches at former sites.
Artist – Zile Zichmanis.

An Assessment of the Protection of Selected Rare Bird Breeding Sites in the Carolinian Forest Region of Ontario

Karen L. McColeman
Paul F. Eagles

Department of Recreation and Leisure Studies
University of Waterloo, Waterloo, Ontario N2L 3G1

Abstract. *The Carolinian Forest region in southwestern Ontario contains significant rare bird breeding habitats. Information on the status of protection for rare bird breeding stations is identified for the Acadian Flycatcher, Hooded Warbler, Tufted Titmouse, Prothonotary Warbler and Louisiana Waterthrush. The breeding stations for these rare birds are correlated with information on the land owner and the location of Carolinian Canada sites to determine the level of protection currently existing for these rare birds. Approximately 28% of the breeding sites are in parks or reserves. Another 18% are in Carolinian Canada sites. Therefore, 54% of the breeding bird populations are in unprotected or unknown situations.*

Introduction

The Carolinian Forest region in southwestern Ontario contains many significant taxa which do not occur elsewhere in Canada. Even though the region was recognized in the early 1900's as a significant area in Canada, very little of the natural ecosystem remains. Only 10 to 15% of the original forest cover has survived the rapid agriculture growth and urban sprawl (Poropat, 1986). Many counties have between five percent and eight percent natural area remaining, while Essex has less than three percent of its forest remaining and Halton has an estimated 20% remaining (Eagles and Beechey, 1985). These remnant natural habitats of the Carolinian forest are significant and must be protected in order to maintain genetic diversity, and to preserve unique ecosystems for future generations.

In 1984, the identification subcommittee of Carolinian Canada identified critical natural areas that were unprotected. Using existing information the subcommittee selected 36 sites and 11 alternative sites to represent the most significant remaining unprotected ecosystems of the Carolinian life zone. Subsequently, two other sites were added to give 38 sites. The goal of the committee was to find sites that, if protected, would conserve, along with existing parks and reserves, the ecological diversity of the life zone. All the sites identified, but one, were privately owned.

The identification of rare birds has traditionally been done by the exhaustive search of museum records, published accounts, fields notes and many other scattered forms of information (McCauley and Eagles, 1982).

Since the identification of unprotected sites in the Carolinian life zone, new information on breeding birds in Ontario has become available. An in depth and systematic inventory of the location of the breeding birds of the province is presented in *The Breeding Bird Atlas of Ontario* (Cadman, Eagles and Helleiner, 1987). This atlas shows accurate and up-to-date maps of the distribution of the breeding birds in the province during the period 1981 to 1985. Using the Universal Transverse Mercator (UTM) grid system, Southern Ontario was divided into

10 x 10 km squares and Northern Ontario was divided into 100 km x 100 km blocks. Over the projects life span volunteer birders spent approximately 123,897 hours collecting field data on breeding birds in these blocks. An estimated 2,000 volunteers contributed to the project. From this information, a list of the rare breeding birds in Ontario and within the Carolinian life zone was generated (Eagles, 1988).

Subsequently, the Ontario Rare Breeding Bird Program started. This is an attempt to field check the status of selected species of breeding birds. It is presently an ongoing effort.

Purpose of Study

The purpose of this study was to identify the status of the protection for rare bird breeding habitats in the Carolinian life zone. The rare birds selected were: Tufted Titmouse, Prothonotary Warbler, Acadian Flycatcher, Louisiana Waterthrush, and the Hooded Warbler. These birds were selected because they are rare in the Carolinian life zone and in Ontario. Furthermore, these birds prefer natural habitats to urban habitats. Using information collected for the *Breeding Bird Atlas of Ontario* and subsequent follow-up reports from the Ontario Rare Breeding Bird Program, the study identified the following:

1. Which rare bird breeding stations were protected in naturalist club nature reserves, conservation areas, provincial parks, national parks and national wildlife areas in the Carolinian life zone?[1]

2. Which of the rare breeding bird stations were not protected in one of the categories listed in (1) above?

3. Which of the rare breeding bird stations were on the sites identified by Carolinian Canada?

4. What percentage of these rare bird breeding habitats are protected in the Carolinian life zone?

Methodology

Information on the identification, location and abundance of rare breeding birds in Ontario was obtained from the data base of the *Ontario Breeding Bird Atlas*, including Unusual Species Report Forms and subsequent reports on stations from the Rare Breeding Bird Program. Thus, the total number of stations for a rare bird may be higher than the total number reported in the *Ontario Breeding Bird Atlas* (1987).

The data analysis involved a comparison of the location of the parks and protected areas with the location of rare breeding bird stations. Rare bird stations determined to be unprotected were then further compared to the location of the critical sites identified by Carolinian Canada. Consequently, rare breeding bird stations not located in parks or in the Carolinian Canada sites were identified.

The research generates the following:

1. a list of the number of protected stations in parks for each of the rare birds,

---

[1] These areas are referred to as "protected" in "parks" throughout this paper.

2. a list of the number of unprotected stations for each of the rare birds,

3. a list of the number of stations identified in #2 that are Carolinian Canada sites, and

4. the percentages of stations that are protected and unprotected for each species.

Results

The results are divided into two sections:

1) Status of Protection, and

2) Carolinian Canada Sites.

The results are reported from data collected up to October 1, 1988. Data collected in the 1989 and 1990 field seasons of the Ontario Rare Breeding Bird Project are not included.

Status of Protection

The total number and percentage of rare breeding bird stations protected, not protected and unknown are presented in Table 1. Records for which station information was not known or was insufficient, are recorded as unknown.

Table 1

The Status of Protection of Selected Rare Bird Breeding Stations

Common Name	Total Protected Stations		Total Unprotected Stations		Unknown		Total Number of Stations
Acadian Flycatcher	13	(45%)	16	(55%)	0		29
Prothonotary Warbler	12	(70%)	3	(18%)	2	(12%)	17
Hooded Warbler	7	(17%)	23	(56%)	11	(27%)	41
Tufted Titmouse	4	(14%)	22	(79%)	2	(7%)	28
Louisiana Waterthrush	2	(11%)	16	(84%)	1	(5%)	19
Total	38		80		16		134
Percent	28%		59%		12%		—

For 88 percent of the stations sufficient information was available for classifying sites as protected or not protected.

Each of these rare birds have breeding stations protected in parks in the Carolinian life zone. However, the majority of the rare bird breeding stations (59%) were not protected in parks.

The Prothonotary Warbler has the highest percentage of stations protected at 70 percent. The Acadian Flycatcher has just below half of its breeding stations protected. The Hooded Warbler, Tufted Titmouse and Louisiana Waterthrush have very few stations protected with 17 percent, 14 percent and 11 percent respectively.

Carolinian Canada Sites

The number of unprotected stations which are Carolinian sites are reported in Table 2. The Carolinian Canada site number and name are listed.

Table 2

Unprotected Rare Bird Breeding Stations that are Carolinian Canada Sites

Common Name	Site No	Site Name
Acadian Flycatcher	5	Big Creek Valley/South Walsingham Sand Ridges
	24	Point Albino Peninsula Sandland Forest
	10a	Delhi Big Creek Valley
Hooded Warbler	20	Middle Point Woods
	36	Walpole Island Indian Reserve
	31	Skunk's Misery
	5	Big Creek Valley-South Walsingham Sand Ridges (10 sites)
	11	Dundas Valley
Tufted Titmouse	15	Grimsby - Winona Escarpment and Beamer Valley (2 sites)
Louisiana Waterthrush	34	Sudden Bog
	7	Catfish Creek Slope and Floodplain Forest
	3a	Beverly Swamp
	15	Grimsby - Winona Escarpment and Beamer Valley (2 sites)
	11	Dundas Valley (2 sites)

A total of 24 breeding bird stations are found in sites identified by Carolinian Canada. The Hooded Warbler has the greatest number of breeding sites on Carolinian Canada sites with a total of 14. The South Walsingham Sand Ridges site was found to contain the most recorded rare breeding bird stations with a total of 11. The Grimsby Winona Escarpment and Beamer Valley is seen to be important because it has two breeding bird sites for both the Tufted Titmouse and the Louisiana Waterthrush.

If all of the Carolinian Canada sites were considered to be protected, the status of protection for these rare bird breeding stations improve significantly. The total number and percentage of stations protected, not protected, and unknown that would occur if the Carolinian Canada sites are considered to be protected are shown in Table 3.

There is a significant increase in the overall status of protection of the rare birds if the Carolinian Canada sites are counted as being protected. The total number of stations protected increases from 38 to 62 or from 28% to 46%. The Hooded Warbler and Louisiana Waterthrush benefit the most from the protection of Carolinian Canada sites. The Hooded Warbler increases from seven to 21 protected breeding stations which is a 200% increase. The Louisiana Waterthrush increases from two to seven protected breeding stations, which is a 250% increase. It is interesting to note that the Tufted Titmouse and Louisiana Waterthrush remain the least protected, even when Carolinian Canada sites are counted as protected.

Table 3

The Status of Protection of Selected Rare Bird Breeding Stations if Carolinian Canada Sites are Included as Protected

Common Name	Total Protected Stations		Total Unprotected Stations		Unknown		Total Number of Stations
Acadian Flycatcher	16	(55%)	13	(45%)	0		29
Prothonotary Warbler	12	(70%)	3	(18%)	2	(12%)	17
Hooded Warbler	21	(51%)	9	(22%)	11	(27%)	41
Tufted Titmouse	6	(21%)	20	(72%)	2	(7%)	28
Louisiana Waterthrush	7	(37%)	11	(58%)	1	(5%)	19
Total	62		56		16		134
Percent	46%		42%		12%		—

Implications of the Study

The need for information on specific species abundance and spatial distribution of breeding habitats is shown in this study. Atlases like the *Ontario Breeding Bird Atlas* provide essential information for species monitoring and for conservation and land use management. The integration of land use data with rare bird site information provides a significant picture of the status of specific species. For example, the Louisiana Waterthrush has few protected breeding habitats. This knowledge can be used to identify the areas that need to be monitored and which require land use practices compatible with this species habitat characteristics. Using this knowledge, certain species can be identified for further research and protection. Therefore, this type of research is an important step towards developing policy for maintaining genetic diversity.

The study also shows how atlas data can be helpful for selecting and ranking areas for land use planning. The rare breeding bird station information can be used to help prioritize sites for protection efforts. The information on rare bird breeding sites can be used to influence owners of the importance of their land. The information is also essential for developing conservation strategies that incorporate knowledge of habitat requirements for these rare birds with appropriate land uses.

The study reveals the need for increased monitoring and protection of the Acadian Flycatcher, Prothonotary Warbler, Hooded Warbler, Tufted Titmouse and Louisiana Waterthrush. Only 28 percent of the identified breeding sites for these rare birds are currently in protected sites such as parks.

With only 10 to 15 percent of the original forest cover left in the Carolinian life zone and increasing pressures from urban development, these rare bird habitats must be protected. Private and public land owners should be knowledgeable about these breeding sites and be encouraged to choose appropriate land use practices that maintain and enhance these habitats.

The work of Carolinian Canada to develop conservation strategies for the suggested and alternative sites will significantly improve the amount of protection for these rare birds. The status of protected breeding sites could be increased from 28 to 46 percent if the Carolinian sites are protected. The concentration of Hooded Warbler breeding sites on Big Creek Valley -South Walsingham Sand Ridges site may be used to give a high priority to this area and influence land owners of the significance of this site. The Grimsby-Winona Escarpment and Beamer Valley also has a concentration of breeding sites that should be recognized and used in planning a conservation strategy for this area.

This research was unable to assess the role of the land owner contact program in bird conservation. What sites are found on lands owned by sympathetic conservationists? This type of analysis could prove to be quite useful in assessing the conservation significance of the voluntary conservation agreements entered into by many landowners in the Carolinian Canada sites.

This analysis presents a static picture of rare bird preservation. In actual fact there is a variation in nest site location over time. A continuous type of data recording and reporting can present a more realistic picture. The analysis should be repeated at frequent intervals as the rare breeding bird data continues to be collected.

Limitations and Problems

The accuracy and certainty of the data is limited due to the method of collection and reporting. Since volunteer birders collected the information, there is some inconsistency in the level of detail and accuracy of the data. Variations exist in the amount of time spent covering the atlas squares, the experience and knowledge of the birders, and the accuracy and detail of individual species site reports. Data on the land use of species sites is uncertain since land uses in some cases were unknown and the ownership of land changes. However, the degree of detail is improving with the specific site studies now being taken within the rare breeding bird program.

The level of protection at each site varies from each other site. The study records sites as either protected, unprotected or unknown. The accuracy of the results would be improved by providing a more comprehensive scale of the levels of protection that occur. For example, a Conservation Area may provide little protection of a rare bird breeding site if the managers are provided with this information.

The measure of protection could further be improved by including other public land agencies which preserve land. For example, including other protected area categories such as: Migratory Bird Sanctuaries, Crown Game Preserves, and Provincial Wildlife Management Areas. There is no existing comprehensive inventory of protected lands for southern Ontario.

The measure of protection is also limited because the specific habitat requirements for the birds were not included. For example, the Hooded Warbler prefers dense undergrowth which may be enhanced by selective logging. A more accurate picture of the present protection of these rare breeding sites must incorporate knowledge of habitat characteristics for each species.

Recommendations

1. This type of study should be completed for all rare birds in the Carolinian. It should include the most recent data from the Ontario Rare Breeding Bird Program.

2. The Big Creek Valley – South Walsingham and Sand Ridges Carolinian Canada site should be given high priority for protection because of the concentration of Hooded Warbler breeding sites it contains.

3. The conservation strategies for Carolinian Canada sites should incorporate this information on rare birds to improve the status of protection of these rare birds.

4. The role of the private conservation agreements on rare breeding populations should be assessed.

References

Cadman, M.D., P.F.J. Eagles, and F.M. Helleiner. 1987. *Atlas of the Breeding Birds of Ontario*. University of Waterloo Press.

Eagles, P.F.J. 1988. *Frequency of Breeding Bird Species in Ontario Summary of Atlas Data*. Occasional Paper #13. Department of Recreation and Leisure Studies, University of Waterloo.

Eagles, P.F.J. and T.J. Beechey. 1985. *Critical Unprotected Natural Areas in the Carolinian Life Zone of Canada*. Nature Conservancy of Canada, Ontario Heritage Foundation and World Wildlife Fund Canada.

McCauley, J.D. and P.F.J. Eagles. 1982. *The Rare Breeding Birds of Ontario*. University of Waterloo Biology Series, No. 24., 1st Edition.

Poropat, E.B. 1986. *Rare Vascular Plants of Selected Protected Areas in the Carolinian Forest Region of Ontario*. Unpublished Thesis, the Department of Recreation and Leisure Studies, University of Waterloo.

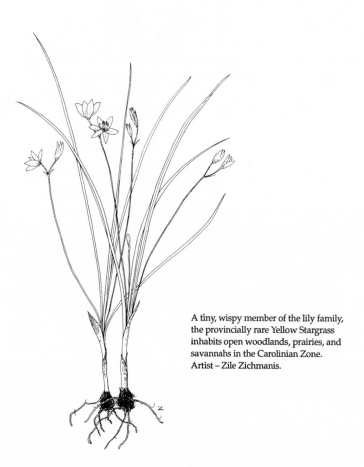

A tiny, wispy member of the lily family,
the provincially rare Yellow Stargrass
inhabits open woodlands, prairies, and
savannahs in the Carolinian Zone.
Artist – Zile Zichmanis.

Reconstruction of Banding Station at Long Point

George E. Wallace

Long Point Bird Observatory
P.O. Box 160, Port Rowan, Ontario N0E 1M0

For 28 years, Long Point Bird Observatory has conducted a migration monitoring program on Long Point. The first station manned on The Point was at the east end. This station has been the most important research site of a three station complex that provides an unparalleled opportunity for studying bird migration.

A key aspect of bird study at the tip of Long Point is the austerity of the habitat. The relatively barren Eastern Cottonwood savannah is a habitat unconducive for birds lingering during migration. Instead, birds tend to arrive and then push on to more productive feeding areas on the mainland of Ontario in spring or the south shore of Lake Erie in fall. Hence, migration monitoring at the tip detects "true migration".

We monitor the passage of all species of birds through the Long Point corridor. To date, over 350 species have been recorded. The most important aspect of the research is the use of migration data to calculate population indices that help us detect fluctuations in avian populations. The work is an important technique useful in the study of population changes that may be a result of habitat alteration on breeding grounds here in Ontario or, in the case of neotropic migrants, decimation of tropical rain forests on the wintering grounds.

The research at the tip of Long Point plays an important role in the study of species native to Canada's Carolinian Zone, found only in southern Ontario.

The migration monitoring program provides a consistent method of sampling relative numbers of Carolinian birds en route to their breeding areas on the adjacent mainland such as Hooded Warbler, White-eyed Vireo and Acadian Flycatcher. Furthermore, Carolinian species using the Point itself can be studied such as Prothonotary Warbler, Red-bellied Woodpecker and King Rail.

The tip station, in combination with our station on Courtright Ridge, Long Point, is a superb study site for research on several reptiles and amphibians that are rare in Canada and/or candidates for threatened or endangered status by COSEWIC. Eastern Fox Snake, Fowler's Toad and Spotted Turtle all have some of their largest Canadian populations on Long Point.

The tip station has other attractive attributes. We are increasingly interested in the use of Long Point by migratory bats. Large numbers of Little Brown Bats congregate on the tip of Long Point in August. Later in the fall, the point becomes an important stopover for highly migratory species such as Red, Hoary and Silver-haired Bat.

Knowing the vital importance of a research station with such diverse resources, the total destruction of the station in the catastrophic storm of December 1-2, 1985 came as a dreadful shock. Over 15 years of gradually increasing lake levels finally took its toll as a tremendous wind-driven surge swept away the building and acres of surrounding trees and dunes.

Fortunately, this story has a happy ending. During the summer of 1987, LPBO rebuilt the station. After careful thought and field examination, we chose a site one km west of the tip on a terrace on the north side of tall dunes along the south shore. Black Creek Marine Contracting of Port Dover installed a rugged steel pipe and I-beam foundation in June. Then during July and August, volunteers from LPBO, with help from the St. Thomas Field Naturalists, built a 16' x 28' 1-1/2 storey cabin on the site. We put the finishing touches on this structure in the spring of 1988.

We are pleased to rekindle our already long-term occupation at the tip. We look forward to continuing our population monitoring and diversifying the scope of our research. More importantly, we want interested researchers to know that LPBO has a facility available for use. The station can be used for educational purposes, the study of Carolinian Canada, and more. LPBO has much to offer scientists and educators who desire to investigate the fantastic ecosystem of Long Point.

Habitat Use by Foraging Insectivorous Bats[1]

C. L. Furlonger
H. J. Dewar
M. B. Fenton*

* Department of Biology, York University,
Downsview, Ontario M3J 1P3

Abstract. *We monitored echolocation calls to measure the activity of insectivorous bats at study sites in southwestern Ontario during the summer of 1985, relying on feeding buzzes to identify foraging activity. The Big Brown Bat* (Eptesicus fuscus) *was the most common and widespread species in the area, while Hoary Bat* (Lasiurus cinereus) *and Red Bat* (Lasiurus borealis) *were widespread. Species in the genus* Myotis *were more restricted in their distribution, being more common in an area with potential hibernacula. None of the species foraged exclusively in one habitat and all species exploited concentrations of insects around lights. Only the Big Brown Bat made significant use of lights as foraging sites in urban areas while in town and rural areas all of the species foraged around lights.*

Introduction

Since extinctions of species usually result from habitat disruption or destruction, and because some habitats in southwestern Ontario are disappearing rapidly, it is important to learn if any resident species are strongly associated with particular habitat types. This information will be essential in preparing a practical conservation plan for this region of high human population density. Within Canada, the Carolinian life zone accounts for less than 0.25% of the land area (Reid 1985) but it harbours more 'rare' species of animals and plants than any other life zone. This high species diversity is also important because 87% of this region lies either on clay or sand plain with little topographic variability.

Our knowledge of the distribution of bats in this environmentally sensitive area is based on occasional specimen records, rather than on the results of systematic surveys (e.g. Peterson 1966; van Zyll de Jong 1985). Indeed, because of the difficulty of capturing them, bats remain the most poorly known mammals in this (and other) parts of Canada. Until recently, surveys of bats have depended upon capture by shooting, netting, or trapping (Tuttle 1974). An alternative approach involves using the echolocation calls of some bats as a means of monitoring their activity (e.g., Fenton 1983). By using an appropriate 'bat detector' it is possible to distinguish one species from another, and to separate feeding from cruising individuals (Simmons *et al.* 1979a; 1979b). Bat detectors, instruments which convert ultrasonic sound into an output accessible to people, come in a variety of guises and may produce visual and/or audio displays of bat calls (Simmons *et al.* 1979b). Work in North America (Fenton and Bell 1981; Fenton *et al.* 1983), Scandinavia (Ahlen 1983), and Australia (Fenton 1982), for example, has demonstrated the feasibility of identifying different species of bats by their echolocation calls.

---

[1] A similar version of this paper was previously published in 1987 in the Canadian Journal of Zoology, Vol. 65, pp. 284-288. It is reprinted here with the kind permission of the National Research Council of Canada.

When one compares studies that have relied on observation of foraging bats (directly, or indirectly by monitoring echolocation calls), only two species appear to forage in just one habitat (Spotted Bat *(Euderma maculatum)*, Leonard and Fenton 1983; African Yellow-winged Bat *(Lavia frons)*, Vaughan and Vaughan 1986), although some others may be as selective (e.g., Grey Bat *(Myotis grisescens)*, Tuttle 1976). Other studies in different areas with different species (e.g., Bell 1980; Geggie and Fenton 1985; Racey and Swift 1985; Barclay 1985a, 1985b) suggest a lack of habitat specificity.

Selection of foraging habitat could be influenced by roost availability and location, particularly for species using roosts (e.g., buildings or caves) that are unevenly distributed (Kunz 1982). Evidence that roost availability could influence activity comes from Geggie and Fenton (1985) who studied the foraging behaviour of the Big Brown Bat in rural and urban settings. Lower feeding rates and longer feeding times led them to suggest that in urban areas insect density was lower than in rural areas, while roost availability (buildings) showed the opposite trend. If prey density has an important effect on activity levels, then the foraging of foliage-roosting bats also should be lower in urban settings.

The purpose of this study was to determine the influence of broad habitat types on the foraging activity of bats in southwestern Ontario (Fig. 1) and to see if increased urbanization was associated with decreased feeding by insectivorous bats which would in turn suggest reduced insect density (Geggie and Fenton 1985). Because our data suggested that proximity to hibernacula influenced activity levels of *Myotis* spp., we sampled additional sites in the Bruce Peninsula in Ontario, a known area of karst. The Big Brown Bat and Little Brown Bats *(Myotis lucifugus)* are the two species that commonly roost in buildings in the study area, while Hoary Bats and Red Bats roost in foliage. We also encountered Northern Long-eared Bats *(Myotis septentrionalis)* and Small-footed Bat *(Myotis leibii)* in the area.

Materials and Methods

We surveyed 181 sites (Fig. 1) in representative habitats in southwestern Ontario between 18 May and 29 August 1985 and 17 additional sites in the Bruce Peninsula (Bruce, Grey, and Simcoe counties) on 20 and 21 July and 16 and 17 August 1985. We characterized the sites with respect to five variables that were not necessarily mutually exclusive: (i) the degree of urbanization (city, town, rural); (ii) the presence of open water; (iii) the type of habitat (field, wooded, or field-wood edge); (iv) the presence or absence of woody vegetation cover; and (v) the presence of lights (which can attract insects and feeding bats, Fenton *et al.* 1983).

In total we collected data for 126 h and 20 min in the main study area, and for 7 h and 20 min in the Bruce Peninsula. Our sampling in habitats with water covered 38 h and 20 min, and in terrestrial sites, 32 h and 40 min, while in habitats with cover, sampling totalled 43 h and 20 min, and without cover, 7 h and 40 min. Sampling forest-edge habitats covered 18 h, and open habitats without edges 4 h and 20 min. In southwestern Ontario, we sampled 12 h and 20 min at sites with lights, and 8 h and 40 min at sites without lights; the distribution of effort between lights in urban, town, and rural settings was 1 h and 20, 3 h and 20 min, and 7 h and 40 min, respectively. Echolocation calls were monitored from within the settings noted above, that is to say, for example, with the microphones pointing over water from shore (aquatic) or parallel to the edge line (forest-edge habitats).

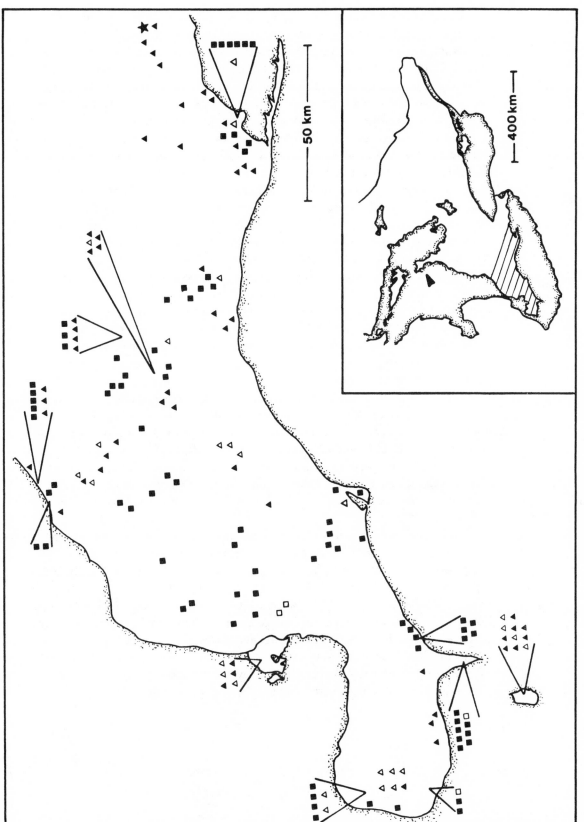

Figure 1: Distribution of permanent (squares) and opportunistic (triangles) sites in the study area with open symbols representing sites where zero bat activity was recorded. The solid star indicates the location of a hibernaculum used by *Myotis*. The shaded portion of the inset map shows the location of the study area within Ontario and the arrow on the inset map indicates the Bruce Peninsula.

Using two different bat detecting systems, we monitored echolocation calls at each site during 10-min observation periods and recorded the number of bat passes and feeding buzzes (high pulse repetition rates associated with attacks on insects, Griffin *et al.* 1960) produced by the species we encountered. Because the incidence of feeding buzzes paralleled general bat activity (bat passes) but at a reduced level (about 10%), we used bat passes in our analysis. In this study, foraging bats were identified by the feeding buzzes they produced.

We used a narrow-band (<5-kHz bandwidth) detector, the QMC Mini (QMC Instruments, 229 Mile End Road, London E1 4AA, England), and a broad-band (ca. 200-kHz bandwidth) system. The broad-band system involved a QMC S200 Bat Detector operated in countdown mode to produce an audio representation of each echolocation call. By feeding the high frequency output of the QMC S200 through a zero-crossing period meter (Simmons *et al.* 1979b), we obtained a simultaneous sonogram display of each call on a Non Linear Systems MS-15 Miniscope (Delmar, California). The calibration of the detecting systems was checked using a signal generator and with an appropriate amplifier and speaker (Simmons *et al.* 1979b). To verify the association of particular calls with the species producing them, we light-tagged (Buchler 1976) and released known individuals and monitored their echolocation calls. All of the species we sampled used high intensity echolocation calls (Fenton and Bell 1981) and appeared to rely on echolocation when foraging. We usually detected the echolocation calls of bats flying within ten m of, and approaching, the microphones.

For each site one set of data (10 min) was obtained from a stationary observer using the broad-band system, and a second set (10 min), by an observer on foot following a transect and using the narrow-band system tuned for 200 s each to 20, 30, and 40 kHz. Data from the two systems were totalled for each site. Our samples covered the 6-h period following sunset divided into three 2-h activity periods. We sampled 89 permanent sites in southwestern Ontario at least once in all three time periods during the study, and 92 sites opportunistically (once or twice) to monitor activity.

We lumped the data for the three *Myotis* species because we rarely encountered them in the southwestern Ontario study area. At sites without lights we compared mean activity (bat passes) for each species across sets of mutually exclusive habitat features (Table 1) and tested the significance of these associations using a modified chi-square test in a form algebraically equivalent to a two-sample Poisson test (Shiue and Bain 1982). We compared activity levels at permanent sites with and without lights in southwestern Ontario and in the Bruce Peninsula (Fig. 2) and analyzed these data using a two-tailed Mann-Whitney U-test (Siegel 1956). We then used a Kruskal-Wallis one-way analysis of variance (Siegel 1956) to determine the effect of setting on activity at lights (rural, town, city in Fig. 3).

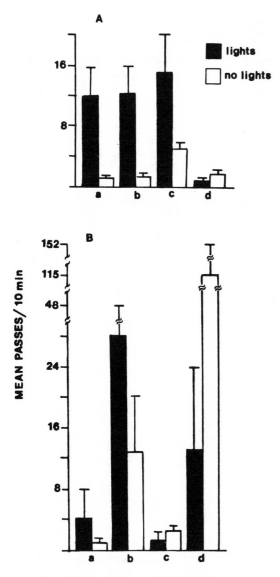

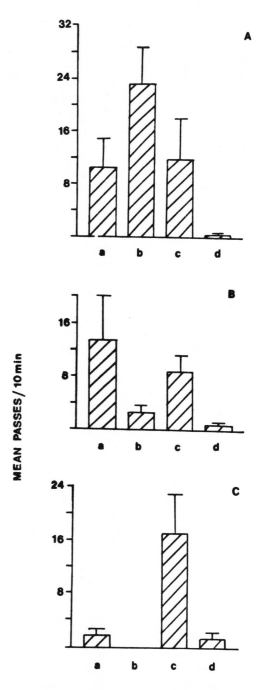

Figure 2: Comparison of bat activity levels (means + standard error) at permanent sites with and without lights in (A) southwestern Ontario: Mann-Whitney *U* values are (a) *L. cinereus:* 1613.5 (p<<0.001), (b) *L. borealis:* 1799.5 (p<<0.001), (c) *E. fuscus:* 1870 (p<0.025), (d) *Myotis:* 2806 (not significant); and (B) the Bruce Peninsula: sampling efforts are 40 and 140 min, respectively, for sites with and without lights; the sample sizes are too small for statistical analysis; species designations as for A.

Figure 3: Comparison of bat activity levels (means + standard error) at sites with lights in (A) rural, (B) town, and (C) urban habitats. Kruskal-Wallis values are (a) *L. cinereus:* 3.504 (not significant), b) *L. borealis:* 8.539 (p<0.025), (c) *E. fuscus:* 6.075 (p<0.05), and (d) *Myotis:* 0.2062 (not significant).

Table 1

Species associations with habitat features in the absence of lights showing values and significant levels for Chi-comparisons of bat activity between pairs of habitat variables.

(df = 1; +, positive association; − ,negative association)

	Habitat Features					
	Land Form		Cover		Edge	
	Water	Terrestrial	Present	Absent	Present	Absent
L. cinnereus						
Association	ns	ns	+***	ns	+***	−***
Chi2	0.66	0.51	19	2	700	656
L. borealis						
Association	−***	+***	+***	ns	+***	−***
Chi2	215	201	78	1	51	64
E. fuscus						
Association	ns	ns	ns	ns	ns	ns
Chi2	2	1	0.3	0.5	1	2
Myotis spp.						
Association	+***	−***	+*	ns	+***	−***
Chi2	113	133	7	2	59	73

Note: ns, not significant; *, p<0.05; ***, p<0.0001.

Results

None of the species we monitored restricted its foraging to a specific habitat type but there were some significant associations between the foraging activity of some species and some mutually exclusive habitat features (Table 1). The Hoary Bat was not significantly more active over water than over terrestrial habitats, but was significantly more active over sites with cover than those without cover, and was positively associated with edge situation. The Red Bat was associated with terrestrial habitats significantly more than with water settings, but otherwise was similar to the Hoary Bat. *Myotis* spp. were significantly associated with water and edge situations, while the Big Brown Bat showed no significant positive or negative associations with any of the habitat features we considered (Table 1).

Although the *Myotis* spp. and the other species we studied all fed in clumps of insects around lights, only three species (Hoary, Red, and Big Brown) showed significant positive associations with lights in southwestern Ontario (Fig. 2). When this relationship is considered in the context of lights set in rural, town, or city situations, the responses of different species are clearer (Fig. 3). While there is no significant effect of setting on the foraging activity of the Hoary Bat or *Myotis* spp., both the Red Bat and Big Brown Bat show a significant effect of setting, with the Big Brown foraging at lights in all areas and the Red Bat avoiding urban situations.

These results suggest that the Big Brown Bat is the most flexible of the species we encountered in terms of the habitats where it forages and in its use of rich food patches in rural, town, or city settings. Throughout southwestern Ontario it was the most widespread species, occurring at 89% of the permanent sites we studied, and being the most active species at 43% of the permanent sites. In comparison, the Hoary Bat occurred at 55% of the permanent sites in southwestern Ontario but was the most active at only 9% of them; comparable figures for Red Bat were 55% and 17%, respectively.

Myotis spp. were encountered at 44% of the permanent sites in southwestern Ontario and were the most active bats at 17% of these sites. There appeared to be more foraging *Myotis* spp. at sites nearer the known hibernaculum (star in Fig. 1) in the southwestern Ontario part of the study area. The potential effect of hibernacula also is suggested by activity data from the Bruce Peninsula where *Myotis* spp. were the most active at 76% of the sites. For comparison, the Hoary Bat was encountered at 53% of the sites, Red Bat at 47% of the sites, and Big Brown at 76% of the Bruce Peninsula sites. In the Bruce Peninsula, *Myotis* spp. were significantly more active around lights ($U = 344$, p < 0.001) than they had been in southwestern Ontario. Their lack of association with lights in southwestern Ontario appears to reflect population levels rather than failure to exploit concentrations of food.

Discussion

Our results support those suggesting no unique associations between different species of foraging bats and specific habitats. Some species were significantly more active along edges which sometimes harbour higher densities of flying insects (Lewis 1970). The bats also showed a propensity to exploit concentrations of insects around lights (albeit ameliorated by the settings in which the lights occurred). These results reflect the data of Racey and Swift (1985) and Swift *et al.* (1985) that showed how Pipistrelles *(Pipistrellus pipistrellus)*, exploited concentrations of insects and that this aspect of their behaviour seemed to prevail over use of particular habitats. Fenton *et al.* (1983), Belwood and Fullard (1984), and Barclay (1985a) also found the Hoary Bat foraging around lights, and the propensity of insectivorous bats to exploit rich patches of prey is widespread both geographically and among different taxonomic groups of bats (e.g. Gould 1978; Vaughan 1980; Bell 1980; Fenton 1982; Bell and Fenton 1984).

To date, African Yellow-winged Bats and Spotted Bats stand out as examples of habitat specificity by foraging insectivorous bats. The data of Leonard and Fenton (1983) do not reflect the behaviour of this species throughout its range in the United States (Fenton *et al.* 1987), but they demonstrate that some bats may select specific habitats in which to forage. There are no comparable studies of African Yellow-winged Bats. Both African Yellow-winged Bats and Spotted Bats are morphologically striking and selection of foraging habitats may be a correlate of morphological specialization where morphology is relatable to foraging or feeding behaviour. Within the Microchiroptera other species could be used to challenge this idea.

Both proximity to roosts and prey availability can influence the distribution of bats. Our observations on foraging activity of two species of *Lasiurus* suggest reduced insect availability in urban areas (cf. Taylor *et al.* 1978) and thus support the suggestion that the Big Brown Bat encounters lower prey densities in urban areas. Our results for *Myotis* spp. demonstrate that proximity to hibernacula may influence activity levels, paralleling Barclay's (1984) observation that activity levels of the Little Brown Bats outside the migration season were influenced by proximity to day roosts. Changes in the relative abundances of different species of bats at different sampling sites as reported here, by Bell (1980), and by Fenton *et al.* (1983)

all are compatible with the hypothesis that at any location, foraging activity could be influenced by roost availability.

To realistically evaluate the influence of different factors on the use of space (roosts or foraging areas) by bats requires data on home range. Radio tracking studies are now producing these kinds of data (e.g., Barclay 1985b; Fenton *et al.* 1985; Brigham and Fenton 1986) and they suggest that foraging strategy may have a greater influence on foraging area than roost location. Furthermore, Barclay (1985a) demonstrated that differences in foraging strategy also influence prey selected. However, Herd and Fenton (1983) and Swift and Racey (1983) have demonstrated that the habitats in which bats forage also can influence prey selected. With the possible exception of Northern Long-eared Bat the species we considered fly continuously in search of flying insects.

Most insectivorous bats studied to date do not show habitat specificity in their foraging behaviour and species using different foraging strategies exploit local concentrations of insects such as those around lights. Although differences in habitat use sometimes have been associated with differences in prey selection, in other cases intraspecific variation in habitat use could override this phenomenon. Differences in techniques of study, the species under examination, and the geographical setting all confound the basic question about habitat specificity and foraging bats.

Conservation Recommendations

Unlike some other organisms, the bats of Ontario's Carolinian area do not show a high level of habitat specificity, and this complicates the formulation of 'simple' recommendations about their conservation. Furthermore, since Big Brown Bats and Little Brown Bats often establish nursery colonies in buildings, some will argue that this commensal behaviour makes conserving them a nonissue. In spite of these problems, three steps are essential to ensure the conservation of bats.

1. The first and most important is changing the public's attitude towards bats. Bats do not CARRY rabies although they are susceptible to it. In Canada there are NO RECORDS of histoplasmosis being associated with bat droppings. And yet, public health is a recurring rationale for Canada's continuing to approve the use of DDT in bat control - even though it is not effective. The continuing registration of DDT for bat control in Canada clearly reflects the public's attitude towards these animals.

2. It is imperative that hibernating bats be protected from disturbance, a situation that puts their welfare in conflict with recreational cavers and some bat researchers. Hibernating bats carry only their body fat to see them through more than six months of fasting and minimizing arousal from hibernation appears to be THE mechanism by which they survive. Arousal, raising the body temperature from ambient (1° to 5°C) to 40°C, is the most expensive part of hibernation and disturbance causes hibernating bats to arouse.

3. We must find out if populations can be enticed into artificial housing. Although we know that some bats regularly roost in buildings, efforts to get them to occupy bat houses have been relatively unsuccessful. Establishing a successful programme of alternate housing may prove to be an important step in the conservation of bats.

Acknowledgements

We are grateful to the many people in southwestern Ontario, particularly staff from national and provincial parks, who provided logistical support during this study. We thank H.D.J.N. Aldridge, R.M. Brigham, D. Audet, M.G. Stoneman, J.P. Balcombe, B. Hickey, and V. Wai-Ping for reading the manuscript and making helpful suggestions. We are grateful to Dr. R.H. Thomas for advice on statistical analysis. This research was supported by a grant from the World Wildlife Fund (Canada).

References

Ahlen, I. 1983. The bat fauna of some isolated islands in Scandinavia. *Oikos* 41:352-358.

Barclay, R. M. R. 1984. Observations on the migration, ecology and behaviour of bats at Delta Marsh, Manitoba. *Can. Field Nat.* 98:331-336.

Barclay, R. M. R. 1985a. Long- versus short-range foraging strategies of hoary *(Lasiurus cinereus)* and silver-haired *(Lasionycteris noctivagans)* bats and the consequences for prey selection. *Can. J. Zool.* 63:2507-2515.

Barclay, R. M. R. 1985b. Foraging behaviour of the African insectivorous bat, *Scotophilus leucogaster. Biotropica* 17:65-70.

Bell, G. P. 1980. Habitat use and response to patches of prey by desert insectivorous bats. *Can. J. Zool.* 58:1876-1883.

Bell, G. P. and M. B. Fenton. 1984. The use of Doppler-shifted echoes as a flutter detection and clutter rejection system: the echolocation and feeding behaviour of *Hipposideros ruber* (Chiroptera: Hipposideridae). *Behav. Ecol. Sociobiol.* 16:109-114.

Belwood, J. J. and J. H. Fullard. 1984. Echolocation and foraging behaviour in the Hawaiian hoary bat, *Lasiurus cinereus semotus. Can. J. Zool.* 62:2113-2120.

Brigham, R. M. and M. B. Fenton. 1986. The influence of roost closure on the roosting and foraging behaviour of *Eptesicus fuscus* (Chiroptera: Vespertilionidae). *Can. J. Zool.* 64:1128-1133.

Buchler, E. R. 1976. A chemiluminescent tag for tracking bats and other small nocturnal mammals. *J. Mammal.* 57:173-176.

Fenton, M. B. and G. P. Bell. 1981. Recognition of species of insectivorous bats by their echolocation calls. *J. Mammal.* 62:233-243.

Fenton, M. B. 1982. Echolocation calls and patterns of hunting and habitat use of bats (Microchiroptera) from Chillagoe, north Queensland. *Aust. J. Zool.* 30:417-425.

Fenton, M. B. 1983. *Just Bats.* University of Toronto Press, Toronto.

Fenton, M. B., H. G. Merriam, and G. L. Holroyd. 1983. Bats of Kootenay, Glacier, and Mount Revelstoke National Parks in Canada: identification by echolocation calls, distribution, and biology. *Can. J. Zool.* 61:2503-2508.

Fenton, M. B., R. M. Brigham, A. M. Mills, and L. L. Rautenbauch. 1985. The roosting and foraging areas of *Epomophorus wahlbergi* (Pteropodidae) and *Scotophilus viridis* (Vespertilionidae) in Kruger National Park, South Africa. *J. Mammal.* 66:461-468.

Fenton, M. B., D. C. Tennant, and J. Wyszecki. 1987. Using echolocation calls to measure the distribution of bats: the case of *Euderma maculatum. J. Mammal* 68:142-144.

Geggie, J. F. and M. B. Fenton. 1985. A comparison of foraging by *Eptesicus fuscus* (Chiroptera: Vespertilionidae) in urban and rural environments. *Can. J. Zool.* 63:263-266.

Gould, E. 1978. Opportunistic feeding by tropical bats. *Biotropica* 10:75-76.

Griffin, D. R., F. A. Webster, and C. R. Michael. 1960. The echolocation of flying insects by bats. *Anim. Behav.* 8:141-154.

Herd, R. M. and M. B. Fenton. 1983. An electrophoretic, morphological, and ecological investigation of a putative hybrid zone between *Myotis lucifugus* and *Myotis yumanensis* (Chiroptera: Vespertilionidae). *Can. J. Zool.* 61:2029-2050.

Kunz, T. H. 1982. Roosting ecology of bats. In: *Ecology of bats*. T. H. Kunz (ed.). Plenum Press, New York. pp. 1-55.

Leonard, M. L. and M. B. Fenton. 1983. Habitat use by spotted bats (*Euderma maculatum*, Chiroptera: Vespertilionidae): roosting and foraging behaviour. *Can. J. Zool.* 61:1487-1491.

Lewis, T. 1970. Patterns of distribution of insects near a wind break of tall trees. *Ann. Appl. Biol.* 65:213-220.

Peterson, R. L. 1966. *The mammals of eastern Canada*. Oxford University Press, Toronto.

Racey, P. A. and S. M. Swift. 1985. Feeding ecology of *Pipistrellus pipistrellus* (Chiroptera: Vespertilionidae) during pregnancy and lactation. I. Foraging behaviour. *J. Anim. Ecol.* 54:205-215.

Reid, R. 1985. The Carolinian Canada Conservation Strategy. *Seasons* 25(2):22-34.

Shiue, W. K. and L. J. Bain. 1982. Experiment size and power comparisons for two sample Poisson tests. *Appl. Stat. Ser. C.* 31:130-134.

Siegel, S. 1956. *Nonparametric statistics for the behavioral sciences*. McGraw-Hill, New York.

Simmons, J. A., M. B. Fenton and M. J. O'Farrell. 1979a. Echolocation and the pursuit of prey by bats. *Science* 203:16-21.

Simmons, J. A., M. B. Fenton, W. R. Ferguson, M. Jutting and J. Palin. 1979b. *Apparatus for research on animal ultrasonic signals*. R. Ont. Mus. Life Sci. Misc. Publ.

Swift, S. M. and P. A. Racey. 1983. Resource partitioning in two species of vespertilionid bats (Chiroptera) occupying the same roost. *J. Zool.* 200:249-259.

Swift, S. M., P. A. Racey and M. I. Avery. 1985. Feeding ecology of *Pipistrellus pipistrellus* (Chiroptera: Vespertilionidae) during pregnancy and lactation. II. Diet. *J. Anim. Ecol.* 54:217-255.

Taylor, L. R., R. A. French and L. P. Woiwod. 1978. The Rothamsted insect survey and the urbanization of land in Great Britain. *Perspectives in urban entomology*. G. W. Frankie and C. S. Koehler (eds). Academic Press, New York. pp. 31-65.

Tuttle, M. D. 1974. An improved trap for bats. *J. Mammal.* 55:475-477.

Tuttle, M. D. 1976. Population ecology of the gray bat *(Myotis grisescens)*: factors influencing growth and survival of newly volant young. *Ecology* 57:587-595.

Van Zyll De Jong, C. G. 1985. *Handbook of Canadian mammals 2. Bats*. National Museum of Natural History, Ottawa, Canada.

Vaughan, T. A. 1980. Opportunistic feeding by two species of *Myotis*. *J. Mammal.* 61:118-119.

Vaughan, T. A. and R. P. Vaughan. 1986. Seasonality and the behaviour of the African yellow-winged bat. *J. Mammal.* 67:91-102.

The Southern Flying Squirrel in Carolinian Canada

M. Stabb[1]
P.L. Aird

Faculty of Forestry, University of Toronto
203 College Street, Toronto, Ontario M5S 1A1

Abstract. *A dual study was conducted to document the status of the Southern Flying Squirrel in Ontario, and to investigate the squirrel's nesting ecology. Population status of the species in the Carolinian Zone ranged from extirpated to abundant, depending on local habitat conditions. The squirrels were found in most forest types, but are known to fare best in mature forests comprised of several mast-producing tree species. Populations are detrimentally affected by reduction and isolation of forests and woodlots; management practices that remove dead or damaged stems may reduce densities in existing habitat. The squirrels used a variety of dead stem types, with little apparent preference for the characteristics that were measured. Winter nests that are the locations of overwintering aggregations are a priority for future research. Conservation recommendations are included. The squirrel has been designated as nationally "rare" by MNR and COSEWIC.*

Introduction

The Southern Flying Squirrel (*Glaucomys volans*) suffers from an identity crisis in Ontario. Not only is this squirrel nocturnal and consequently rarely noticed by people, but it often lives in close proximity to the similar Northern Flying Squirrel (*Glaucomys sabrinus*), which can make species identification difficult. As a result, the distribution, habits, and habitat, of the Southern Flying Squirrel, are poorly known in the province, including the Carolinian Zone. This comes at a time when obvious impingements on the species' habitat are increasing.

Being a secondary cavity-nesting species, the squirrel depends heavily on chicots (alias snags) and dead portions of live trees for denning sites, and during many other periods of its life history. The habitat features that support cavities are often selected against during contemporary management of forests and woodlots, and may lead to a decline in this cavity-dependent squirrel. As well, habitat is being completely replaced by agriculture or urban development in many portions of the species' Ontario range.

In light of these problems a dual study was established: to document the status of the squirrel in Ontario, and to investigate aspects of the squirrel's nesting ecology. This paper is an overview of the results of these studies.

Distribution

The Southern Flying Squirrel inhabits the eastern deciduous forest of North America, with some subspecies located in the forests of Mexico and Central America. The subspecies in Canada, *G. v. volans*, is found in southern Ontario,

---

[1] Current address: Wildlife Branch, Ministry of Natural Resources, Whitney Block, Queen's Park, Toronto M7A 1W3.

extreme southwestern Quebec, and in isolated portions of Nova Scotia. The range of the Southern Flying Squirrel and the limits of Canada's Carolinian Zone coincide in southwestern Ontario (Figure 1); north and east of the Carolinian Zone the forests are inhabited by the Northern Flying Squirrel as well. Based on personal observations and historical records from museums and the literature, it appears that *Glaucomys volans* is *the* flying squirrel of Carolinian Canada. North of Lake Ontario and further east the ranges of the two species overlap considerably.

Within the Carolinian Zone, the population status of the squirrel varies with habitat conditions from extirpated to common, and can even be locally abundant. In a very general sense, the status can be broken down as follows:

Essex and Kent	Rare to extirpated
Lambton, Elgin, Niagara, Hamilton-Wentworth, and Middlesex	Uncommon to rare
Haldimand-Norfolk	Common to locally abundant

A detailed breakdown of the geographical status and existing records of the Southern Flying Squirrel can be found in a status report of the species (Stabb 1987) available from the Wildlife Branch of the Ontario Ministry of Natural Resources. The authors would be interested in any observations beyond those areas noted in Figure 1.

Habitat

We reconnoitred potential flying squirrel habitat in the Carolinian Zone in the summer of 1985. More than 50 woodlots were intensively checked for flying squirrels by rapping on dead stems, live-trapping, and by using spotlight searches. Dead stem surveys proved to be the most productive technique, and were employed during most of the field season. Flying squirrels were found in 23 of the sites surveyed. Forest types associated with these observations were as follows: mixed oak-hickory-tulip-pine (44%), maple-beech (22%), oak-hickory (13%), Silver/Red maple swamps (13%), and moist maple-aspen (8%). It became obvious that the observations recorded depended more on the presence or absence of cavity-bearing trees than on forest type. No systematic measure was made of cavity availability in the reconnaissance survey.

Southern Flying Squirrels are often characterized as inhabitants of "heavy timber" or mature hardwood forests. This certainly can be the case, although we have found the species in younger stands, including one young pine plantation. However the younger sites with squirrels were always associated with a mature section of deciduous woods, or contained mature components (i.e. dead stems or mast-producing trees).

We spent the 1986 field season in Backus Woods and found the squirrels in virtually every major forest community, including flooded Silver Maple swamps. It appears that given enough mature habitat, the squirrels can inhabit most forests in the Carolinian Zone. Forest type may influence distribution more at the extreme northern edge of the squirrel's range, such as the Muskoka region.

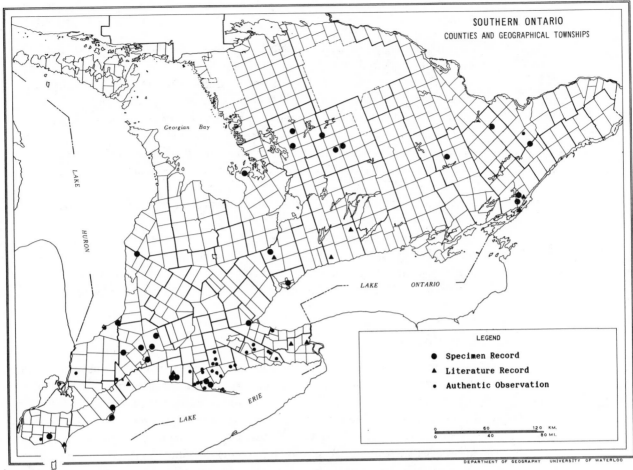

Figure 1: Distribution of Southern Flying Squirrel in Ontario. Source: Stabb 1987.

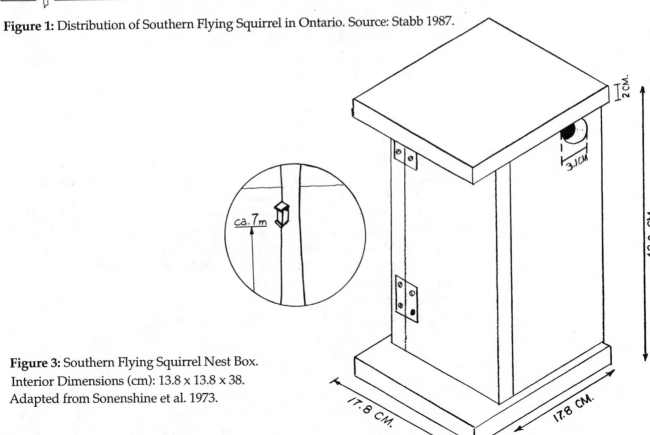

Figure 3: Southern Flying Squirrel Nest Box.
Interior Dimensions (cm): 13.8 x 13.8 x 38.
Adapted from Sonenshine et al. 1973.

Food

Southern Flying Squirrels are primarily omnivorous, although the most crucial food sources are undoubtedly nuts and seeds of mast-bearing trees. Stored nuts and acorns are the primary source of energy during the winter months. Hickory nuts are preferred over acorns, and both presumably over beech nuts and other more perishable items. Due to a lower tannin content (which affects digestibility), acorns from the White Oak group of trees are preferred over those of the Red Oak group. Several studies have linked reproductive output of Southern Flying Squirrels to the variety, availability, and abundance of nuts and acorns (e.g. VanVoorhees 1976, Doby 1984, Thomas 1986). In fact, the northern range of the species may be limited by the presence or absence of such trees as Red Oak or American Beech (Weigl 1978).

The evidence suggests that the Carolinian Zone is the most productive habitat for Southern Flying Squirrels in Canada, due to the large number of mast-producing tree species. Beyond the zone, populations may be highly unstable and/or exist at low densities since they must subsist on lower quality food sources.

Limiting Factors

Flying squirrel populations are likely limited mostly by habitat quantity and quality in southern Ontario. The species is obviously eliminated with the loss of forest cover. Contraction of extant woodland to smaller woodlots may threaten the future of local populations. Several authors report that the squirrels rarely travel across open areas (e.g. Bendel and Gates 1987) and that they are no longer found in small isolated woods. Southern Flying Squirrel populations are limited in size by the number of available nest sites. Thus, they may be detrimentally affected by intensive forest management practices that remove dead, diseased, or dying trees – the progenitors of potential nest sites. Thinning of sub-canopy trees during management operations may eliminate the precursors to snags that may eventually bear cavities.

Reduction in the numbers of mast-producing trees (individuals and species) in particular woodlands can reduce reproductive output of Southern Flying Squirrels. The squirrels are non-hibernatory, so stored acorns and nuts are especially important to the species in the winter. To cope with severe cold, the squirrels form winter aggregations that can include 30 or more animals. Presumably the cavities and trees in which these groups form would have to be large and solid (e.g. windfirm), but this question requires study.

Domestic and feral cats have been termed the chief mammalian predators of Southern Flying Squirrels, and may be the most important of all predators in suburban and rural areas (Banfield 1974, Hamilton and Whitaker 1979). The effects of these free-ranging felines could be especially detrimental in small, isolated squirrel populations, such as those found in farm woodlots.

Surprisingly, owl pellet analysis from Backus Woods, and most other areas, failed to turn up remains of Southern Flying Squirrels.

Status

Records of the Southern Flying Squirrel are uncommon in Ontario for a variety of reasons. Conventional small mammal trapping techniques are not often successful for Southern Flying Squirrels. Because of their nocturnal habits, they are rarely observed. When they are seen, their close resemblance to the Northern Flying Squirrel can lead to ambiguous observation records for "flying squirrel". Museum specimens do exist, but they are few in number.

Still, there is sufficient evidence to suggest that the squirrel has suffered a significant decline in Ontario following settlement, primarily due to the wholesale removal of forest cover in southern Ontario. This is continuing – during the period of this study we saw much evidence of woodlots being razed or severely cut, particularly in tobacco-growing areas. A compilation of observations indicates that the range of the Southern Flying Squirrel is much more restricted in southern Ontario than is presumed by several authors, although their range may be expanding somewhat north of Lake Ontario.

Forest fragmentation may be affecting local survival of Southern Flying Squirrel populations. Of greater importance is the increasing intensity of forest management. Firewood cutting has removed dead, dying, and diseased trees, and interest in high quality timber leads to thinning and stand management that reduces severely the number of cavities that remain in hardwood forests.

The species reaches its northern limit in Canada, and has always had a restricted distribution in Ontario. It is locally abundant in a few areas (e.g. Haldimand-Norfolk) but is uncommon, rare, or extirpated, in most of its southern Ontario range. Due to the species' spotty distribution, the biology of the species, and continued reduction in forest cover and cavity-bearing trees, the Southern Flying Squirrel was proposed as a rare species in Canada (Stabb 1987). This designation was accepted both by the Wildlife Branch (Non-game Program) of the Ontario Ministry of Natural Resources, and the Committee on the Status of Endangered Wildlife in Canada. A "Rare" designation is defined by COSEWIC as:

> "Any indigenous species of fauna or flora that, because of its biological characteristics, or because it occurs at the fringe of its range, or for some other reasons, exists in low numbers or in very restricted areas in Canada, and so is vulnerable, but is not a threatened species".

The existing distribution records for the species are still relatively few, so with further field study it may be determined that the Southern Flying Squirrel is a marginal member of the "rare" category. It is safe to say, however, that forest management and clearing will intensify in the future. This makes the species vulnerable.

A rare designation gives no official protection to a species whatsoever. In the author's view its main value is in identifying a species that requires the special attention of the public, researchers, and resource managers. Forest managers in particular should be aware of the requirements of cavity-nesters such as Southern Flying Squirrels. There is evidence that conservation of the species is not inconsistent with forest management.

Nesting Ecology

Foresters must have access to specific information if they are to include wildlife conservation in their management prescriptions for forest areas. To help determine the habitat requirements of the Southern Flying Squirrel, we undertook an intensive search for nest sites in Backus Woods in the summer of 1986. Backus was selected as a study site because it is large and probably contains the nearest-to-natural ecological conditions of any Carolinian forest. The forest is also demarcated with permanent stakes that facilitate identification of survey plots. A vegetation survey has been prepared based on the grid system, the combination of which creates an excellent research resource for floral and faunal studies.

We surveyed 50 transects, 15 metres wide, in an east-west direction across Backus Woods in early summer, and in mid-summer surveyed 50 adjoining transects 20 metres in width, adjoining the first. Approximately 180 ha were sampled in total. Within the transects we noted the abundance and characteristics of all dead stems and took specific measurements on all dead stems with visible cavities. Approximately 200 trees with cavities were identified, of which 42 had squirrels (20%). This seems to be an inordinately high occupancy rate, especially considering that there appeared to be substantial differences in success between observers in detecting flying squirrels in the stems. This can be explained in part by the possibility that we observed the same squirrel using different trees. No squirrels were marked, so our extended observation period could easily have resulted in this "double detection".

Our rudimentary but rapid technique for locating and rousting squirrels from nest sites involved rapping the stem, usually with an open palm, such that a tremor was sent up the stem. Squirrels would appear at cavity entrances and would occasionally leap out to an adjacent tree. We could not determine the exact number of squirrels in many stems, as there was often no way of knowing whether more squirrels remained in the cavity after one squirrel emerged.

Our information, therefore, elucidates dead stem use primarily, rather than occupancy rate *per se* or population density. Interestingly, if we tabulate our observations on a per-area basis, we arrive at a very low density (54 squirrels in 180 ha = 0.5 squirrels/ha), far lower than any reported in the literature. This may indicate that we did not observe a substantial portion of the population. Bendel and Gates (1987) recently determined that in Maryland, cavities in live trees provided more den sites for Southern Flying Squirrels than dead stems.

The average height of dead stems used in Backus Woods was 8.5 metres, but ranged from three to 14.6 metres. Average diameter at breast height was 29.7 centimetres and ranged from 14.1 to 62.4 centimetres. One half of the nests located were in relatively fresh woodpecker holes, the remainder appeared in natural cavities or in older woodpecker holes that had deteriorated or had been enlarged. Interestingly, one of the most consistent of the parameters measured was the height of the cavities in which squirrels were found (ca. seven metres), which may reflect hole height preference of woodpeckers.

Tree species were used as follows: Silver Maple (33% of observations), Yellow Birch (16.7%), White Pine (13.3%), oak (13.3%), Largetooth Aspen (13.3%), and others (10%). Figure 2 shows dead stem use both in Backus and the remainder of southern Ontario. In general, the species and characteristics of the stems favoured by the squirrels appeared related to their availability, but this requires further analysis of data on unused dead stems.

The average number of squirrels per tree increased with tree size, which may be due to larger cavity size. More juveniles were discovered in the larger stems as well, suggesting that females may choose to defend larger stems as nesting sites. Larger trees, as was mentioned earlier, may support the winter aggregations that are crucial to the survival of these squirrels.

Fifty percent of the trees used were located within flooded swamps, that is with water abutting the stem. It may be that these locations provide some protection from predators (e.g. raccoons) that may climb trees and ambush squirrels in cavities.

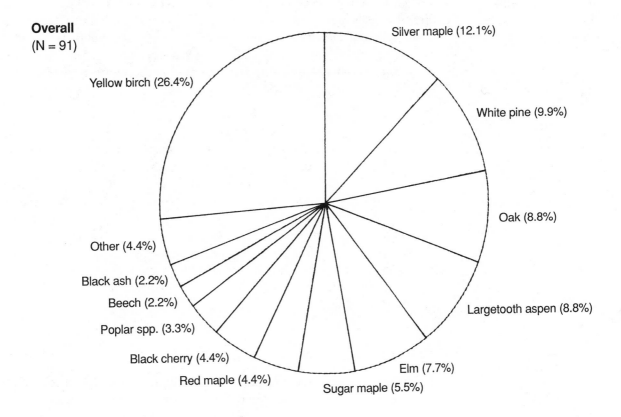

Overall
(N = 91)

Silver maple (12.1%)

White pine (9.9%)

Oak (8.8%)

Largetooth aspen (8.8%)

Elm (7.7%)

Sugar maple (5.5%)

Red maple (4.4%)

Black cherry (4.4%)

Poplar spp. (3.3%)

Beech (2.2%)

Black ash (2.2%)

Other (4.4%)

Yellow birch (26.4%)

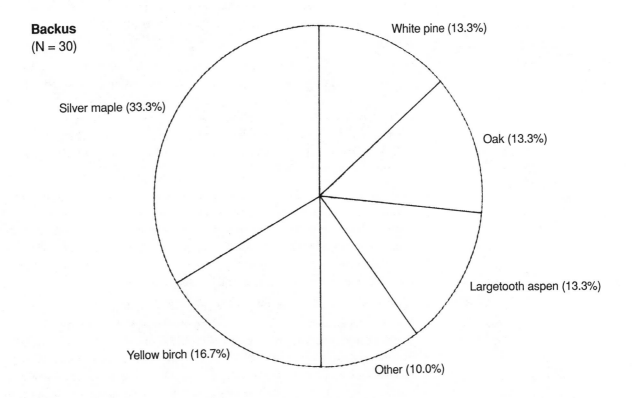

Backus
(N = 30)

White pine (13.3%)

Oak (13.3%)

Largetooth aspen (13.3%)

Other (10.0%)

Yellow birch (16.7%)

Silver maple (33.3%)

Figure 2: Dead Stem Use by Southern Flying Squirrel in Ontario (1985-1986).
Source: Stabb 1987.

We undertook incidental trips to areas outside of Backus to examine dead stem use outside of a "protected" area. We found that girdled trees with broken tops, especially Yellow Birch, provided many nest sites for Southern Flying Squirrels in managed forests. We found as well that squirrels could live in close proximity to clearcuts, if mature trees and cavity-nest sites were available.

Discussion

These data are in a preliminary state of analysis, and as such generate more questions than answers to particular management problems. With further scrutiny more specific management prescriptions may arise.

At this time, though, we can say that Southern Flying Squirrels appeared less selective than expected in their choice of dead stems. The squirrels used dead stems with a wide variety of sizes, locations, and decay characteristics. Dead stems with broken tops in the 20 to 30 centimetre diameter range seem ideal for Southern Flying Squirrels. Larger stems are presumably more desirable for actual nest sites, although an undetermined number of lesser sites are required to support a local squirrel population.

Conservation Recommendations

1. Research priorities for Southern Flying Squirrel conservation include: the identification of wintering areas and preferred wintering trees; a comparative evaluation of flying squirrel survey techniques; studies of re-introduction potential; and, dispersal habits and capabilities. As well, the habitat and distribution of the species still needs to be more completely identified in Ontario, including the Carolinian zone.

2. Many dead stems with cavities are required for the survival of healthy Southern Flying Squirrel populations in a given stand. Retention of wolf trees, long recognized as a valuable wildlife management objective, is especially important if they provide winter aggregation sites for flying squirrels. Flying squirrels will often reveal their presence by leaping from a tree that is in the process of being cut. Such trees could be harvested after the coldest part of winter, or, ideally, should be retained indefinitely.

3. "Soft snags" are used extensively by woodpeckers and Southern Flying Squirrels. These stems are characteristically broken-topped, branchless, shaky, and soft enough to allow easy penetration by a sharp object. Leaving these stems standing in managed forests may accommodate a portion of the squirrel population, and other members of the cavity-nesting community, at little loss to the firewood or timber value of the forest stand.

4. Habitat management guidelines for cavity-nesting birds have been prepared for the Ontario Ministry of Natural Resources (James 1984), the implementation of which would go a long way to ensuring the squirrels (both northern and southern species) are maintained within managed forests. Management that accommodates smaller cavity-nesters such as the Downy Woodpecker, would be particularly valuable for *Glaucomys volans*. James suggests that six large and perhaps a dozen small snags per hectare be left standing in managed forests to conserve cavity-nesters. Another approach would be to maintain small blocks of unmanaged forest within managed woodlots.

5. Nest boxes are readily used by Southern Flying Squirrels, and are a valuable means of assisting the species to recover from a loss or lack of available natural cavities. Figure 3 shows a successful design employed in the United States (Sonenshine *et al.* 1973) to capture and monitor *G. volans*. Small holes are preferable (e.g. 3.1 to 4.3 cm) due to competition for cavities with other squirrels and cavity-nesting birds. In areas where Gray Squirrels are abundant, metal plates, i.e. excluders, can be placed around nest box entrances to ensure the holes cannot be enlarged by competitors. We suggest placing the boxes about seven metres above the ground, in areas where natural cavities are (or are expected to be) few, so as to maximize effectiveness of the artificial structures.

6. Finally, reintroductions should be attempted to return the squirrels to areas where they have been extirpated. This may only be feasible or necessary in places such as Point Pelee National Park, where reintroduction attempts can be conducted with the appropriate habitat assessment, handling techniques, monitoring, and management practice.

Acknowledgements

This paper is contribution #3 of a cooperative project funded by World Wildlife Fund (Canada), Ontario Ministry of Natural Resources, Natural Sciences and Engineering Research Council of Canada, University of Toronto's Faculty of Forestry, Canadian Wildlife Service, and Canadian Wildlife Foundation. The authors would like to thank T. Kurvits, A. Jaramillo, M. Gartshore, and dozens of other individuals who contributed information to this study.

References

Banfield, A.W.F. 1974. *The Mammals of Canada.* Univ. of Toronto Press. 438 pp.

Bendel, P.R. and J.E. Gates. 1987. Home range and microhabitat partitioning of the southern flying squirrel (*Glaucomys volans*). *J. Mammal.* 68:243-255.

Doby, W.J. 1984. *Resource base as a determinant of abundance in the southern flying squirrel* (Glaucomys volans). Unpubl. Ph.D. dissertation. Wake Forest University, Winston-Salem, North Carolina.

Hamilton, W.J. and J.O. Whitaker, Jr. 1979. *Mammals of the Eastern United States.* 2nd Ed. Cornell Univ. Press, London. 346 pp.

James, R. D. 1984. *Habitat management guidelines for cavity-nesting birds in Ontario.* Unpubl. report to Ontario Ministry of Natural Resources, Wildlife Branch, Toronto. 51pp.

Sonenshine, D.E., D.G. Cerretani, G. Enlow and B.L. Elisberg. 1973. Improved methods for capturing wild flying squirrels. *J. Wildl. Manage.* 37:588-590.

Stabb, M. 1987. *The status of the southern flying squirrel* (Glaucomys volans) *in Canada.* Unpubl. report to Ontario Ministry of Natural Resources, Wildlife Branch, Toronto. 83pp.

Thomas, R.B. 1986. *Dynamic optimization in the southern flying squirrel* Glaucomys volans. M. Sc. thesis. Wake Forest University, Winston-Salem, North Carolina.

VanVoorhees, D.A. 1976. *Feeding energetics and winter survival in the southern flying squirrel,* Glaucomys volans. M.A. thesis, Wake Forest University, Winston-Salem, North Carolina.

Weigl, P. D. 1978. Resource overlap, interspecific interactions and the distribution of the flying squirrels, *Glaucomys volans* and *Glaucomys sabrinus. Am. Midl. Nat.* 100:83-96.

Reptiles, Amphibians and Invertebrates

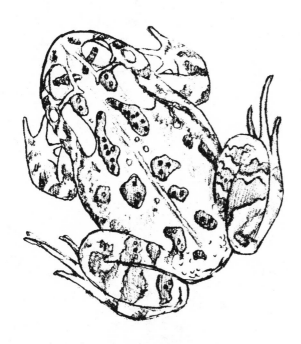

The Fowler's Toad is restricted in Canada to a few sites on the north shore of Lake Erie. Its breeding calls, reminiscent of the short wail of a baby, can be heard in May from the beaches of Rondeau, Long Point, and Point Abino.
Artist – E.B.S. Logier (from a preliminary sketch circa 1950).

Ontario Herpetofaunal Summary

Michael J. Oldham

Ontario Ministry of Natural Resources
Aylmer District Office
353 Talbot Street West
Aylmer, Ontario N5H 2S8

Abstract. *The Ontario Herpetofaunal Summary is a volunteer project to collect and disseminate information on the distribution, abundance, and ecology of the province's amphibians and reptiles. This paper outlines the history, objectives, and results of the project. Updated information and distribution maps are presented for eight largely Carolinian species: Fowler's Toad, Blanchard's Cricket Frog, Eastern Spiny Softshell, Butler's Garter Snake, Lake Erie Water Snake, Queen Snake, Eastern Fox Snake, and Blue Racer. Conservation recommendations for Ontario amphibians and reptiles are provided.*

History and Background

The Ontario Herpetofaunal Summary (OHS) began in 1984 on an informal basis. Letters were sent to potentially interested individuals asking them to record amphibian and reptile sightings for the year and submit them to the organizers, Michael J. Oldham and Donald A. Sutherland. At the end of the year over 100 individuals had contributed 2,696 records. Response to the initial letters was far greater than expected, and the project soon grew beyond the capabilities of two individuals working in their spare time. In order to help cover printing, mailing, and other costs, a grant through the Carolinian Canada program was applied for and received. These records were summarized and mapped in the *1984 Ontario Herpetofaunal Summary* (Oldham and Sutherland 1986).

In its second year, the OHS continued to grow. The 1985 report (Oldham 1988) summarized 4,648 records submitted by over 300 contributors. The number of records also increased in 1986 (6,136 records; Weller and Oldham 1988, Oldham and Weller 1989) and 1987 (9,156 records).

Objectives

The OHS is modelled after the highly successful *Atlas of the Breeding Birds of Ontario* (Cadman *et al.* 1987), with additional ideas from the Toronto Entomological Association's annual summaries of Lepidoptera sightings in Ontario, and the seasonal bird summaries in *American Birds*. Major objectives of the OHS are:

1. To gather and publish distributional data on Ontario amphibians and reptiles. The distribution of many species is still very poorly known, particularly in the north. Some species are secretive and hard to find, even if they may be relatively common and widespread (eg. Four-toed Salamander and Stinkpot).

2. To gather and publish ecological data such as dates of entry into and emergence from hibernation, calling dates for frogs and toads, egg-laying dates, incubation periods, larval periods, habitat preferences, etc.. Much of this type of information is poorly known for populations near their northern range limits (such as

3. To provide baseline data on distribution and abundance for future studies.
4. To monitor the status of rare or endangered species.
5. To increase public awareness and disseminate information on these often maligned and misunderstood animals.

How It Works

In order to contribute records to the OHS, observers are asked to record the details of their sightings on printed sightings cards (Figure 1). Completed cards are returned to the compilers, where the data are entered into a computer file and the records mapped by UTM grid to a resolution of 10 km. Data are stored in a dBASE file, and contributors with an IBM compatible computer can enter data directly into this file. Since the records are computerized, it is relatively easy to extract lists by date, county, atlas square, species, observer, etc. At the conclusion of each year, an annual summary is written which summarizes and maps the year's records. The most recent annual report (1986) includes computer-generated maps and graphs of seasonal occurrence, as well as a written summary of distribution and noteworthy observations. These annual reports are sold to contributors and other interested individuals, with the proceeds going towards printing cards and future annual summaries. Starting with the 1985 annual report, species accounts have been authored by a variety of different individuals. For example, in 1985, the 46 species accounts were written by 20 different authors. Long-term plans call for a 7-year summary report (1984-1990) which will incorporate pre-OHS literature, museum, and other records. Following this report, periodic up-dates will be produced as time and funding permit. At the conclusion of the OHS project, all records will be deposited at the Herpetology Section of the National Museum of Natural Sciences in Ottawa.

Figure 1

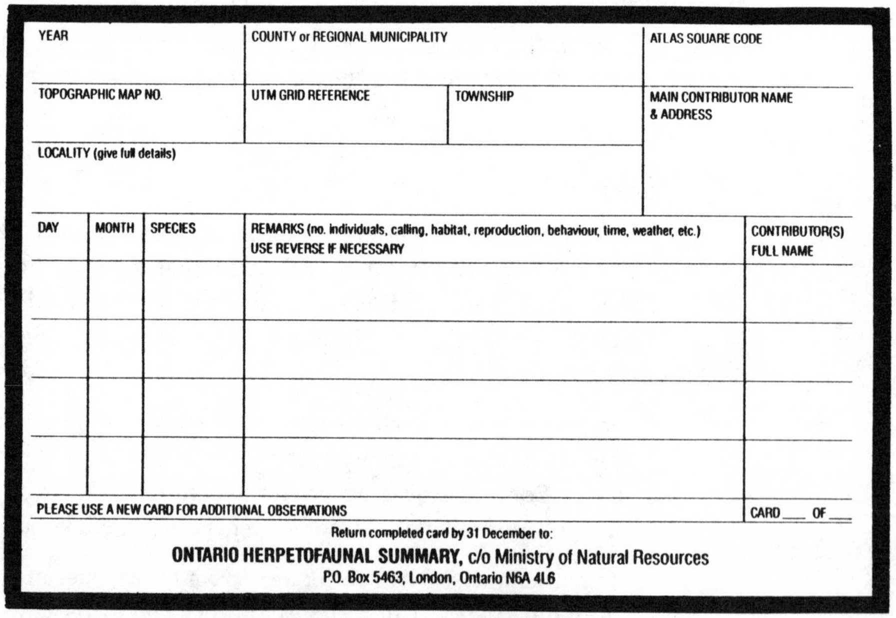
YEAR | COUNTY or REGIONAL MUNICIPALITY | ATLAS SQUARE CODE

TOPOGRAPHIC MAP NO. | UTM GRID REFERENCE | TOWNSHIP | MAIN CONTRIBUTOR NAME & ADDRESS

LOCALITY (give full details)

DAY	MONTH	SPECIES	REMARKS (no. individuals, calling, habitat, reproduction, behaviour, time, weather, etc.) USE REVERSE IF NECESSARY	CONTRIBUTOR(S) FULL NAME

PLEASE USE A NEW CARD FOR ADDITIONAL OBSERVATIONS | CARD ___ OF ___

Return completed card by 31 December to:

ONTARIO HERPETOFAUNAL SUMMARY, c/o Ministry of Natural Resources

P.O. Box 5463, London, Ontario N6A 4L6

OHS SIGHTINGS CARD

Table 1

1984-1988 OHS Species Total

	1984	1985	1986	1987	1988	Total
Mudpuppy	7	15	26	27	18	93
Red-spotted Newt	30	57	72	108	122	389
Central Newt	0	0	1	0	0	1
Jefferson Salamander	2	3	4	0	0	9
Blue-spotted Salamander	3	3	6	0	3	15
Jefferson Complex hybrids	9	20	25	0	2	56
Jefferson Complex undet.	59	95	136	133	101	524
Yellow-Spotted Salamander	25	65	47	49	39	225
Two-lined Salamander	15	8	11	8	15	57
Four-toed Salamander	4	7	25	14	9	59
Redback Salamander	92	167	200	243	267	969
American Toad	157	299	542	758	897	2653
Fowler's Toad	16	25	30	22	9	102
Spring Peeper	161	306	432	812	1203	2914
Gray Treefrog	65	126	250	330	596	1367
Midland Chorus Frog	84	163	192	334	298	1071
Boreal Chorus Frog	3	2	2	5	3	15
Cricket Frog	3	0	0	1	0	4
Wood Frog	146	307	304	364	358	1479
Leopard Frog	217	375	564	915	918	2989
Pickerel Frog	21	28	30	25	26	130
Green Frog	211	352	532	858	696	2649
Mink Frog	66	40	69	66	54	295
Bullfrog	108	148	236	333	279	1104
Snapping Turtle	92	110	311	459	328	1300
Stinkpot	7	2	3	9	27	48
Midland Painted Turtle	165	312	442	813	823	2555
Western Painted Turtle	4	9	4	4	3	24
Red-eared Slider	1	0	2	2	3	8
Map Turtle	35	48	75	115	69	342
Blanding's Turtle	73	204	143	131	141	692
Wood Turtle	2	2	8	63	98	173
Spotted Turtle	44	61	50	34	30	219
Box Turtle	1	3	3	2	5	14
Softshell Turtle	18	25	20	31	27	121
Five-lined Skink	19	31	39	58	50	197
Eastern Garter Snake	220	448	511	923	667	2769
Red-sided Garter Snake	1	2	0	0	0	3
Ribbon Snake	14	33	22	52	37	158
Butler's Garter Snake	16	14	28	11	3	72
Northern Water Snake	69	86	136	213	186	690
Lake Erie Water Snake	10	24	21	15	36	106
Queen Snake	2	3	7	6	5	23
Redbelly Snake	37	50	88	136	97	408
Brown Snake	53	94	116	182	111	556
Smooth Green Snake	28	53	43	69	75	268
Ringneck Snake	5	12	19	26	19	81
Hognose Snake	19	52	49	40	35	195
Rat Snake	16	78	48	76	12	230
Fox Snake	57	112	125	104	70	468
Milk Snake	44	64	72	120	83	383
Blue Racer	7	5	4	3	19	38
Massasauga	133	100	79	54	30	396
TOTAL	2696	4648	6204	9156	9002	31706

Results

As of January 1989, over 31,000 records of 52 species and subspecies of Ontario amphibians and reptiles had been received by the OHS (Table 1); over 15,000 records have been computerized. Over 1,700 participants have contributed to the project. Two regional amphibian and reptile atlas projects have begun, one in Northumberland County coordinated by John McLaughlin, the other in the Hamilton area coordinated by Bill Lamond and Christine Bishop. Three other ongoing projects are contributing data to the OHS: the Toronto Amphibian and Reptile Survey coordinated by Bob Johnson, the Bruce County Herpetofaunal Atlas coordinated by Martin Parker, and the Muskoka Herpetofaunal Atlas coordinated by Bob Bowles. Coverage of southern Ontario has been quite extensive to date and most ten km squares have received at least some field investigation (Figure 2). Coverage has been particularly good in the Carolinian Zone, largely due to Carolinian Canada supported projects such as the Haldimand-Norfolk Natural Areas Inventory (over 2,000 records over two years; Gartshore et al. 1987), the Kent-Elgin Environmentally Significant Areas study, and the Walpole Island Natural Areas Inventory. Coverage in northern Ontario has not been as extensive (Figure 3), with several hundred records received.

Our knowledge of certain rare species largely restricted to the Carolinian Zone has increased since the OHS began:

1. Fowler's Toad *(Bufo fowleri)* – About 100 records between 1984 and 1988, largely from areas of known occurrence in Kent (Rondeau Provincial Park and area), Elgin (Iroquois Beach Provincial Park), Haldimand-Norfolk, and Niagara. Several new sites have been documented by Gartshore et al. (1987) in Haldimand-Norfolk, and Tim Seburn has reported healthy populations in Niagara. No evidence has been found for the continued presence of this species in Essex County, where it is known from historic records (Green 1985). Reported from a total of 20 atlas squares (Figure 4).

2. Blanchard's Cricket Frog *(Acris crepitans blanchardi)* – Only four records from a single atlas square have been reported to the OHS (Figure 5). Oldham and Campbell (1987) have documented a dramatic decline of this species on Pelee Island, and recommend it for endangered status in Canada and Ontario.

3. Eastern Spiny Softshell *(Trionyx spiniferus spiniferus)* – One hundred and twenty-one records of this highly aquatic turtle have come from 28 southern Ontario atlas squares (Figure 6). As suggested by Campbell and Donaldson (1980), Spiny Softshells are largely restricted to Lake Erie (particularly Long Point and Rondeau) and the Thames and Sydenham River systems. A 1986 record from the Ottawa River at Westmeath is of particular significance, since there are very few records from this part of the province. A 1988 report from the Ausable River is also significant since it is the first reliable report from the Lake Huron drainage basin in Ontario.

4. Butler's Garter Snake *(Thamnophis butleri)* – Most of the 72 records of this species have come from the Windsor and Walpole Island areas, where it is locally common. Other reports are from Amherstburg, the south shore of Lake St. Clair, along the St. Clair River to Sarnia, and apparently disjunct populations at Skunk's Misery and Luther Marsh. Records for 15 atlas squares have been reported to the OHS (Figure 7).

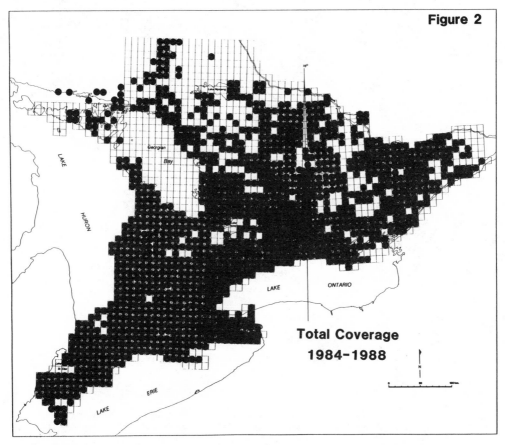

Figure 2

Total Coverage
1984-1988

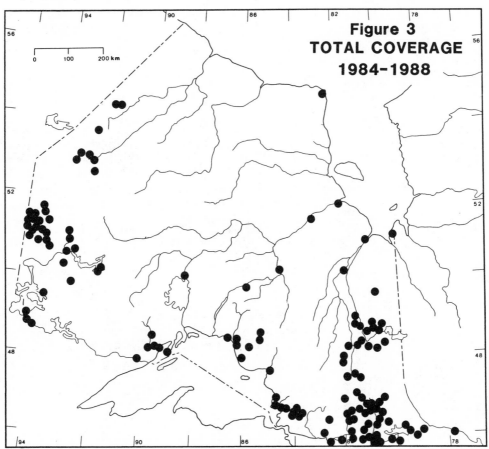

Figure 3
TOTAL COVERAGE
1984-1988

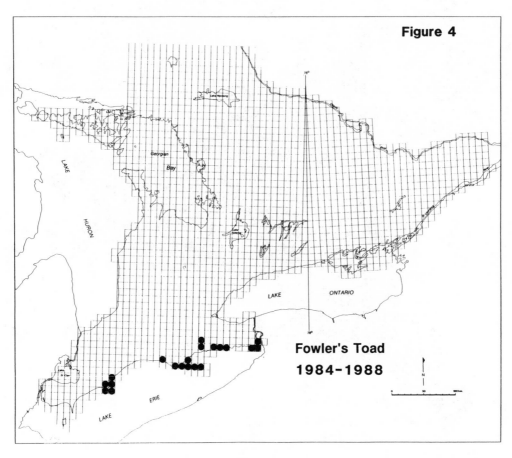

Figure 4

Fowler's Toad
1984-1988

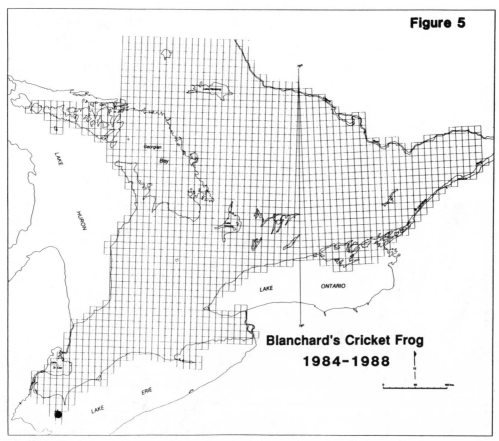

Figure 5

Blanchard's Cricket Frog
1984-1988

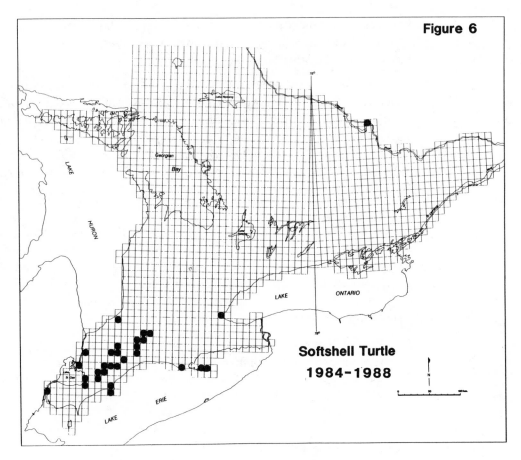

Figure 6

Softshell Turtle
1984-1988

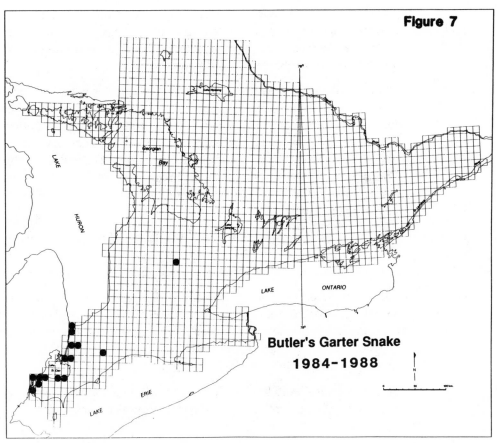

Figure 7

Butler's Garter Snake
1984-1988

5. Lake Erie Water Snake *(Nerodia sipedon insularum)* – This endangered subspecies of water snake has been reported 106 times, from seven atlas squares covering the western Lake Erie islands (Figure 8).

6. Queen Snake *(Regina septemvittata)* – Twenty-three records of this secretive water snake have been reported to the OHS, from 12 atlas squares (Figure 9). Sightings have come from the Canard River, Maitland River, Ausable River, Thames River, Grand River, Nanticoke Creek, Whiteman's Creek, and Walpole Island. Although very rare in Ontario, this snake can be locally common, as indicated by sightings of eleven Queen Snakes on the Ausable River in August 1988, and 12 basking on branches of a cedar tree along Whiteman's Creek in October 1986.

7. Eastern Fox Snake *(Elaphe vulpina gloydi)* – Because this species is locally common at relatively well studied sites such as Long Point, Point Pelee, Pelee Island, and Walpole Island, over 468 records have been received by the OHS. Fox Snakes are most common around the western end of Lake Erie, the Lake St. Clair area, Long Point, and southern Georgian Bay. Sixty-six atlas squares have records since 1984 (Figure 10).

8. Blue Racer *(Coluber constrictor foxi)* – Thirty-eight Blue Racer sightings have been reported to the OHS, all from two Pelee Island atlas squares (Figure 11). This species is protected in Ontario by the Endangered Species Act, but unfortunately about half of the records reported to the OHS are found dead on roads.

Conservation Recommendations

1. The Ontario Herpetofaunal Summary and Ontario Breeding Bird Atlas have done the background work and set up an observer network for atlas projects in Ontario. Sufficient funding and sponsoring agencies are needed to expand the atlassing effort to other faunal and floral groups.

2. Ontario desperately needs a Conservation Data Centre where computerized records and detailed mapping of rare species and vegetation community in formation can be gathered and stored. At the present this type of information is being assembled by a wide variety of individuals and agencies, with little standardization and exchange of information. In many US states, the Nature Conservancy has set up State Heritage Programs to oversee the gathering, storage, and dissemination of this type of information; such a system should be instituted in Canada also.

3. Natural area surveys are needed for several parts of the Carolinian Zone (and elsewhere in the province), for example Niagara Region. The Haldimand-Norfolk Natural Areas Inventory would be an excellent model to follow.

4. Periodic monitoring of rare species localities is needed. For example, a decade ago Blanchard's Cricket Frogs were common and widespread on Pelee Island, now they are very rare and restricted to a single site. A more active monitoring program might have detected this decline earlier, and created the opportunity to study it and possibly reverse it.

5. Several species should be considered for addition to Ontario's Endangered Species Act (Blanchard's Cricket Frog is a prime example).

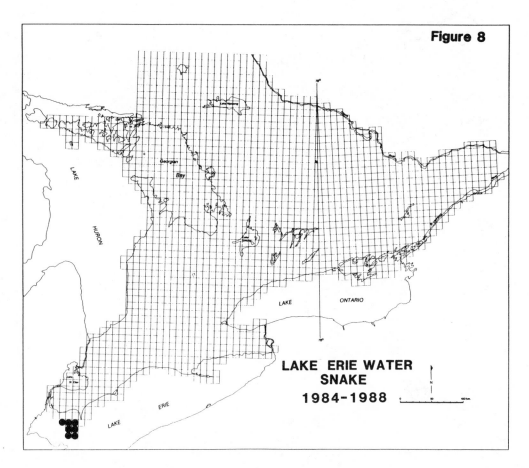

Figure 8

LAKE ERIE WATER
SNAKE
1984-1988

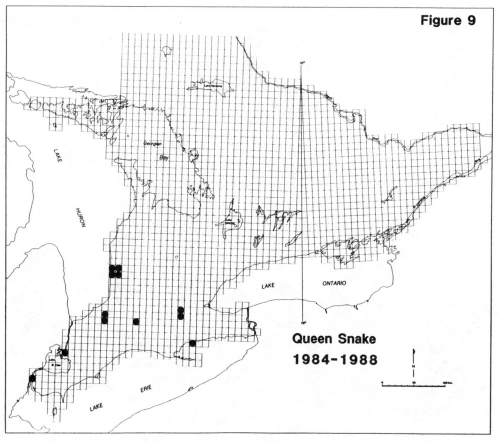

Figure 9

Queen Snake
1984-1988

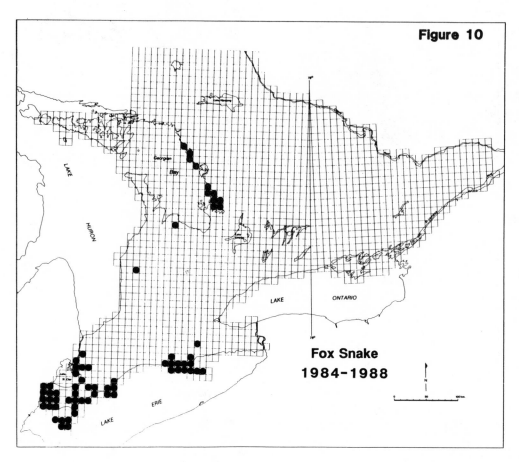

Figure 10

Fox Snake
1984-1988

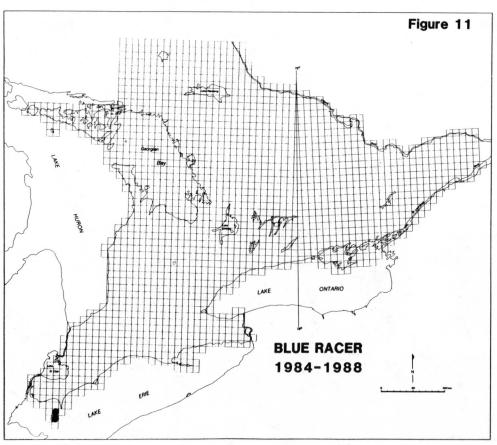

Figure 11

BLUE RACER
1984-1988

6. Updated COSEWIC reports are needed for a number of rare amphibian and reptile species, such as the Queen Snake, Fox Snake, and Black Rat Snake. These reports should utilize recent data gathered by the Ontario Herpetofaunal Summary.

7. The possibility of captive breeding and/or reintroduction should be considered for several rare species such as the Blue Racer, Black Rat Snake, and Blanchard's Cricket Frog.

8. Increased emphasis on amphibians and reptiles in interpretive activities would help improve their public image.

Acknowledgements

Funding and support for the Ontario Herpetofaunal Summary have come from the World Wildlife Fund, Essex Region Conservation Authority, Ontario Ministry of Natural Resources, and Canadian Amphibian and Reptile Conservation Society. The author is a member of a small Ontario Herpetofaunal Summary working group, and the responsibilities undertaken by the other members, Wayne Weller, Martyn Obbard, Donald Sutherland, Peter Carson, and Mary Gartshore, is much appreciated. Many others have assisted in various ways, including Gary Allen, Mireille Delisle-Oldham, Diane Hansen, Sue House, James Kamstra, Cynthia Kember, Bill Lamond, Sharlene McGugan, Linda Nuttall, Martha Orlocci, Paul Pratt, Christy Slasor, and Phil Taylor. The OHS would not be possible of course were it not for the 1,700 plus participants. The comments of Gary Allen, Phil Taylor, and Donald Sutherland helped improve this paper.

References

Cadman, M.D., P.F.J. Eagles, and F.W. Helleiner. 1987. *Atlas of the Breeding Birds of Ontario*. University of Waterloo Press, Waterloo. 617 pp.

Campbell, C.A. and G.R. Donaldson. 1980. *A status report for the Eastern Spiny Softshell Turtle* (Trionyx spiniferus spiniferus) *in Canada*. Edited and revised in 1985 by M.E. Obbard. Unpublished report, Ontario Ministry of Natural Resources, Toronto. 50 pp.

Gartshore, M.E., D.A. Sutherland, and J.D. McCracken. 1987. *The Natural Areas Inventory of the Regional Municipality of Haldimand-Norfolk*. 2 volumes. Norfolk Field Naturalists, Simcoe.

Green, D.M. 1985. *The status of* Bufo fowleri *(Fowler's Toad) in Canada*. Report to the Committee on the Status of Endangered Wildlife in Canada, Ottawa. 31 pp.

Oldham, M.J., ed. 1988. *Ontario Herpetofaunal Summary 1985*. World Wildlife Fund, Ontario Ministry of Natural Resources, Essex Region Conservation Authority. London. 206 pp.

Oldham, M.J. and C.A. Campbell. 1987. *The status of Blanchard's Cricket Frog* (Acris crepitans blanchardi) *in Canada*. Report to the Committee on the Status of Endangered Wildlife in Canada, Ottawa.

Oldham, M.J. and D.A. Sutherland. 1986. *Ontario Herpetofaunal Summary 1984*. World Wildlife Fund and Essex Region Conservation Authority. Essex. 214 pp.

Oldham, M.J. and W.F. Weller. 1989. *Ontario Herpetofaunal Summary 1986, Technical Supplement*. Ontario Field Herpetologists. 197 pp.

Weller, W.F. and M.J. Oldham, eds. 1989. *Ontario Herpetofaunal Summary 1986*. Ontario Field Herpetologists. 221 pp.

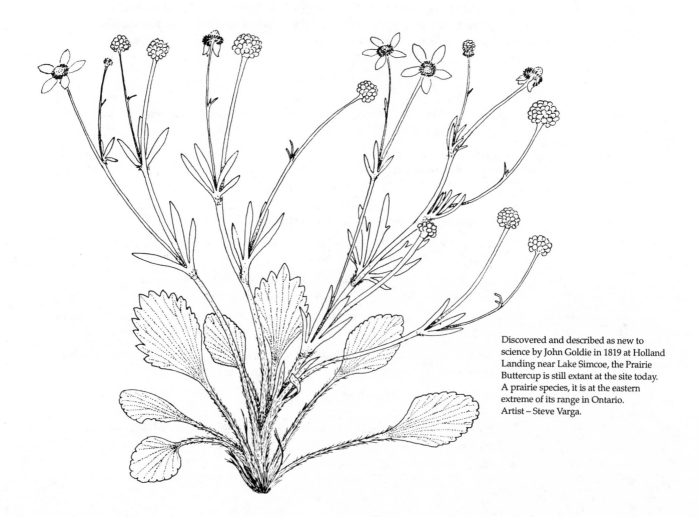

Discovered and described as new to
science by John Goldie in 1819 at Holland
Landing near Lake Simcoe, the Prairie
Buttercup is still extant at the site today.
A prairie species, it is at the eastern
extreme of its range in Ontario.
Artist – Steve Varga.

Status, Distribution and Life History Characteristics of Some Butterflies at Risk in the Carolinian Forest Zone of Ontario

C.A. Campbell

294 Albert St., Waterloo, Ontario N2L 3T8

D.P. Coulson

Ontario Ministry of Natural Resources
P.O. Box 2186, Cambridge, Ontario N3C 2W1

A.A. Bryant

P.O. Box 553
Okanagan Falls, British Columbia V0H 1R0

Abstract. *The status of 63 taxa of butterflies within the Carolinian forest zone of Ontario was assessed during 1981-1982. A total of 22 was considered to be either extirpated, endangered, threatened, or vulnerable. For each of these a synopsis of life history, distribution, general ecology, status, and conservation recommendations is provided. Nine species were determined to be non-resident but were assigned to a watch list to monitor for evidence of breeding. The remaining 32 species were deemed to be under no threat at present.*

Introduction

Butterflies are an integral part of many natural ecosystems, yet their conservation has received relatively little popular or legal support in North America (Opler and Krizek 1984). We suggest that this is largely because relatively few data are available on the distribution, abundance or breeding status of native butterflies. As a step towards rectifying this situation, we assessed the status of 63 taxa of butterflies within the Carolinian forest zone of Ontario.

The present study was derived from a survey of abiotic and biotic features of the Great Lakes Canadian coastal areas done by Campbell *et al.* (1981) for the Nature Conservancy of Canada, and contained a preliminary list of possible rare butterflies. Further impetus for the study came from the earliest conceptions of the Carolinian Canada Program, the multi-agency strategy developed by the World Wildlife Fund to research the biota of the Carolinian Zone of Canada with a view to protecting those representative and specialized habitats most threatened with development. The purpose of our work was to provide one piece of this Carolinian conservation strategy and compile a preliminary report on the status of the most threatened butterflies in the Carolinian Zone of southern Ontario with recommendations for their conservation.

Methods

1. Study Area

The area covered was the Upper Austral Life Zone in Ontario, for butterflies east of the Great Plains as defined by Opler and Krizek (1984), but herein referred to as the Carolinian Life Zone (Eagles and Beechey 1985). All counties or regional municipalities along the lower Great Lakes shorelines were included, as well as inland counties and regions having a portion of the Carolinian Life Zone within them. Our limits for the Carolinian Zone corresponded quite closely with those prescribed by Hosie (1973) for the Deciduous Forest Region, with a slight extension eastward and northward to the end of Lake Ontario (Figure 1). Our study area encompassed the following counties and regional municipalities: Essex, Lambton, Kent, Elgin, Middlesex, Haldimand-Norfolk, Brant, Hamilton-Wentworth, Oxford, Huron, Perth, Waterloo, Halton, Peel, York, Durham, Northumberland and Prince Edward. Parts of Lennox and Addington, Frontenac, and Leeds and Grenville are also included.

2. Literature, Collections and Authorities Consulted

A literature review was undertaken and a working bibliography on rare Ontario butterflies was prepared (see References). Standard works consulted were:

– Toronto Entomologists' Association (TEA) annual summaries for Ontario (1969 to 1989),
– *The Skipper Butterflies of the Province of Quebec* (Duffy and Garland 1978),
– *Checklist of the Butterflies and Skippers of Canada* (Gregory 1975).

Records were examined for: date of capture/observation, collector/observer, location, reference (number, collection), determiner, sex, brood/form, habitat, and abundance.

Major public collections of lepidoptera in southern Ontario were examined. The following public collections were examined for potentially significant species: CNC (Canadian National Collection), ROM (Royal Ontario Museum), OAC (University of Guelph), HAM (McMaster University), WAT (University of Waterloo, including the Lanktree Collection), WLU (Wilfrid Laurier University), and UWO (University of Western Ontario). The following private collections were searched: K. Stricker (Kitchener), C.A. Campbell (including the Millman Collection) (Waterloo), L.E. Lamb (Kitchener), A. Wormington (Leamington), A. Macnaughton (Kitchener), and D.P. Coulson (Guelph).

Lastly, an effort was made to contact many amateur and professional entomologists to solicit their records, advice, and impressions about specific butterflies.

3. Field Study Methods

At all localities visited we attempted to determine whether individuals were residents or simply strays by noting such factors as: the presence and distribution of the host plant(s), suitable habitat, number of individuals observed, condition of specimens (i.e. fresh *vs.* worn), how the flight capture date compared with the optimum for the species, food preferences, behaviour of adults including such typical functions as perching and patrolling, as well as ovipositing in some cases. These field visits also served to: supplement the TEA summaries, verify occurrence of reported taxa, permit photographs and/or collections of specimens, and attempt to more accurately document the distribution of the taxa. Several hours to several days were spent at the survey sites in optimal periods of butterfly activity.

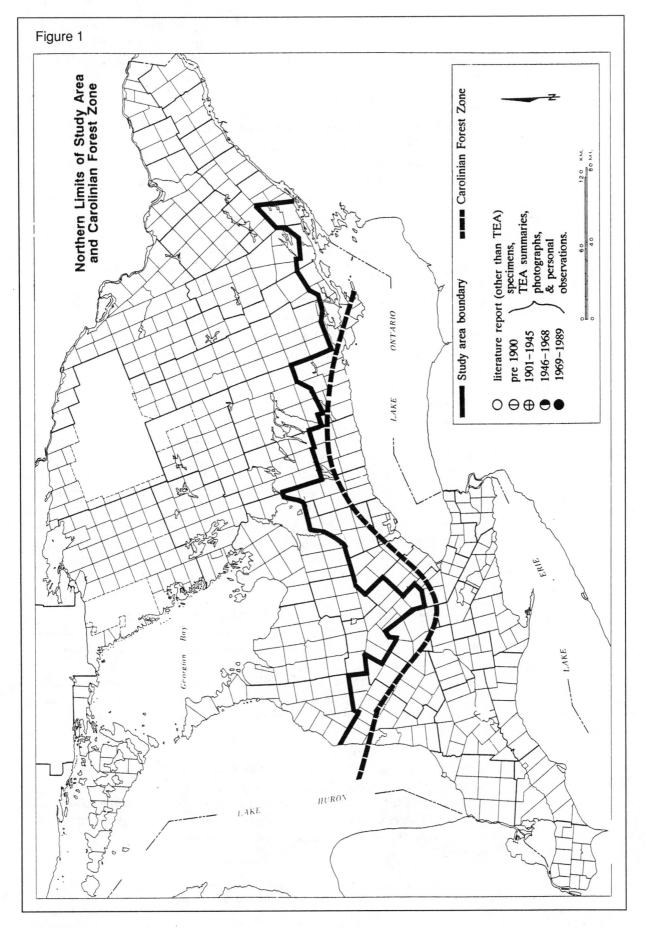

Figure 1

Northern Limits of Study Area
and Carolinian Forest Zone

— Study area boundary

■■■ Carolinian Forest Zone

literature report (other than TEA)

○ pre 1900
⊖ 1901–1945   specimens,
⊕ 1946–1968   TEA summaries,
◐ 1969–1989   photographs,
●   & personal
                    observations.

120 KM.
80 MI.
60
40
0

N

LAKE ONTARIO

LAKE ERIE

Georgian Bay

LAKE HURON

Some specimens were collected and will be deposited by Campbell in the entomology collection, University of Guelph, Ontario. Slides and field notes of rare species which were photographed only or described *in situ* are currently held by Campbell.

4. Field Study Sites

Only a relatively small number of field sites, deemed to be of greatest biogeographical significance, were visited during the two available field seasons of 1981 and 1982. Taxa on our working list were entered on cards by locality and flight dates, to assist in selecting sites to visit. These were (from west to east): Windsor Prairie, Kingsville area, Point Pelee, Pelee Island, Squirrel Island, Walpole Island, St. Clair National Wildlife Area, Mitchell's Bay, Thamesville Moor, Kettle Point Road, Ipperwash Military Reserve, Ipperwash Provincial Park, Port Franks, Pinery Provincial Park, Grand Bend, Highway 21 roadside sites, Port Bruce, Straffordville, Southwold area, Fingal airport, Vienna (Pawpaw stands), Iroquois Beach, Port Burwell, Port Royal, Charlotteville, Clear Creek, Houghton sandhills, Fisher's Glen, Spooky Hollow, Big Creek Marsh, Long Point, Turkey Point, Port Rowan, St. Williams, Camp Ryerson sand plain, southern Waterloo Region, Brant County area, Wainfleet Bog, Point Abino, Oshawa Second Marsh, Shannonville area, Salmon River, and Prince Edward County. Unfortunately Rondeau Provincial Park was not field or museum-searched.

5. Coverage and Mapping for Species

Sites were mapped with separate symbols if their centres were greater than 16 km (10 mi) apart; otherwise the scale of mapping (1:4,500,000) constrained us to one symbol to represent one or more sites.

On the maps, an open circle (○) represents a report in the literature other than TEA; a divided open circle (◑), a pre-1900 record[1]; a circle containing a cross (⊕), a record from 1900 to 1945 inclusive; a half-shaded circle (◑), a record from 1946 to 1968 (the post-pesticide era); and a solid circle (●), specimens or TEA summaries 1969 to 1988. It must be emphasized that a certain lack of precision in mapping is involved in interpreting some records, particularly historical ones. It should also be noted that there is no distinction made between strays and residents in the specie's distribution maps.

Extralimital records (i.e. beyond the study area) were not mapped. Extralimital records are given in the text for Ontario only. Specimens from outside Ontario were not considered, but taxa known to occur elsewhere in Canada were noted.

Flight bars were based on dates within our study area from personal communications, specimens examined, personal observations and collections, and reports in the literature, both published and unpublished, in particular TEA summaries.

6. Taxonomy and Nomenclature

There have been a great many changes with the taxonomy of North American butterflies during the 20th century, and we have tried to include the major ones. A more complete treatment of historic and modern synonyms for the taxa dealt with in this paper is in preparation by Coulson. Where appropriate, subspecies and forms have been treated. Especially useful were several publications on butterflies

---

[1] A record is defined here as one of our field observations, a specimen or photograph seen by us, and reports accepted as valid by TEA and included in their annual summaries.

of the Great Lakes States (see Bibliography). Opler and Krizek (1984) were followed for nomenclature and Klots (1951) and Howe (1975) were sometimes used for subspecific determinations. Also consulted frequently were Ehrlich and Ehrlich (1961), Pyle (1981), Holland (1898, revised ed. 1931), Scudder (1889), and Edwards (1868-1897). Taxonomic order follows Scott (1986). Tietz (1972) and Scott (1986) were used extensively for host plants. Botanical nomenclature follows Voss, 1972, 1985 (Taxaceae to Cornaceae); and Gleason and Cronquist, 1963 (Pyrolaceae to Asteraceae).

7. Criteria for Species' Evaluations

A list of threatened butterflies and their habitats was circulated to lepidopterists as part of a research project the senior author was conducting for the Nature Conservancy of Canada in 1980 on significant natural areas on the Great Lakes shoreline of Ontario. A preliminary list of 63 taxa was compiled from these reviewers' comments (Table 1) for further consideration. Published reports, personal communications, photographs, and collections of adult specimens were accepted. The exception was historical reports where there was some uncertainty with regard to identification or nomenclature, e.g. dusky wings, and these were rejected.

Table 1

A Preliminary List of Butterflies for Further Study

I. True Butterflies – Papilionidea

PAPILIONIDAE: Swallowtails

Papilio troilus	Spicebush Swallowtail
Eurytides marcellus	Zebra Swallowtail
Papilio cresphontes	Giant Swallowtail
Battus philenor	Pipe Vine Swallowtail

PIERIDAE: Whites and Sulphurs

Eurema mexicana	Mexican Sulphur
Eurema lisa	Little Sulphur
Nathalis iole	Dainty Sulphur
Euchloe ausonides	Large Marble
Pieris virginiensis	West Virginia White
Ascia monuste	Great Southern White
Pontia protodice	Checkered White
Colias cesonia	Dog Face Butterfly
Phoebis sennae eubule	Cloudless Giant Sulphur
Phoebis philea	Orange-barred Sulphur
Abaeis nicippe	Sleepy Orange
Euchloe olympia	Olympia Marble (dune form/*rosa*)

Table 1 continued

Table 1 (continued)

NYMPHALIDAE: Brush-footed Butterflies

Satyrodes appalachia	Appalachian Eyed Brown
Coenonympha nipisiquit	Nipisiquit Ringlet
Limenitis archippus floridensis	Florida Viceroy
Junonia coenia	Buckeye
Chlosyne gorgone gorgone	Gorgone Checkerspot
Chlosyne harrisii harrisii	Harris' Checkerspot
Phycoides batesii	Tawny Crescent
Boloria selene	Silver-bordered Fritillary
Euptoieta claudia	Variegated Fritillary
Asterocampa celtis	Hackberry Butterfly
Asterocampa clyton	Tawny Emperor
Speyeria idalia	Regal Fritillary

LIBYTHEIDAE: Snout Butterflies

Libytheana b. bachmanii	Snout Butterfly

LYCAENIDAE: Hairstreaks, Coppers and Blues

Incisalia p. polios	Hoary Elfin
Incisalia augustus	Brown Elfin
Parrhasius m-album	White 'M' Hairstreak
Strymon melinus humili	Gray Hairstreak
Plebejus saepiolus amica	Greenish Blue
Incisalia irus	Frosted Elfin
Mitoura g.gryneus	Olive Hairstreak
Fixsenia o. ontario	Northern Hairstreak
Lycaeides melissa samuelis	Karner Blue

II. Skippers – Hesperioidea

HESPERIIDAE: Skippers

Oarisma garita	Garita Skipper
Hylephila phyleus	Fiery Skipper
Polites vibex	Whirlabout
Pompeius verna	Little Glassy Wing
Atalopedes campestris	Sachem
Atrytone logan	Delaware Skipper
Poanes massasoit	Mulberry Wing
Poanes viator	Broad-winged Skipper
Euphyes conspicua	Black Dash
Euphyes dion	Dion Skipper
Euphyes bimacula	Two-spotted Skipper
Euphyes dukesi	Duke's Skipper
Atrytonopsis hianna	Dusted Skipper
Amblyscirtes vialis	Roadside Skipper
Achalarus lyciadas	Hoary Edge
Thorybes bathyllus	Southern Cloudy Wing
Staphylus hayhurstii	Scalloped Sooty Wing
Erynnis brizo	Sleepy Dusky Wing
Erynnis martialis	Mottled Dusky Wing
Erynnis horatius	Horace's Dusky Wing
Erynnis zarucco	Zarucco Dusky Wing
Erynnis persius	Persius Dusky Wing
Erynnis baptisiae	Wild Indigo Dusky Wing
Pyrgus communis	Common Checkered Skipper
Pholisora catullus	Common Sooty Wing

Three main criteria were applied to reduce this list to priority taxa for this study. The first was that there could be no more than 20 recent localities for a taxon (post-1969). Secondly, there had to be evidence of residency in Ontario, rather than the species simply being recorded as a migrant or vagrant. In determining Ontario residency, the following definition was used, "A butterfly taxon which spends at least one entire life cycle, and to the best of our knowledge appears to overwinter, in Ontario".[2] The third criterion was that the main part of the species' Ontario range had to be within the Carolinian Zone. Several taxa, although worthy of consideration, can best be protected within other vegetation zones in the province, for example those with northern affinities. This cannot be said for species specific to host plants at their range limits in the Carolinian Zone, or those found only in specialized habitats best represented in this Zone. The priority taxa derived from the application of the above criteria were then refined by a subsequent application of the "COSEWIC (Committee on the Status of Endangered Wildlife in Canada) Criteria for Assigning Conservation Status to Species of Wildlife" (Appendix III).

Results

Applying the first set of criteria to the target list of 63 taxa excluded 41 species from further consideration (see Appendices I and II) and reduced the list to 22 priority taxa. With the application of the COSEWIC criteria to these, nine taxa were determined to be vulnerable in Ontario, five threatened, seven endangered, and one was found to be extirpated (no recent records) (Table 2). The seven endangered and one extirpated taxa are proposed for consideration under Ontario's Endangered Species Act.

Species which could not be confirmed as having had established populations in the Carolinian Zone but are recorded rarely as vagrants were relegated to a "Watch" category (Appendix I). The purpose of the list is to act as a guide to those species which are potential candidates for the Carolinian "rare" list, should breeding ever be confirmed.

[2] The one exception to this definition is the Monarch. Otherwise we find the definition serves the practical purpose of butterfly conservation.

Table 2

Proposed Status of Some Butterflies at Risk in the Carolinian Forest Zone of Ontario

Extirpated

Fixsenia o. ontario	Northern Hairstreak

Endangered

Eurytides marcellus	Zebra Swallowtail
Battus philenor	Pipe Vine Swallowtail
Colias cesonia	Dog Face Butterfly
Speyeria idalia	Regal Fritillary
Incisalia irus	Frosted Elfin
Lycaeides melissa samuelis	Karner Blue
Achalarus lyciadas	Hoary Edge

Threatened

Euphyes dukesi	Duke's Skipper
Erynnis horatius	Horace's Dusky Wing
Erynnis persius	Persius Dusky Wing
Erynnis baptisiae	Wild Indigo Dusky Wing
Staphylus hayhurstii	Scalloped Sooty Wing

Vulnerable

Euchloe olympia	Olympia Marble (dune form/*rosa*)
Papilio cresphontes	Giant Swallowtail
Asterocampa celtis	Hackberry Butterfly
Asterocampa clyton	Tawny Emperor
Mitoura g. gryneus	Olive Hairstreak
Atrytonopsis hianna	Dusted Skipper
Erynnis brizo	Sleepy Dusky Wing
Erynnis martialis	Mottled Dusky Wing
Pyrgus communis	Common Checkered Skipper

Accounts of Taxa

Accounts of taxa are grouped according to the status categories, and within these taxonomically.

1. Northern Hairstreak *(Fixsenia o. ontario)*

Distribution. The type locality for this subspecies is Port Stanley, Ontario (Klots 1951) where a specimen was collected about 1870. Since then, only three additional specimens have been reported from Ontario for certain: Toronto (no date); Grimsby, where a specimen was reported in 1894; and St. Thomas, where a specimen was taken in 1919. Pyle (1981) states that it is a rare butterfly in the northeast United States.

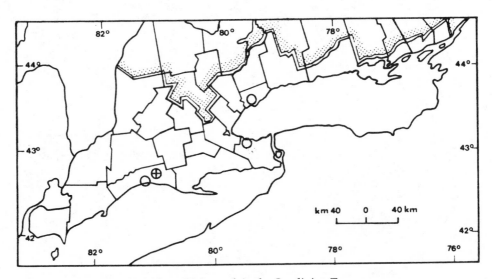

Fig. 2. Distribution of Northern Hairstreak in the Carolinian Zone.

Flight Season

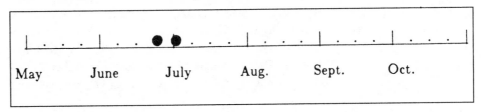

Notes. This butterfly is dull-coloured and easily overlooked. It does not appear to be limited by its host plants, Hog-peanut (*Amphicarpa bracteata* or hawthorns (*Crataegus* spp.).

Status. The Northern Hairstreak is very rare and peripheral in Ontario and Quebec. There are no recent records or specimens, suggesting that this species no longer occurs in Ontario. The proposed status is EXTIRPATED in the Carolinian Zone.

2. Zebra Swallowtail (*Eurytides marcellus*)

Distribution. Recent records are for the Dundas area in 1980 (1); Harrow in 1981 (1), 1987 (11), and 1988 (3), and 1989 (1); Kingsville in 1983 (1) and 1988 (1); Point Pelee in 1987 (1); Windsor in 1988 (1 nectaring) (Campbell pers. obs.; Larson pers. comm. 1989; Pratt pers. comm. 1989; Hess 1989).

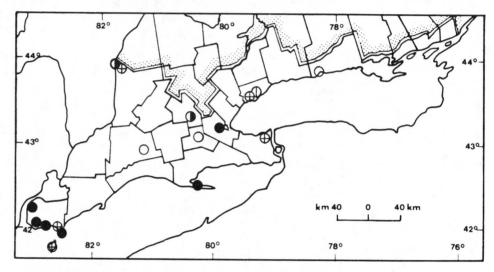

Fig. 3. Distribution of Zebra Swallowtail in the Carolinian Zone.

Flight Season

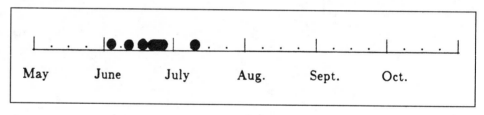

Notes. For northern Zebras most authorities list only Pawpaw (*Asimina triloba*) as a host plant. Tietz (1972) adds Spicebush (*Lindera benzoin*) and blueberries (*Vaccinium* spp.) as well. The scarcity of Pawpaw in Ontario is well known (Argus *et al.* 1982-1987). However, in Wisconsin, Zebra Swallowtails have been recorded up to 200 miles from the nearest stand of Pawpaw (Ebner 1970).

Status. This species is seemingly dependent upon a single host plant species in Ontario and has a history of declining abundance. Surviving as a resident in very low numbers at only two sites in Ontario, this is probably one of Ontario's rarest butterflies. It is very susceptible to collecting. The proposed status is ENDANGERED in the Carolinian Zone.

3. Pipe Vine Swallowtail *(Battus philenor)*

Distribution. The Pipe Vine Swallowtail has experienced a dramatic change of status in recent times, with decline in the Niagara Frontier Region having been noted between 1939 (Wild 1939) and 1969 (Bailey 1970). Breeding has been noted as far north as Kitchener in 1955 (Campbell pers. obs.) and migrants may reach Ontario in some numbers. Totals of 20 and 12 were seen at Point Pelee in 1981 and 1985 respectively (Hess 1984, 1986) and 23 at Pelee Island in 1988 (Hess 1989) and stragglers have occurred at Caribou Island in Lake Superior (A. Wormington pers. comm.). Ontario constitutes the only Canadian range for this species (Gregory 1975).

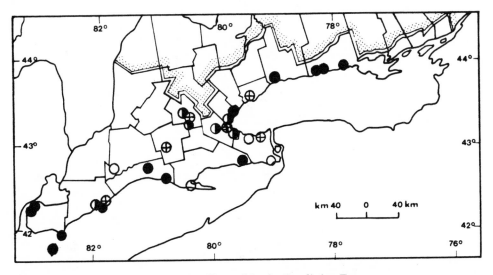

Fig. 4. Distribution of Pipe Vine Swallowtail in the Carolinian Zone.

Extralimital Records. Thunder Bay District (Caribou Island, Lake Superior).

Flight Season

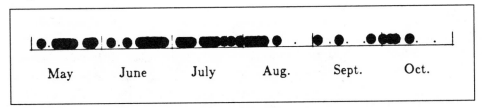

Notes. Host plants include Black Bindweed *(Polygonum convolvulus)*, Common Smartweed *(Polygonum hydropiper)*, and Dutchman's Pipe *(Aristolochia macrophylla)* (Scott 1986). In Ontario the butterfly would rely on the presence of garden specimens of the latter host, since naturalized populations are extremely rare.

Status. The Pipe Vine Swallowtail was historically rare and peripheral to Ontario, but it was also formerly more widespread and frequently bred here. There are few recent records. The proposed status is ENDANGERED in the Carolinian Zone.

4. Dog Face Butterfly *(Colias cesonia)*

Distribution. The last Ontario record for this species was in 1971 in Toronto (5 July) (Hess 1972). Older specimen data indicate a wide distribution from Essex County to York Region. At one time it may have been fairly common near Toronto (Gibson 1896) and even reached Orillia (Bethune 1896; Grant 1896).

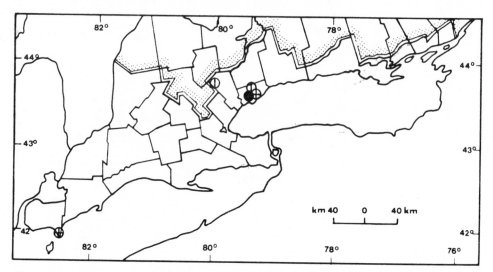

Fig. 5. Distribution of Dog Face Butterfly in the Carolinian Zone.

Extralimital Records. Simcoe and Wellington Counties.

Flight Season

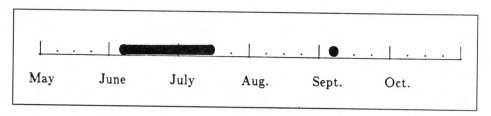

Notes. The preferred host plant, False Indigo *(Amorpha fruticosa)*, is native to Ontario only on Pelee Island but is rarely adventive through southern Ontario (Argus *et al*. 1982-1987). Howe (1975) and Scott (1986) also note Soybean *(Glycine max)* and Alfalfa *(Medicago sativa)* as hosts.

Status. The Dog Face Butterfly is possibly now extirpated in Ontario. The preferred host plant species *(Amorpha* spp.) are very rare in Ontario (Argus *et al*. 1982-1987) and there is no evidence that the insect will breed here on Alfalfa or Soybean. The proposed status is ENDANGERED in the Carolinian Zone.

5. Regal Fritillary *(Speyeria idalia)*

Distribution. The last specimen taken in Ontario was in 1976 from Langton, Haldimand-Norfolk Regional Municipality, by J. Troubridge. However, there is an unconfirmed 1979 sight record from Kitchener (by Campbell) and another on the Norfolk Sand Plain in 1981 (by Campbell and R.J. Sutherland). The habitat at the Kitchener site has been disturbed by development. Oldham (1983) states that it occasionally immigrates into Essex County. In Canada it also occurs in Manitoba, New Brunswick and Nova Scotia (Gregory 1975). The species is Appalachian and montane (Holland 1931) as well as prairie/mid-western.

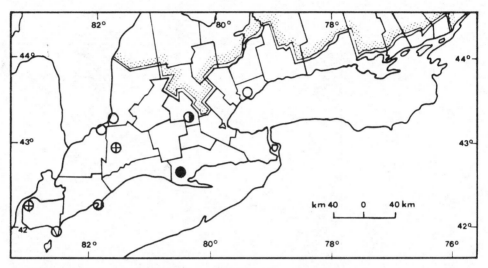

Fig. 6. Distribution of Regal Fritillary in the Carolinian Zone.

Flight Season

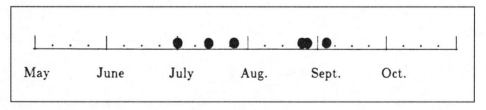

Notes. Howe (1975) attributes the increased rarity of the Regal Fritillary to the loss of native prairie vegetation. A major factor in its decline may be the loss of host plants such as Bird's-foot Violet *(Viola pedata).* This violet was once known in Ontario from eight populations; seven of these have apparently been extirpated and only one 'new' population has been recently discovered (Kavanagh *et al.* 1989). Other violets noted as hosts are the Lance-leaved Violet *(Viola lanceolata)* and the Common Blue Violet *(Viola papilionacea)* (Scott 1986).

Status. The loss of prairie and meadow habitat has apparently caused a serious decline in this species in Ontario; indeed, this butterfly may already be extirpated here. The status of other Canadian populations is not known. The proposed status is ENDANGERED in the Carolinian Zone.

6. Frosted Elfin *(Incisalia i. irus)*

Distribution. There appears to be only a single recent station in Canada, near St. Williams, Ontario, with another, historic station at the Pinery (Packer 1987b). The species was not recorded at St. Williams between 1980 and 1985 but a previously unknown population was discovered at St. Williams in 1986 (Gartshore *et al.* 1987). Packer (1987b) believes the Canadian population to be declining and probably does not exceed 100 adults in any year. He considered it to be the most critically endangered butterfly in Canada. A maximum of eight individuals have been observed in one day (Packer 1987b). Small dispersed populations that are decidedly local "and never abundant" appear typical of this species (Pyle 1981). Holland (1931) and Klots (1951) concur that it is usually a rare species.

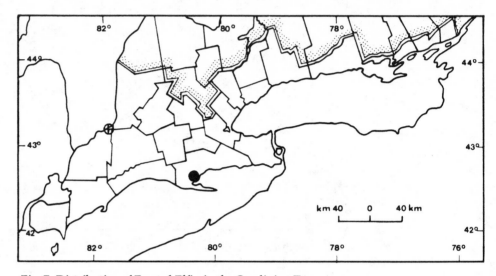

Fig: 7. Distribution of Frosted Elfin in the Carolinian Zone.

Flight Season

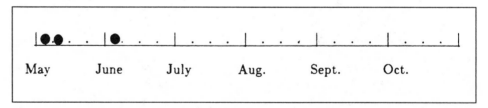

Notes. The Frosted Elfin favours open second-growth woods, brushy fields, pine stands and other semi-open areas near the host plant (Klots 1951; Pyle 1981). The larva will feed only on Wild Lupine *(Lupinus perennis)* or Wild Indigo *(Baptisia tinctoria)* according to Klots (1951) and Pyle (1981). Both species are rare in Ontario (Argus *et al.* 1982-1987).

The Frosted Elfin population at St. Williams was intensively collected from 1967 to 1979 (Campbell pers. obs.). The St. Williams site provides habitat for the Spicebush Swallowtail, Karner Blue, Wild Indigo Dusky Wing and other uncommon species, as well as for this species.

Status. This butterfly is very rare in Ontario. Increasing rarity of its host plants and the single population's vulnerability to over-collecting and habitat destruction make protection measures essential. The site on which this species occurs was purchased in 1989 through the Carolinian Canada Program and is now owned by the Nature Conservancy of Canada. The proposed status is ENDANGERED in the Carolinian Zone.

7. Karner Blue *(Lycaeides melissa samuelis)*

Distribution. The Karner Blue was once more widespread in southern Ontario, with colonies at High Park in Toronto until at least 1920. Recent populations have been recorded from Port Franks just south of the Pinery Provincial Park, and the St. Williams Forestry Station and an adjacent tract. Recent census work at Port Franks indicates a downward trend in the population with maximum daily totals from 200-300 in 1980 (Hess 1981), 170-230 in 1983 (Crabe 1984), 109 in 1984 (Schweitzer 1985), 55 in 1986 (Hess 1987), and 40 in 1987 (Hess 1988). The situation at St. Williams is more drastic. By 1986 the known population had become extirpated but a 'new' population was discovered on an adjacent property. This population is extremely small if not already extirpated with a total of only two adults observed in 1987 and none in 1988 (Hess 1988, 1989).

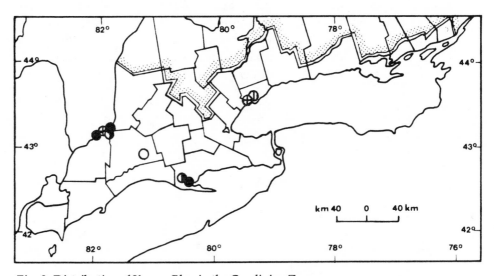

Fig. 8. Distribution of Karner Blue in the Carolinian Zone.

Flight Season

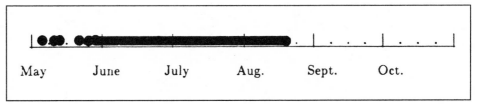

Notes. Several factors have been cited as causes in the decline of the Ontario populations, including community succession, fire suppression, soil erosion by trail bikes, limited distribution of Wild Lupine in isolated portions of some of the sites, possible shortage of nectar sources, and a drastic decline in the population of wood ants which protects the larvae at St. Williams (Packer 1987a).

Only Wild Lupine *(Lupinus perennis)* is listed as a host plant for the Karner Blue by Howe (1975) and it is stated to be preferred by Pyle (1981). Wild Lupine is now a rare plant in Ontario (Argus *et al.* 1982-1987). Areas where this plant occurs may harbour other populations of the Karner Blue. At Pinery Provincial Park, the numbers of lupine are small.

Status. Within its global range from Wisconsin to New York, this subspecies has been recorded from New Hampshire, Massachusetts, and all the states bordering the Great Lakes. However, between 1975 and 1987 it was found in only 21 localities in the US and is in serious decline. Despite its high public profile and several ongoing conservation efforts, the Karner Blue is now considered to be extirpated in Massachusetts and Pennsylvania, is possibly extirpated in Ohio, and is endangered in New Hampshire, New York, and Indiana. Its only stongholds appear to be in Michigan and Wisconsin (Packer 1987a).

The Karner Blue is rare, peripheral, and declining in Ontario. Its host plant *(Lupinus perennis)* is also rare and patchy in distribution. A small property now owned by Lambton Wildlife Incorporated encompasses the main population at Port Franks. The critical habitat adjacent to the St. Williams Forestry Station was designated as a Carolinian Canada site in 1988, acquired through the program in 1989, and is now owned by the Nature Conservancy of Canada. Both sites are in need of immediate management to restore savannah habitat. The proposed status is ENDANGERED in the Carolinian Zone.

8. Hoary Edge *(Achalarus lyciades)*

Distribution. Two individuals were recorded by J. Larson in June and July of 1988 and one in June of 1989 at Sandwich West Township in Essex County (Hess 1989; Larson 1989; Larson pers. comm. 1989). Wild (1939) stated that it was "very rare" in the Niagara-Frontier region, and Wormington (pers. comm. 1981) believes that there is a specimen from Dunnville that may be in the Buffalo Museum of Science.

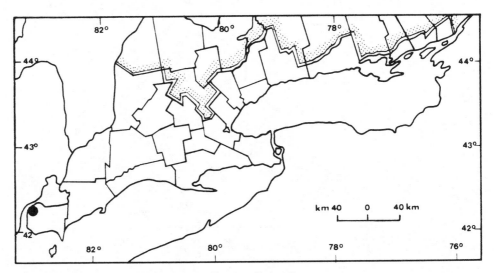

Fig. 9. Distribution of Hoary Edge in the Carolinian Zone.

Flight Season

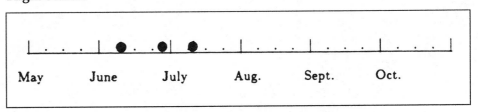

Notes. Howe (1975) notes three species of Tick-trefoil *(Desmodium ciliare, D. dillenii, D. paniculatum)*, and Bush-clover *(Lespedeza hirta)*, and possibly Wild Indigo *(Baptisia tinctoria)* as hosts. All these hosts are strongly associated with prairie and savannah vegetation in Ontario, and *D. ciliare* and *B. tinctoria* are provincially rare (Argus *et al.* 1982-1987). Scott (1986) however, adds *Desmodium rotundifolium, D. nudiflorum, D. canadense,* and *D. cuspidatum,* only the first of which is considered rare in Ontario.

Status. One small population which is probably established has recently been discovered in the Windsor area. The habitat at this site is currently being developed for housing. The proposed status is ENDANGERED in the Carolinian Zone.

9. Duke's or Scarce Swamp Skipper *(Euphyes dukesi)*

Distribution. There are only nine known localities for this species in Canada, all from Essex County, in wetlands or dry deciduous woods. The species does not occur elsewhere in Canada (Gregory 1975).

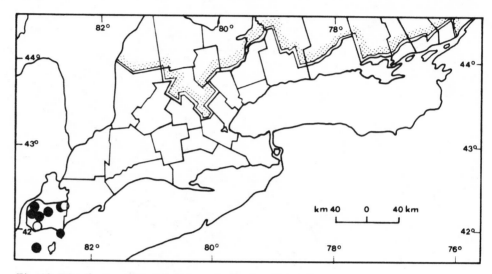

Fig. 10. Distribution of Duke's Skipper in the Carolinian Zone.

Flight Season

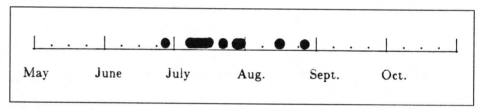

Notes. The species is specific to the Cyperaceae family, with host plants in Ontario being the sedges *Carex lacustris* and *Carex hyalinolepis* (Scott 1986). The former is widespread in southern Ontario while the latter is rare in Ontario (Argus *et al.* 1982-1987) and is restricted to Essex, Kent, and Lambton Counties.

Status. The species was not described until 1923 and extremely little is known about the its distribution or ecology. However several wetland habitats in Essex County supporting populations are under drainage and development pressures (Oldham pers. comm. 1988). The proposed status is THREATENED in the Carolinian Zone.

10. Scalloped Sooty Wing *(Staphylus hayhurstii)*

Distribution. Gregory (1975) lists this taxon for Canada only in Ontario; indeed, it appears to have one of the most restricted ranges of any Canadian butterfly. Fortunately, good populations occur within two nature reserves on Pelee Island (Fish and Lighthouse Points). At Point Pelee National Park the species is considered rare (Wormington 1983). This species seems to occur chiefly in the Mississippi drainage, west of the Great Lakes and east of the Rockies as far as Pennsylvania (Pyle 1981).

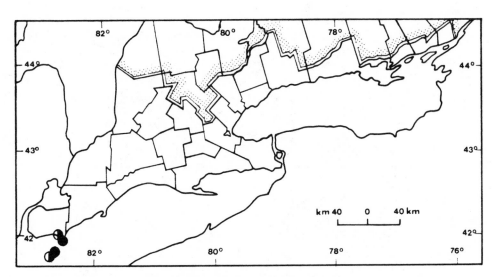

Fig. 11. Distribution of Scalloped Sooty Wing in the Carolinian Zone.

Flight Season

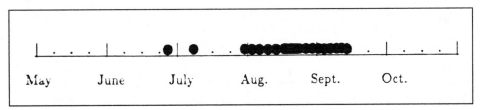

May   June   July   Aug.   Sept.   Oct.

Notes. The only Ontario host species cited by Scott (1986) is Lamb's-quarters *(Chenopodium album)*, which is a widespread alien through the Carolinian Zone. The species was observed ovipositing on *C. foggii* at the south end of Pelee Island in 1981 (M.J. Sharp pers. comm.).

Evans (1953), having examined five specimens in the British Museum from "Canada", considered these to be a subspecies of *Staphylus mazans*, the Mazans or Southern Scalloped Sooty Wing. Gregory (1975) agreed with this nomenclature; however, most recent authorities (Howe 1975; Pyle 1981; Miller and Brown 1981) consider the two as separate species.

Status. This species is known in Canada only from Point Pelee and Pelee Island, where existing populations are currently afforded some measure of protection. The proposed status is THREATENED in the Carolinian Zone.

11. Horace's Dusky Wing *(Erynnis horatius)*

Distribution. In Ontario this species has been reported from the St. Williams Forestry Station in 1964 and 1984 through 1987, Backus Woods in 1985, the Pinery in 1985 and 1986, Oxley (Essex County) in 1988, Point Pelee National Park in 1988, and Springarden Prairie (Essex County) in 1989 (Hess 1979, 1985, 1986, 1987, 1988; Kulon pers. comm. 1988; Larson pers. comm 1989; Pratt pers. comm. 1989). Two additional specimens were located by us in the ROM: Dunnville (1959) and Rondeau Park (1965).

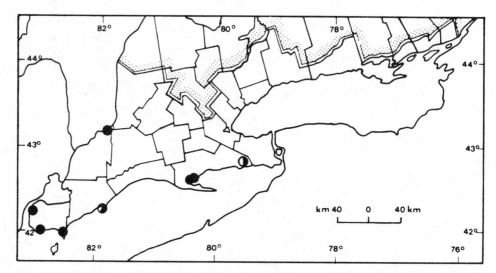

Fig. 12. Distribution of Horace's Dusky Wing in the Carolinian Zone.

Flight Season

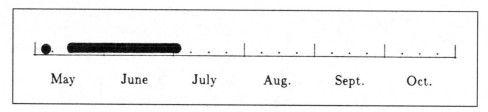

Notes. Its host plants in the east include Red Oak *(Quercus rubra)* and Black Oak *(Q. velutina)* (Opler and Krizek 1984; Scott 1986); and Chinquapin Oak *(Q. muhlenbergii)* and Shumard Oak *(Q. shumardii)* (Howe 1975; Scott 1986). The latter species is rare in Ontario (Argus *et al.* 1982-1987).

Status. This butterfly is at the edge of its range in Ontario and probably does not occur elsewhere in Canada. It apparently occurs in low numbers, the highest recent count being three individuals at St. Williams in 1985 (Hess 1986). The proposed status is THREATENED in the Carolinian Zone.

12. Persius Dusky Wing *(Erynnis persius)*

Distribution. The Persius Dusky Wing has only recently been confirmed for Ontario as a result of records from Backus Woods in 1984, St. Williams in 1984, the Pinery in 1987, Walpole Island in 1987, and Bracebridge in 1984 (Hess 1986, 1988). The latter four reports are substantiated by collections. Unconfirmed records exist for Moosonee and Algonquin Park (Hess 1981). Howe (1975) stated that the species' range probably extended to Quebec and Ontario, while Gregory (1975) shows it extending from Quebec and Manitoba to the Yukon Territory, but not to Ontario. In Quebec, the species has been reported from at least eight localities (Duffy and Garland 1978).

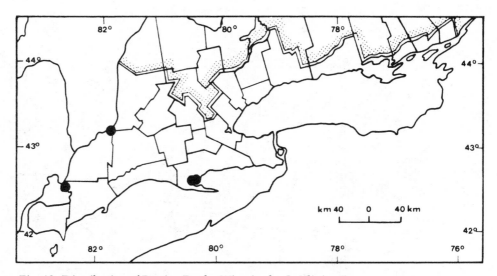

Fig. 13. Distribution of Persius Dusky Wing in the Carolinian Zone.

Extralimital Records. Moosonee District, Bracebridge, and Algonquin Park.

Flight Season

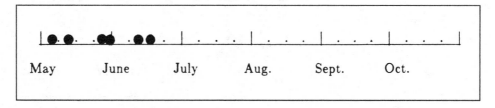

Notes. There appears to have been some confusion between *E. persius* and the closely related *E. baptisiae*. Klots (1951) believes that "many eastern records of *persius* actually refer to *E. baptisiae*".

The preferred host plant in southern Ontario, the Wild Lupine *(Lupinus perennis)* is listed as rare in the Province (Argus *et al.* 1982-1987). The extent to which the species uses the other eastern North American hosts noted by Scott (1986), Upland Willow *(Salix humilis)*, Balsam Poplar *(Populus balsamifera)*, and Trembling Aspen *(Populus tremuloides)*, is unknown.

Status. The Persius Dusky Wing is only known from four locations in the Carolinian Zone and is apparently present in low numbers at all these stations, the highest recorded total being three at St. Williams in 1984. The preferred host plant species there is also rare. This Dusky Wing is much more common elsewhere in Canada. For these reasons, the proposed status is THREATENED in the Carolinian Zone.

13. Wild Indigo Dusky Wing *(Erynnis baptisiae)*

Distribution. There are only five localities for this species in Ontario, the South Walsingham Sand Ridges (1987), St. Williams (1976, 1978, 1979), Ojibway Prairie area (Windsor 1985), Brunet Park (1988), and Walpole Island (1986) (Hess 1977, 1986, 1987, 1988, 1989; Carson 1987).

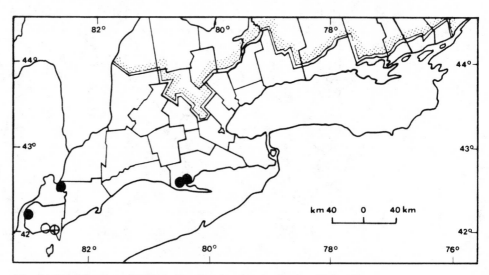

Fig. 14: Distribution of Wild Indigo Duskywing in the Carolinian Zone.

Flight Season

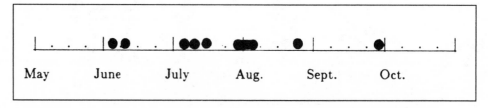

| May | June | July | Aug. | Sept. | Oct. |

Notes. This butterfly already receives some protection at Ojibway Park and Windsor Prairie Provincial Nature Reserve where it is common. At these sites it shows a strong preference for one of its noted hosts Wild Indigo *(Baptisia tinctoria)* (Pratt pers. comm. 1989) (Scott 1986), which is listed as rare in Ontario by Argus *et al.* (1982-1987). Other Ontario hosts, Leadplant *(Amorpha canescens)* (Ebner 1970), and Wild Lupine *(Lupinus perennis)* (Scott 1986) are also listed as rare by Argus *et al.* (1982-1987), while Canada Milk-vetch *(Astragalus canadensis)* (Scott 1986), is rare to uncommon through the Carolinian Zone. However both Cow Vetch *(Vicia* *cracca)* (Pyle 1981), and the introduced Crown Vetch *(Coronilla varia)* (Scott 1986), are common and widespread in southern Ontario.

Status. This is a legume-specific butterfly and one which is only peripheral in Ontario, where its occurrence is apparently limited by factors other than the host plants. The proposed status is THREATENED in the Carolinian Zone.

14. Giant Swallowtail *(Papilio cresphontes)*

Distribution. Although the Giant Swallowtail strays rarely into southern Quebec, it is essentially a Carolinian and tropical species (Scott 1986). In Ontario there are only a few Great Lakes-St. Lawrence Forest records, for the Muskoka District (Rothschild and Jordan 1906), and from Wellington and Simcoe Counties.

There are recent locality records, all concentrated towards the extreme south-west of the Province. Good numbers are found at Walpole Island, Ojibway Prairie, Skunk's Misery, Point Pelee, and Pelee Island. It has always been considered "rare" in the north (Ehrlich and Ehrlich 1961; Howe 1975) but its range expands and contracts sporadically (Klots 1951). Such an expansion was noted in 1988 when individuals were observed at Hay Swamp, Huron County, and Port Franks (Kulon pers. comm. 1988). The latter was the first Pinery area record of the species in about 50 years (Hess pers. comm. 1988).

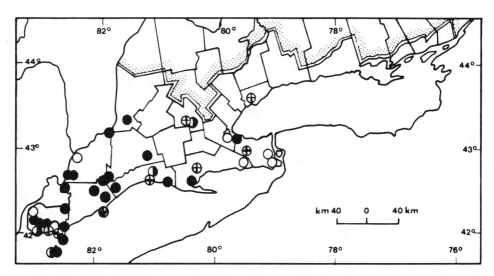

Fig. 15. Distribution of Giant Swallowtail in the Carolinian Zone.

Extralimital Records. Muskoka District and Wellington and Simcoe Counties.

Flight Season

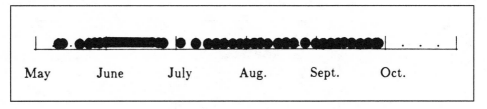

229

Notes. As the largest Ontario butterfly and a very showy species, this swallowtail is subject to considerable collecting. The species is a citrus feeder (family Rutaceae), restricting it in Ontario to only three species, Hop-tree *(Ptelea trifoliata)*, which is rare in Ontario (Argus *et al.* 1982-1987), Northern Prickly-ash *(Zanthoxylem americanum)*, and Rue *(Ruta graveolans)*, a very rare introduction.

Status. This species is rare to uncommon and peripheral in Ontario, its main Canadian range. There have been rare occurrences in Quebec and Nova Scotia. It is restricted by the distribution of its host plants and is probably further restricted by climate. The proposed status is VULNERABLE in the Carolinian Zone.

15. Olympia Marble *(Euchloe olympia)* (dune form/*rosa*)

Distribution. This species occurs in Canada from Quebec to Alberta, often north of the edge of the Canadian Shield in Ontario (Gregory 1975). South of the Shield, the dune form of the Olympia Marble, which may represent a geographic isolate (Opler and Krizek 1984), is restricted to the western portions of the Great Lakes. There are fewer than ten known extant colonies of this dune form in Canada, all confined to the Pinery - Grand Bend area of Lake Huron.

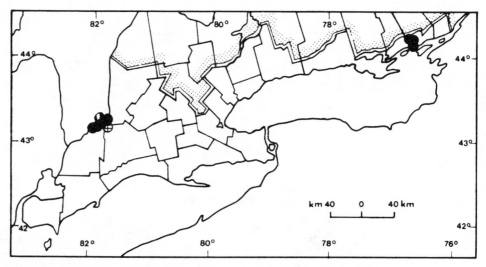

*Fig. 16. Distribution of Olympia Marble (dune form/*rosa) in the Carolinian Zone.*

Extralimital Records (for the species). Muskoka, Parry Sound, and Manitoulin Districts, Renfrew, Haliburton, Peterborough, Victoria, Frontenac, Hastings, Lanark, and Leeds Counties, and Ottawa-Carleton RM.

Flight Season

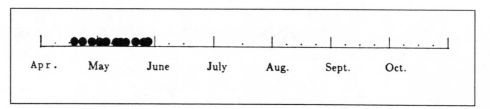

Notes. Wagner's (1977) Great Lakes dune "form" resembles in some ways the typical eastern race of *E. olympia*. Subspecies *rosa*, a Great Lakes/inland form and a more western subspecies, is of dubious taxonomic status. We captured, examined and released specimens of *E. olympia* in the Pinery-Ipperwash area in May 1982, and recorded the amount of rosy flush. We agree with Pyle (1981) that it may only be an ephemeral character at best; however, some authors (e.g. Hodges 1983) recognize this as a valid subspecies. Also, we are in agreement with the observation made by Howe (1975) that because of their marked territorial behaviour, males in spring are very vulnerable to collecting.

Fluctuations in numbers appear marked in this species (Pyle 1981). Occasional wandering may result in new colonies such as the ones recently increasing in the Ottawa district (Layberry *et al.* 1982). These colonies are dependent on Smooth Rock-cress *(Arabis laevigata)*, Tower Mustard *(Arabis glabra)*, Drummond's Rock-cress *(Arabis drummondii)*, and Lyre-leaved Rock-cress *(Arabis lyrata)* (Opler and Krizek 1984), whereas the dune form seems to feed only on Lyre-leaved Rock-cress (Wagner 1977) (Campbell and M.J. Sharp, pers. obs. 1982).

Status. The dune form of this butterfly is rare in Canada. The subspecies *rosa*, if valid, is rather uncommon in Ontario but more widely distributed in Canada (Gregory 1976). The dune form may be restricted by its chief host plant, *Arabis lyrata*, and it is therefore vulnerable. The proposed status is VULNERABLE in the Carolinian Zone.

16. Hackberry Butterfly *(Asterocampa celtis)*

Distribution. There appear to be three main areas of concentration in Ontario. Large numbers have been recorded from Pelee Island, Point Pelee and the Delaware area near the Thames River in Middlesex County. Individuals have been recorded from Holiday Beach Provincial Park in 1980 (Hess 1981), Hamilton in 1984 (M.J. Sharp, pers. comm.), Windsor in 1989 (Larson pers. comm.), Harrow in 1987 and 1988 (Hess 1988, 1989), and an unconfirmed sighting from a Hackberry stand at Rattlesnake Point Conservation Area, Halton RM (Paton and Sharp 1979). It also occurs in Quebec (Gregory 1975).

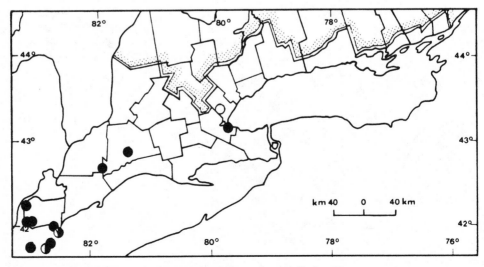

Fig. 17. Distribution of Hackberry Butterfly in the Carolinian Zone.

Flight Season

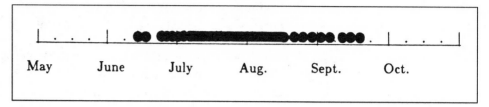

Notes. It is restricted to several species in the genus *Celtis* (Scott 1986), which in Ontario is represented only by Common Hackberry *(Celtis occidentalis)* and Dwarf Hackberry *(Celtis tenuifolia)*.

Status. This species is apparently rare and peripheral in southern Ontario. The only other Canadian occurrences are along the St. Lawrence and Ottawa Rivers near Montreal and Ottawa (Layberry *et al.* 1982). It does not appear to be threatened or vulnerable but, like its host plants, it is confined to southern zones. The proposed status is VULNERABLE in the Carolinian Zone.

17. Tawny Emperor *(Asterocampa c. clyton)*

Distribution. There are a few locations for this species in southern Ontario. The smallest centre appears to be near Cambridge, Ontario, on the Grand River, where a grove of its host plant Common Hackberry *(Celtis occidentalis)* occurs (e.g., August 1981, Campbell specimen). Other populations are scattered along or near the Thames River in Middlesex County, Elgin, and Kent Counties, at Point Pelee, the Erie Islands, Goderich, the Pinery Provincial Park, Big Creek (near Amherstburg), and Windsor. It was discovered for the first time at the latter four sites in 1987, 1988, 1989, and 1989 respectively (Hess 1988, 1989, and Larson pers. comm.). Ontario is its only Canadian range (Gregory 1975).

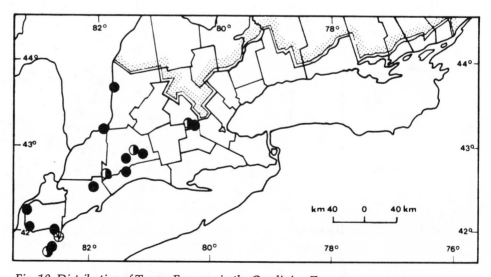

Fig. 18. Distribution of Tawny Emperor in the Carolinian Zone.

Flight Season

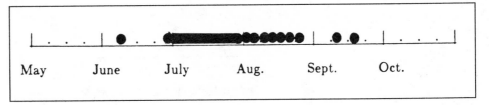

| May | June | July | Aug. | Sept. | Oct. |

Notes. The larvae are highly specific to *Celtis* (Scudder 1889). Tietz (1972) also lists American Plum *(Prunus americana)* and Dutchman's Pipe *(Aristolochia macrophylla)*.

There is a darker form occurring in Ontario known as *proserpina*, in addition to the more typical eye-spotted form. It is suspected that both forms of the Tawny Emperor are intensively collected in Ontario.

Status. The Tawny Emperor is rare and peripheral in Ontario, and it may be limited by climate and the distribution of its host plants. The proposed status is VULNERABLE in the Carolinian Zone.

18. Olive Hairstreak *(Mitoura g. gryneus)*

Distribution. This species occurs only rarely in Ontario (Gregory 1975). Recent records appear to cluster around the Red Cedar groves north of Prince Edward County where it is at least locally common and even sometimes locally abundant. Recent captures have been made in the Shannonville area. It formerly occurred on Pelee Island, with 36 specimens taken in 1918 (Wormington 1983), but no recent observations have been made despite censusing in 1981 (Campbell and M.J. Sharp), and intense inventory work in 1988 (Kamstra pers. comm. 1989). At Point Pelee, the species seems to be barely maintaining itself. Wormington (1983) has described its status there as "declining rapidly" and "now rare". There were no Pelee records between 1981 and 1983 and the maximum count since has been two in 1984 (Hess 1985).

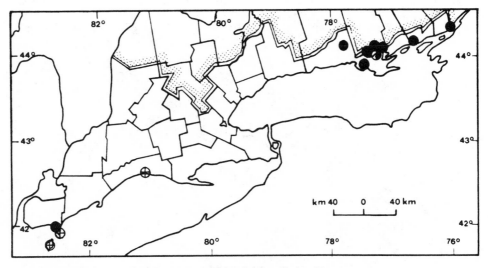

Fig. 19. Distribution of Olive Hairstreak in the Carolinian Zone.

Flight Season

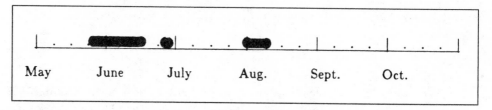

Notes. Most authorities mention only Red Cedar (*Juniperus virginiana*) as a host (e.g. Klots 1951; Tietz 1972; Opler and Krizek 1984; Scott 1986). Once formerly extensively cut for furniture, pencils and oil, Red Cedar is now regenerating on abandoned farm land (Hosie 1973). Pyle (1981) states that the decline of agriculture in New England has increased the available habitat as above; however, both forest regeneration and urbanization contribute to declines of this insect.

It is possible that this species is sometimes overlooked because of its swift flight, small size, and habit of perching in or on cedars (Klots 1951; Ebner 1970).

Status. The Olive Hairstreak is rare and peripheral in Ontario, its only Canadian range. There appear to be two discrete occurrences at present, the Point Pelee area and southeastern Ontario. The Pelee population appears to be declining and may be vulnerable to collecting. The eastern population is apparently healthy and the Red Cedar habitats are increasing. The proposed status is VULNERABLE in the Carolinian Zone.

19. Dusted Skipper (*Atrytonopsis h. hianna*)

Distribution. The Dusted Skipper is a rare species in Ontario, occurring only in the Pinery-Ipperwash area with no historical records elsewhere (Packer 1987b). The same subspecies occurs in both Saskatchewan and Manitoba (Gregory 1975).

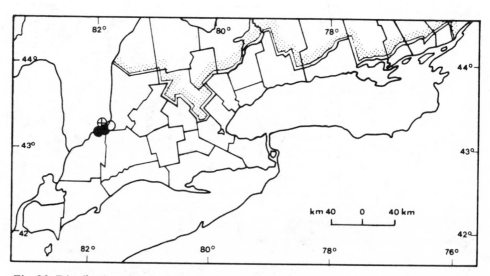

Fig. 20. Distribution of Dusted Skipper in the Carolinian Zone.

Flight Season

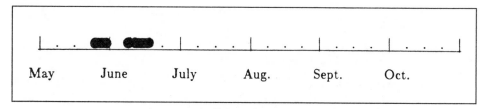

Notes. Howe (1975) considers the species to be a pioneering and transient one; Pyle (1981) found it colonizing recently burned areas and acid, sandy oak pine barrens. The occurrence of this community type elsewhere in Ontario, combined with the widely scattered distribution of the host grasses, Big Blue Stem *(Andropogon gerardii)* and Little Blue Stem *(Andropogon scoparius)* (Scott 1986), may indicate the possibility of other provincial populations of this skipper.

Status. The Dusted Skipper population in Ontario is disjunct from those of the prairie provinces; however, it is not known to be unusual either taxonomically or ecologically. Packer (1987b) found it in low densities over a wide area, in all areas of suitable habitat in the Pinery-Ipperwash area. Efforts currently underway at the Pinery Provincial Park to restore oak savannah will benefit this species. The proposed status is VULNERABLE in the Carolinian Zone.

20. Sleepy Dusky Wing *(Erynnis b. brizo)*

Distribution. This species appears to reach its centre of abundance in Canada in the Carolinian Zone. The same subspecies also occurs in Saskatchewan and Manitoba (Gregory 1975) and although not listed by that author for Quebec, it has apparently been recorded from seven locations in the province (Duffy and Garland 1978).

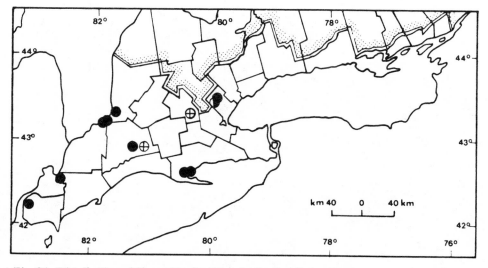

Fig. 21. Distribution of Sleepy Dusky Wing in the Carolinian Zone.

Extralimital Records. Nipissing and Parry Sound Districts, Bruce and Simcoe Counties, Ottawa and Orillia.

Flight Season

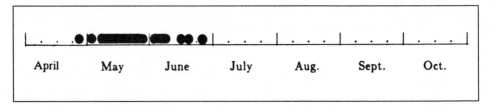

| April | May | June | July | Aug. | Sept. | Oct. |

Notes. Opler and Krizek (1984) cite open oak barrens and scrub as predictable habitat for this species. Oaks are listed as a primary host throughout its range (Howe 1975). Scott (1986) also lists American Chestnut (*Castanea dentata*) as a host.

The species is often confused with the more common Dreamy Dusky Wing *(E. icelus)* and may be sometimes overlooked. *E. brizo* can only be reliably distinguished from *E. icelus* by dissecting the genitalia. They are morphologically variable and cannot be separated on the wing or *in situ* by anybody but perhaps taxonomists who work on them consistently.

Status. Insofar as oak savannas and barrens are being lost, there is some cause for concern about the future of this species in the province. Therefore the proposed status is VULNERABLE in the Carolinian Zone.

21. Mottled Dusky Wing *(Erynnis martialis)*

Distribution. This species is rare and restricted to several extensive sand dunes and sandy woods in southern Ontario, sites at which New Jersey Tea *(Ceanothus americanus)*, one of its host plants, commonly occurs. These sites include the Pinery-Port Franks area, the London area, Point Pelee National Park, St. Williams, Hamilton, Walpole Island, Skunk's Misery, and Constance Bay and Huntley Twp. in Ottawa-Carleton RM. It also occurs in Manitoba and Quebec (Gregory 1975). In Quebec it is listed as "local" and has been collected from only one site, Norway Bay (Duffy and Garland 1978).

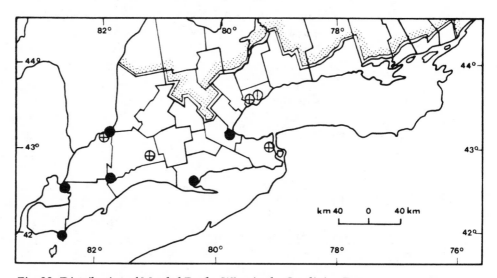

Fig. 22. Distribution of Mottled Dusky Wing in the Carolinian Zone.

Extralimital Records. Ottawa-Carleton RM, Hastings and Victoria Counties.

Flight Season

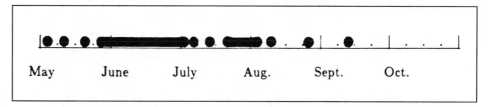

Notes. The host plant New Jersey Tea is most common in the Carolinian Zone, but occurs north into the Great Lakes-St. Lawrence Forest, well into the Ottawa Valley (Soper and Heimburger 1982). The only other known host plant (Scott 1986) in Ontario is the Narrow-leaved New Jersey Tea *(Ceanothus herbaceus)*, which in the south of the province is restricted to a few sites along the Great Lakes shoreline (Soper and Heimburger 1982).

Status. This butterfly is local and dependent upon a habitat type that is often targeted for development by man (e.g. the sandy headland areas along Lake Ontario near Toronto). Several populations are known to be extant, and some habitat is already protected in the Pinery area. The proposed status is VULNERABLE in the Carolinian Zone.

22. Common Checkered Skipper *(Pyrgus communis)*

Distribution. This skipper ranges from British Columbia across the prairies to Ontario (Gregory 1975). Pyle (1981) states that many authorities consider it to be "the most common skipper in North America", especially because it can exploit both rural and urban habitats. However, in Ontario it seems to be confined to the Carolinian Zone, with very few inland occurrences and very few recent ones. At St. Catharines a colony survived for several years but recent censusing here has proven unsuccessful and the population is believed extirpated (Hess pers. comm. 1989). During this decade only three individuals have been recorded, a collection by A.F. Wigg in Toronto in 1982 (Hess 1983) and two observations, by Campbell on Pelee Island in 1985, and by Larson at Brunet Park south of Windsor in 1988 (Hess 1989).

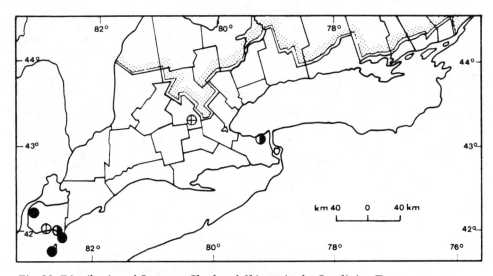

Fig. 23. Distribution of Common Checkered Skipper in the Carolinian Zone.

Flight Season

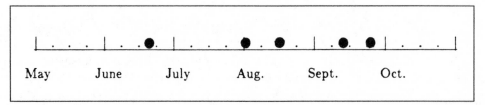

Notes. This species is highly territorial and may thus be more vulnerable to collecting. The larvae feed on all members of the mallow family, including (in Canada), Musk Mallow (*Malva moschata*), Round-leaved Mallow (*Malva neglecta*) (Scott 1986), Hollyhock (*Althaea rosea*), Velvet-leaf (*Abutilon theophrasti*), Flower-of-an-Hour (*Hibiscus trionum*), Swamp Rose Mallow (*Hibiscus moscheutos*) and Prickly Mallow (*Sida spinosa*) (Tietz 1972; Scott 1986). Velvet-leaf is considered a problem "weed" by the agricultural community. Swamp Rose Mallow has been accorded a status of rare in Canada by COSEWIC (Ford 1985) and is rare in Ontario (Argus *et al.* 1982-1987).

Status. The disjunct southern Ontario population is not a separate subspecies, and this butterfly is common elsewhere. Nevertheless, excessive collecting or loss of host plants may eliminate this species from Ontario. While the species has a long history in Ontario, including sometimes several broods per year, more evidence is required to determine its life history characteristics in the province. The proposed status is VULNERABLE in the Carolinian Zone.

Conclusions and Recommendations

We recognize the inherent difficulties of attempting to assign status on the basis of specimens and published accounts. Some species, because of their appearance or behaviour, are more prone to capture than others. In addition, large areas within the Carolinian Zone have never been properly surveyed for their butterfly fauna. Finally, changes in taxonomic relationships make it difficult to determine the actual taxa documented in old records. This problem is compounded in some groups (particularly the Lycaenidae) by the difficulty of determining subspecific status. *Our list must therefore be considered a preliminary one.* However, the changes to our eastern butterfly fauna that have resulted from such developments as major destruction of mature forest, loss of relict prairie and savannah, wetland drainage, the indiscriminate application of pesticides, forest fire protection, and tree planting operations, all of which disturb natural systems, are readily apparent in southern Ontario. Rapid alteration of Ontario's coastal dune lands may also have a serious effect. Overcollecting of certain taxa may have been a factor contributing to the decline of some. The following conservation recommendations are intended as a guide toward stemming this trend.

1. Of the 22 taxa identified in our report as being at risk in the Carolinian Zone of Canada, it is striking that at least 13 of these are largely dependent on savannah habitat (oak, oak-pine, Common Hackberry-Chinquapin Oak-Blue Ash, or Red Cedar). This situation reflects a distressing trend throughout the tallgrass prairie biome in the wholesale conversion of savannah habitat to other uses and in the succession of habitat due to alteration or elimination of natural fire regimes.

   While substantial sections of some of our best quality savannah sites have been protected, e.g. Turkey Point, Long Point, Stone Road (Pelee Island), The Pinery, and Point Pelee, nearly all are in serious need of successional management. Several others are mainly in private hands and under heavy development pressure, e.g. Spooky Hollow, Walpole and Squirrel Islands, Sandwich West prairies and others in the south Windsor-LaSalle area, and the sand barrens at Skunk's Misery (Middlesex and Kent Counties). The lepidopteran history of Ontario parallels that of other fields of natural history – a tale of species-rich sites which no longer exist – the Leamington Prairies, Thamesville Moor, and the Humber Plains; or are so degraded as to no longer support the necessary host plants, e.g. High Park, Toronto.

We suggest not only increased attention to the already noted significant savannah-prairie sites, but also to the need for a systematic inventory of small savannah remnants throughout the Carolinian Zone of southern Ontario. We believe that populations of the 13 savannah-dependent taxa noted certainly exist which have never been identified, and that other taxa may remain to be discovered in this, and other Carolinian community types.

2. The Karner Blue should be protected under the Endangered Species Act. COSEWIC status reports should be prepared for those species proposed for endangered status in this report: Zebra Swallowtail, Pipe Vine Swallowtail, Dog Face Butterfly, Regal Fritillary, Frosted Elfin, and Hoary Edge. Assuming concurrence with our findings, these species, together with the sites where their host plants occur, should also be protected under the Endangered Species Act.

3. Because the Regal Fritillary is monotypic throughout Canada, consideration should be given to the possibility of reintroducing this butterfly to Ontario. We suggest that the meadows at Spooky Hollow and Turkey Point, or the oak openings at Skunk's Misery, would provide suitable conditions for such an experiment.

4. Wild Lupine (*Lupinus perennis*) is critical to the survival of three of the 22 butterflies at risk in the Carolinian Zone; Karner Blue, Frosted Elfin, and Persius Dusky Wing. A rare species itself in Ontario, the Wild Lupine should be a high priority for protection and management efforts. Known stands should be monitored and 'new' stands of the lupine carefully checked for populations of the three butterfly species.

5. Existing stands of *Lupinus perennis* in the Pinery-Ipperwash corridor and at St. Williams should be protected and possibly augmented by the sowing of native lupine.

6. The St. Williams site should be managed (i.e. brushed out or burned) to create additional habitat for Wild Lupine. Packer (1987a) provides detailed guidelines.

7. Southwestern Ontario and Manitoba should be investigated for populations of the Dog Face Butterfly and its chief host plant, *Amorpha fruticosa*.

8. Known stands of Pawpaw should be protected and monitored for the presence of Zebra Swallowtails and protected. Likely additional sites should be surveyed for this critically important food source and evidence of the butterfly.

9. Prairie and savannah habitats in the Windsor area and at Walpole Island should be searched for 'new' populations of the Hoary Edge. The habitat supporting the population in Sandwich West Township should be protected and further research conducted to determine the population size at this location.

10. Because of the relatively recent elevation of Wild Indigo Dusky Wing to full-species rank in 1936 by Forbes (Opler and Krizek 1984) (separated from the similar Persius Dusky Wing, *E. persius*), old museum specimens of the pre-1940s should be carefully examined.

11. Very little research has been conducted on the consequences of genetic isolation (e.g. morphological aberrations, skewed sex ratios), on butterfly populations in southern Ontario. Related to this is the paucity of quantitative or even good descriptive data on habitats utilized by the 22 taxa discussed in our report. Successful management for these species in Ontario will depend on ascertaining their ecological requirements, behaviour, and genetics. Research focusing on these important aspects should be increased.

Appendix I

Watch List – Species Determined as Rare in the Carolinian Zone but Currently Known Only as Vagrants. These Species Should be Monitored for Establishment of Reproducing Populations.

---

1. Cloudless Giant Sulphur *(Phoebis sennae eubule)*

Distribution. The Cloudless Giant Sulphur has not been collected in Ontario since 1953. However, specimens have been observed in a Toronto garden in 1980 (Hess 1981), at Port Credit in 1985 (Hess 1986), at Ojibway Prairie in 1988 (Larson pers. comm. 1988), and one was photographed on Middle Sister Island in 1987 (Hess 1988). Its status as a resident in Ontario remains in considerable doubt, despite the fact the larvae feed on many species of legumes, including several which occur in Ontario. Pyle (1981) considers it an immigrant in all of the northeast, including Canada, and rare northward except during unusual summer and autumn movements.

Notes. The presence of some of its host plants, e.g. Wild Senna *(Cassia hebecarpa)* and clovers (*Trifolium* spp.) (Tietz 1972), in southern Ontario, facilitates the possibility of breeding.

2. Zarucco Dusky Wing *(Erynnis zarucco)*

Distribution. The Zarucco Dusky Wing has not been collected in Ontario since 1935 (three at Kitchener and one on the Rouge River, Toronto). Pyle (1981) considers the Zarucco to be "largely a coastal butterfly", while Macy and Shepard (1941) consider that, "from Virginia north, the species is only a summer visitor, occasionally reaching Massachusetts."

Notes. It is possible that the Ontario specimens may actually refer to the closely-related *Erynnis funeralis,* a widely-wandering western species. There are no Canadian specimens of *E. funeralis,* although there is one hypothetical sight record (from the dock at Colchester, Ontario, *fide* T. Hince, in 1982).

Several of the host plants, e.g. Black Locust *(Robinia pseudo-acacia),* bush-clovers (*Lespedeza* spp.), and Alfalfa *(Medicago sativa)* (Klots 1951; Howe 1975; Scott 1986), are common and widespread in southern Ontario. Klots (1951) also lists Wild Indigo *(Baptisia tinctoria)* as a possible host.

Recommendation. The existing Canadian specimens should be re-examined to confirm that they are actually those of *E. zarucco.*

3. Gorgone Checkerspot *(Chlosyne gorgone gorgone)*

Distribution. This species has not been collected in Ontario since 1891 when several specimens were obtained in the Humber Valley, Toronto, by C.W. Nash. It may never have bred in Ontario, and was probably always rare here. Elsewhere, the species is largely limited to central North America with disjunct colonies near the Atlantic coast (Pyle 1981).

Notes. This butterfly frequents dry prairie-like areas and Jack Pine barrens (Hess 1979). The larvae feed on many weedy species which are widespread in the Carolinian Zone such as sunflowers (*Helianthus* spp.), ragweeds (*Ambrosia* spp.), and asters (*Aster* spp.) (Hess 1979).

The *C. g. gorgone* taxon is single-brooded in the north and flies only in June (Hess 1984). It may be primarily a western subspecies, and perhaps overlooked because of its similarity to the Pearly Crescentspot (*Phyciodes tharos*) (Ebner 1970).

Recommendation. We recommend that the former habitat around the Humber River be thoroughly searched during the breeding season. Should a breeding population be discovered, this taxon should be considered for protection under the Endangered Species Act.

4. Checkered White *(Pontia protodice)*

Distribution. Recorded at Zurich, Huron County in the 1930s, where a large flight appeared in a clover field (specimens at ROM, Hess pers. comm. 1989), closely observed and collected during the late 1960s as fresh individuals at Cambridge (site now developed) (Lamb pers. comm. 1989), at St. Williams from 1969 to 1974 (Hess 1981), and at Caledonia in 1974 (Troubridge pers. comm. *in* Carson 1987). Four individuals were observed at LaSalle on 11 Sept. 1988 and one individual was observed on 23 Sept. 1988 at Point Pelee (Hess 1989).

Notes. Several of its Cruciferae host plants e.g. Tower Mustard *(Arabis glabra)*, Yellow Rocket *(Barbarea vulgaris)*, Black Mustard *(Brassica nigra)*, Shepherd's-purse *(Capsella bursa-pastoris)*, Penny-cress *(Thlaspi arvense)*, and Tall Mustard *(Sisymbrium altissimum)* (Scott 1986), are common and widespread in southern Ontario, indicating the possibility of breeding.

The fact that the northward breeding limits are poorly known and adults travel many kilometres to establish new colonies (Scott 1986), is further cause to search for this species.

Recommendation. Potential breeding sites for this species should be surveyed, e.g. sandy or gravelly, often disturbed sites on the Norfolk Sand Plain.

5. Sleepy Orange *(Abaeis nicippe)*

Distribution. A very rare straggler into Ontario, there are no records of this species for the 1982-1988 period. This species has been recently recorded only once in Ontario, at Quetico Provincial Park in June 1978 (Hess 1979). Reports in the literature of a collection at Point Pelee (Klots 1951; Hess 1979) were confirmed (specimen CNC, year unknown). A specimen collected from Kitchener in 1934 (15 Sept.) has been examined by us.

Notes. The presence of its host plants Wild Senna *(Cassia hebecarpa)* and clovers (*Trifolium* spp.) Tietz 1972; Scott 1986) in Ontario might facilitate the possibility of breeding.

6. Great Southern White *(Ascia monuste)*

Distribution. A. Wormington closely observed an individual at Point Pelee National Park in June, 1981 (Wormington 1983). There are no records for the 1982 to 1988 period.

Notes. Host plants noted (Scott 1986) which occur in southern Ontario include Bird Rape *(Brassica rapa)*, Sea Rocket *(Cakile edentula)*, and Poor-man's Pepper *(Lepidium virginicum)*.

7. Orange-barred Sulphur *(Phoebis philea)*

Distribution. Prior to a collection of a female by J. Pilkington in a garden in Windsor in 1986 (21 Sept.), the last Ontario collection was 1930 (13 Oct.) at Zurich, Huron County (Hess 1981). Several recent observations have been made of this species including one in flight on the Leslie St. Spit, Toronto (15 June, 1987) (Hess 1988).

Notes. The only host noted by Tietz (1972) or Scott (1986) which occurs in southern Ontario is Wild Senna *(Cassia hebecarpa)*, which is rare (Argus *et al.* 1982-1987).

8. White 'M' Hairstreak *(Parrhasius m-album)*

Distribution. A rare visitor to Ontario, the last provincial collections were in 1960, when two were captured at Point Pelee on August 31 by R.W. Holzman, and a third at Essex on September 11 by D.M. Wood (Hess 1983). The species is resident in Northern Ohio (Scott 1986).

Notes. Scott (1986) notes White Oak *(Quercus alba)* and Basswood *(Tilia americana)* as probable hosts. In addition to the latter species Tietz (1972) notes hawthorns (*Crataegus* spp.), Common Hop *(Humulus lupulus)*, and Common Vetch *(Vicia sativa)*. All of these species are common and widespread in southern Ontario.

Recommendation. White Oak stands at Long Point would be ideal sites to survey for possible breeding.

9. Sachem *(Atalopedes campestris)*

Distribution. Prior to 1988, when there was a substantial invasion of the species recorded at Windsor, Pelee Island, Point Pelee, and Hillman Marsh (Hess 1989), the only previous Ontario record is a 1968 collection in London by K. Thorne. Observations at Point Pelee by A. Wormington included ovipositing females, several fresh individuals, and a probably locally produced brood.

Notes. Three of the grasses noted by Scott (1986) as hosts occur in southern Ontario: Red Fescue *(Festuca rubra)*, Goose Grass *(Eleusine indica)*, and Large Crab Grass *(Digitaria sanguinalis)*. Only the latter one can be considered common and widespread.

Recommendation. Further work should be conducted at Point Pelee to determine if the species has been able to establish itself, i.e. overwinter successfully.

Appendix II

Species excluded from this report

(Criteria met for exclusion from the priority taxa list: 1) Greater than 20 recent localities (post-1969) within the Carolinian Zone, 2) No evidence of residency in Ontario, recorded only as a migrant or vagrant, and 3) Main part of the species' range not within the Carolinian Zone).

		Criteria
PAPILIONIDAE: Swallowtails		
Papilio troilus	Spicebush Swallowtail	1
PIERIDAE: Whites and Sulphurs		
Eurema mexicana	Mexican Sulphur	2
Eurema lisa	Little Sulphur	2
Nathalis iole	Dainty Sulphur	2
Euchloe ausonides	Large Marble	3
Pieris virginiensis	West Virginia White	3
NYMPHALIDAE: Brush-footed Butterflies		
Satyrodes appalachia	Appalachian Eyed Brown	1
Coenonympha nipisiquit	Nipisquit Ringlet	3
Limenitis archippus floridensis	Florida Viceroy	2
Junonia coenia	Buckeye	1
Chlosyne harrisii harrisii	Harris' Checkerspot	3
Phycoides batesii	Tawny Crescent	3
Boloria selene	Silver-bordered Fritillary	3
Euptoieta claudia	Variegated Fritillary	1
LYCAENIDAE: Hairstreaks, Coppers and Blues		
Incisalia p. polios	Hoary Elfin	3
Incisalia augustus	Brown Elfin	3
Strymon melinus humili	Gray Hairstreak	1
Plebejus saepiolus amica	Greenish Blue	3
LIBYTHEIDAE: Snout Butterflies		
Libytheana b. bachmanii	Snout Butterfly	1
HESPERIIDAE: Skippers		
Oarisma garita	Garita Skipper	3
Hylephila phyleus	Fiery Skipper	2
Polites vibex	Whirlabout	2
Pompeius verna	Little Glassywing	1
Atrytone logan	Delaware Skipper	1
Poanes massasoit	Mulberry Wing	1
Poanes viator	Broad-winged Skipper	1
Euphyes conspicua	Black Dash	1
Euphyes dion	Dion Skipper	1
Euphyes bimacula	Two-spotted Skipper	3
Amblyscirtes vialis	Roadside Skipper	3
Thorybes bathyllus	Southern Cloudy Wing	1
Pholisora catullus	Common Sooty Wing	1

Appendix III

COSEWIC Criteria for Assigning Conservation Status to Species of Wildlife

Species — "Species" means any species, subspecies, or geographically separate population.

Vulnerable Species — Any indigenous species of fauna or flora that is at particular risk because of low or declining numbers, occurrence at the fringe of its range or in restricted areas, or for some other reason, but is not a threatened species.

Threatened Species — Any indigenous species of fauna or flora that is likely to become endangered in Canada if the factors affecting its vulnerability do not become reversed.

Endangered Species — Any indigenous species of fauna or flora that is threatened with imminent extinction or extirpation throughout all or a significant portion of its Canadian range, owing to human action.

Extirpated Species — Any indigenous species of fauna or flora no longer existing in the wild in Canada but occurring elsewhere.

Extinct Species — Any species of fauna or flora formerly indigenous to Canada but no longer existing anywhere.

Acknowledgements

Numerous individuals and government departments contributed information critical to the report and made information readily accessible. The latter include the Biosystematics Research Institute, Agriculture Canada, Ottawa; the Royal Ontario Museum, Department of Entomology; the National Museums of Canada, Department of Entomology; various members of the Toronto Entomological Association; Ontario Ministry of Natural Resources; and staff at Point Pelee National Park, Pinery Provincial Park, and Ipperwash Provincial Park. Permits were issued for Camp Ipperwash (by the Commandant), The Pinery, and for Point Pelee National Park.

The services provided by the Inter-library Loan Service at Wilfrid Laurier University (Mrs. M. Martin) in obtaining many obscure old publications, and by the Toronto Public Library, are much appreciated.

Field assistance was provided by G.M. Allen, J. Campbell, J. Goltz, C. Klein-Lebbink, M.J. Oldham, D. Perrin, P.D. Pratt, A. Sandilands, R.J. Sutherland, and especially M.J. and G.E. Sharp.

The original manuscript was revised by A.A. Bryant in 1986 with supervision by Dr. S. Smith, Department of Biology, University of Waterloo. Improvements between the 1986 report and the current version were made possible by substantial editorial changes and new information provided by a number of reviewers. In particular, we would like to thank G.M. Allen, Q. Hess, J. Kamstra, B. and B. Kulon, L.E. Lamb, J. Larson, M.J. Oldham, P.D. Pratt, J.P. Prevett, and M.J. Sharp. The range maps and flight bar graphs are by D.P. Coulson.

The World Wildlife Fund provided supervision and funding; thanks to M. Hummel who originally conceived the project and S. Price; to Mr. A. Hanks of T.E.A.; and to Col. Pat Torry of the British Butterfly Conservation Society, who visited us in Waterloo.

The senior author also wishes to thank his wife, Dr. J. Campbell, G. Dennison, Dr. J. Fancy, Ms. S. Gutenberg, Dr. C. Hollidge, Dr. J. Lee, C. Spooner, and Jo Brewer of the Xerces Society, and other colleagues, especially G.M. Allen, for their support and encouragement during the numerous revisions to the manuscript. Also, he is indebted to his late friend D. Schachinger.

The work was funded by the World Wildlife Fund and the University of Waterloo.

References

Anonymous. 1975. Endangered Butterflies. *Nature Canada* 4(3):18.

Argus, G.W., K.M. Pryer, D.J. White and C.J. Keddy, eds. 1982-1987. *Atlas of the rare vascular plants of Ontario*. Four parts. National Museum of Natural Sciences, Ottawa.

Bailey, E.G. 1970. *Butterflies of the Niagara Peninsula*. Niagara Falls Nature Club, Special Publication No.1. 19pp.

Barnes, W. and J. McDunnough. 1917. *Check list of the Lepidoptera of boreal America*. Herald Press, Decatur, Illinois. 392 pp.

Beirne, B.P. 1955. Natural fluctuations in the abundance of British Lepidoptera. *Entomologists' Gazette* 6:21-52.

Bethune, C.J.S. 1872. Insects affecting the hop. *Proceedings of the Entomological Society of Ontario* 2(32):399.

Bethune, C.J.S. 1894. The butterflies of the eastern provinces of Canada. *Proceedings of the Entomological Society of Ontario* 25:31.

Bethune, C.J.S. 1896. The butterflies of the eastern provinces of Canada. *Proceedings of the Entomological Society of Ontario* 27:107-109.

Bethune, C.J.S. 1897. Notes on the season of 1897. *Proceedings of the Entomological Society of Ontario* 28:33.

Bethune, C.J.S. 1899. Notes of the season of 1899. *Proceedings of the Entomological Society of Ontario* 30:101.

Bird, C.D. 1982. Endangered species/habitats – butterflies. *Alberta Naturalist* 12:50-52.

Botham, W. 1981. *Plants of Essex County, a preliminary list*. Essex Region Conservation Authority, Essex, Ontario. 210 pp.

Brown, L.U. 1974. Haven for rare butterflies. *National Parks and Conservation Magazine* July:10-13.

Caesar, L. 1932. Insects of the season 1932 in Ontario. *Entomological Society of Ontario* 63:19.

Campbell, C.A., B.W. Evered, D.W. Perrin, M.C. Sharp, and B.B. Weller. 1981. *The Great Lakes biogeographic province: a Canadian review of source material*. The Nature Conservancy of Canada, Toronto. 2 volumes.

Carson, P. 1987. Annotated checklist to the butterflies of Haldimand-Norfolk. pp. 1-8 *In*: Gartshore M.E., D.A. Sutherland, and J.D. McCracken. *The Natural Areas Inventory of the Regional Municipality of Haldimand-Norfolk*. Volume II: Annotated Checklists. The Norfolk Field Naturalists.

Catling, P.M., W. Edmonds and C.H. Walker. 1971. *Annual summary of the Papilionoidea and Hesperioidea encountered in Ontario for 1970*. Toronto Entomologists' Association, Occasional Publication No. 2. 18 pp.

Catling, P.M. and C.H. Walker. 1970. *Annual summary of the Rhopalocera encountered in Ontario for the year 1969*. Toronto Entomologists' Association, Occasional Publication No. 1. 11 pp.

Catling, P.M. and C.H. Walker. 1974. *Annual summary of Rhopalocera encountered in Ontario in 1971*. Toronto Entomologists' Association, Occasional Publication No. 3. 18 pp.

Clench, H.K. 1971. Some records of *Euristrymon ontario* (Lycaenidae). *Journal of Lepidopterists' Society* 25(1):80-82.

Cosens, A. 1919. Reports on insects for the year; Division No.3 (Toronto District). *Proceedings of the Entomological Society of Ontario* 50:14.

Crabe, T.J. 1984. *Status of* Lupinus perennis *(Wild Lupine) and* Lycaeides melissa samuelis *Nabokov (Karner Blue) in the Pinery Provincial Park/Port Franks Area – 1983*. Unpublished. 3 pp. + 2 maps.

Daniel, J.W. 1908. Notes of captures. *Proceedings of the Entomological Society of Ontario* 39:103.

Dennis, R.L.H. 1977. *The British butterflies, their origin and establishment*. E.W. Classey Ltd., Faringdon, Oxon, England. 318 pp.

Dore, W.G. and J. McNeill. 1980. *Grasses of Ontario*. Agriculture Canada, Research Branch. Monograph 26. 566 pp.

Duffy, D.N. and J.A. Garland. 1978. *The skipper butterflies of the Province of Quebec*. Lyman Entomological Museum and Research Laboratory, Memoir No. 5 (Special Publication No. 13). 165 pp.

Dunn, D.B. and J.M. Gillett. 1966. *The lupines of Canada and Alaska*. Canadian Department of Agriculture. Research Branch Monograph 2. 89 pp.

Ebner, J.A. 1970. *The butterflies of Wisconsin*. Milwaukee Public Museum, Popular Science Handbook No. 12. 205 pp.

Edwards, W.H. 1868-1897. *The butterflies of North America*. 3 vols. American Entomological Society. Houghton-Mifflin, Boston. 1068 pp.

Edwards, W.H. 1884. *Revised catalogue of the diurnal Lepidoptera of America north of Mexico*. Transactions of the American Entomological Society. Philadelphia. 83 pp.

Ehrlich, P.R. and A.H. Ehrlich. 1961. *How to know the butterflies*. Wm. C. Brown Company Publishers, Dubuque, IA. 262 pp.

Evans, W.H. 1952. *A catalogue of the American Hesperiidae indicating the classification and nomenclature adopted in the British Museum*. Part II. Jarrold and Sons Ltd., Norwich, Great Britain.

Evans, W.H. 1953. *A catalogue of the American Hesperiidae indicating the classification and nomenclature adopted in the British Museum*. Part III. Jarrold and Sons Ltd., Norwich, Great Britain.

Evans, W.H. 1955. *A catalogue of the American Hesperiidae indicating the classification and nomenclature adopted in the British Museum*. Part IV. Jarrold and Sons Ltd., Norwich, Great Britain.

Fernald, M.L. 1950. *Gray's manual of botany*. 8th ed. American Book Company, New York. 1632 pp.

Field, W.D., C.F. Dos Passos, J.H. Masters. 1974. *A bibliography of the catalogues, lists, faunal and other papers on the butterflies of North America north of Mexico, arranged by state and province (Lepidoptera: Rhopalocera)*. Smithsonian Contributions to Zoology, No. 157. Smithsonian Institute Press. 104 pp.

Ford, B.A. 1985. *Status report on Swamp Rose Mallow* Hibiscus moscheutos *subsp.* moscheutos, *a rare species in Canada*. Prepared for the Committee on the Status of Endangered Wildlife in Canada. 25 pp. + appendices.

Ford, E.B. 1975. *Butterflies*. The Fontana New Naturalist. Collins Sons & Co. Ltd., Glasgow. 368 pp.

Frankton, C. and G.A. Mulligan. 1970. *Weeds of Canada*. Canada Department of Agriculture. Publication 948. 217 pp.

Gibson, A. 1896. Rare captures during the season of 1896. *Entomological Society of Ontario* 27:105.

Gleason, H.A. and A. Cronquist. 1963. *Manual of Vascular Plants of Northeastern United States and Adjacent Canada*. Van Nostrand Reinhold Co., Toronto. 810 pp.

Grant, C.E. 1896. Butterflies taken at Orillia, Ontario. *Canadian Entomologist* 28:271-274.

Grant, C.E. 1897. Notes on the season of 1897. *Proceedings of the Entomological Society of Ontario* 28:76.

Grant, C.E. 1901. Notes on captures. *Proceedings of the Entomological Society of Ontario* 32:102.

Gregory, W.W. 1975. *Checklist of the butterflies and skippers of Canada*. Lyman Entomological Museum and Research Laboratory, Memoir No. 3 (Special Publication No. 10). i + 44 pp.

Heitzman, J.R. and R.L. Heitzman. 1974. *Atrytonopsis hianna* biology and life cycle in the Ozarks. *Journal of Research on Lepidoptera* 13:239-245.

Hess, Q.F. 1975. *Summaries of Rhopalocera encountered in Ontario in 1972, 1973 and 1974*. Toronto Entomologists' Association, Occasional Publication No. 4-75. 26 pp.

Hess, Q.F. 1979. *Butterflies of Ontario and summaries of Lepidoptera encountered in Ontario in 1978*. Toronto Entomologists' Association, Occasional Publication No. 10- 79. 78 pp.

Hess, Q.F. 1980. *Butterflies of Ontario and summaries of Lepidoptera encountered in Ontario in 1979*. Toronto Entomologists' Association, Occasional Publication No. 11-80. 46 pp.

Hess, Q.F. 1981. *Butterflies of Ontario and summaries of Lepidoptera encountered in Ontario in 1980*. Toronto Entomologists' Association, Occasional Publication No. 12-81. 80 pp.

Hess, Q.F. 1982. *Butterflies of Ontario and summaries of Lepidoptera encountered in Ontario in 1981*. Toronto Entomologists' Association, Occasional Publication No. 13-82. 68 pp.

Hess, Q.F. 1983. *Butterflies of Ontario and summaries of Lepidoptera encountered in Ontario in 1982*. Toronto Entomologists' Association, Occasional Publication No. 14-83. 73 pp.

Hess, Q.F. 1984. *Butterflies of Ontario and summaries of Lepidoptera encountered in Ontario in 1983*. Toronto Entomologists' Association, Occasional Publication No. 15-84. 67 pp.

Hess, Q.F. 1985. *Butterflies of Ontario and summaries of Lepidoptera encountered in Ontario in 1984*. Toronto Entomologists' Association, Occasional Publication No. 16-85. 67 pp.

Hess, Q.F. 1986. *Butterflies of Ontario and summaries of Lepidoptera encountered in Ontario in 1985*. Toronto Entomologists' Association, Occasional Publication No. 17-86. 79 pp.

Hess, Q.F. 1987. *Butterflies of Ontario and summaries of Lepidoptera encountered in Ontario in 1986*. Toronto Entomologists' Association, Occasional Publication No. 18-87. 83 pp.

Hess, Q.F. 1988. *Butterflies of Ontario and summaries of Lepidoptera encountered in Ontario in 1987*. Toronto Entomologists' Association, Occasional Publication No. 19-88. 82 pp.

Hess, Q.F. 1989. *Butterflies of Ontario and summaries of Lepidoptera encountered in Ontario in 1988*. Toronto Entomologists' Association, Occasional Publication No. 20-89. 62 pp.

Hess, Q.F. and A.J. Hanks. 1976. *Butterflies of Ontario and summaries of Lepidoptera encountered in Ontario in 1975*. Toronto Entomologists' Association, Occasional Publication No. 6-76. 21 pp.

Hess, Q.F. and A.J. Hanks. 1978. *Butterflies of Ontario and summaries of Lepidoptera encountered in Ontario in 1977*. Toronto Entomologists' Association, Occasional Publication No.9-78. 51 pp.

Hess, Q.F., W. Plath, Jr., and A.J. Hanks. 1977. *Butterflies of Ontario and summaries of Lepidoptera encountered in Ontario in 1976.* Toronto Entomologists' Association, Occasional Publication No. 7-77. 29 pp.

Hodges, R.W., ed. 1983. *Check list of the Lepidoptera of America north of Mexico.* E.W. Classey Ltd. and the Wedge Entomological Research Foundation, London. 284 pp.

Holland, W.J. 1898, revised ed. 1931. *The butterfly book.* Doubleday and Company Inc., Garden City, New York. 424 pp. + 77 plates.

Hosie, R.C. 1973. *Native trees of Canada.* Seventh Edition. Canadian Forestry Service, Department of the Environment. 380 pp.

Howe, W.H. 1975. *The butterflies of North America.* Doubleday and Company, Inc., Garden City, New York. 633 pp. + plates.

Judd, W.W. 1963. The butterflies of Dunn Township, Ontario. *Ontario Field Biologist* 17:1-14.

Judd, W.W. 1970. Additional observations on butterflies of Dunn Township, Ontario. *Ontario Field Biologist,* 24:13-16.

Kavanagh, K.C., L. Hutchison and S. Varga. 1989. *Status report on Bird's-foot Violet* Viola pedata *L. in Canada.* Prepared for the Committee on the Status of Endangered Wildlife in Canada (COSEWIC). 29 pp.

Kirby, W.F. 1871. *A synonymic catalogue of diurnal Lepidoptera.* John Van Voorst, London. 690 pp.

Kirby, W.F. 1877. *A synonymic catalogue of diurnal Lepidoptera.* John Van Voorst, London. pp. 691-883.

Klots, A.B. 1951. *A field guide to the butterflies of North America, east of the great plains.* The Peterson Field Guide Series. Houghton Mifflin Company, Boston. 349 pp.

Kohler, S. 1977. Revision of North American *Boloria selene* (Nymphalidae) with description of a new subspecies. *Journal of the Lepidopterists' Society* 31:243-265.

Konecny, A. 1986. *A status report on the Karner Blue butterfly* (Lycaeides melissa samuelis *Nabokov) in Canada.* A report prepared for the Ontario Ministry of Natural Resources. 48 pp.

Lafontaine, J.D. 1968. The butterflies of the Ottawa Region. *Trail and Landscape* 2(4):94-97.

Lamb, L. 1967. *A checklist of Waterloo County Lepidoptera, Papilionoidea, the butterflies.* Kitchener-Waterloo Field Naturalists. 9 pp.

Larson, J. 1989. *Achalarus lyciades* in Sandwich West Township of Essex County. *The Egret* 6(1):12-13.

Layberry, R.A., J.D. Lafontaine and P.W. Hall. 1981. Butterflies: some old, some new, some help from you. *Trail and Landscape* 15(3):118-122.

Layberry, R.A., J.D. Lafontaine and P.W. Hall. 1982. Butterflies of the Ottawa district. *Trail and Landscape* 16(1):359.

Lyman, H.H. 1908. Life history of *Euchaetias oregonensis* (Stretch). *Entomological Society of Ontario* 39:145.

Macy, R.W. and H.H. Shepard. 1941. *Butterflies.* University of Minnesota Press, Minneapolis, MN. 247 pp.

Maynard, C.J. 1891. *A manual of North American butterflies.* Dewolfe, Fiske and Company, Boston. 226 pp.

McDounnough, J. 1938. *Check list of the Lepidoptera of Canada and the United States of America. Part I, Macrolepidoptera.* Memoirs of the Southern California Academy of Science, Los Angeles, California, Vol. 1. 275 pp.

McMurrich, J.R. 1910. Notes of captures. *Proceedings of the Entomological Society of Ontario* 41:107.

Measures, D.G. 1976. *Bright wings of summer: watching butterflies.* Prentice-Hall, Incorporated, Englewood Cliffs, N.J. 160 pp.

Miller, L.D. and F.M. Brown. 1981. *A catalogue/checklist of the butterflies of America north of Mexico.* The Lepidopterists' Society, Memoir No. 2. 280 pp.

Moffat, A. 1895. Observations of the season of 1895. *Proceedings of the Entomological Society of Ontario* 26:38.

Morton, A. 1982. The importance of farming butterflies. *New Scientist* 30:503-508.

Munroe, E. 1978. Lepidoptera. pp. 427-481 *In:* Danks H.V., ed. *Canada and its insect fauna.* Memoirs of the Entomological Society of Canada No. 108. 573 pp.

Nabokov, V. 1949. The Nearctic forms of *Lycaeides* Hubner. *Psyche* 50:87-99.

Oldham, M.J. 1983. *Environmentally significant areas of the Essex Region*. A background report to the Essex Region Conservation Plan. Essex Region Conservation Authority, Essex, Ontario. 426 pp.

Opler, P.A. and G.O. Krizek. 1984. *Butterflies East of the Great Plains*. John Hopkins Univ. Press, Baltimore, MD. 294 pp.

Packer, L. 1987a. *Status report on the Karner Blue butterfly,* Lycaeides melissa samuelis *Nabokov, in Canada*. A report prepared for the World Wildlife Fund and the Ontario Ministry of Natural Resources, Wildlife Branch, Nongame Program. Unpublished. 66 pp.

Packer, L. 1987b. *Status report on some rare Lepidopteran species in southern Ontario*. Prepared for the World wildlife Fund and the Ontario Ministry of Natural Resources, Wildlife Branch, Nongame Program. 38 pp.

Paton, D.G. and M.J. Sharp. 1979. *A biological inventory of Halton Region Conservation Authority properties*. Halton Region Conservation Authority. 147 pp.

Pierce, N.E. and S. Easteal. 1986. The selective advantage of attendant ants for the larvae of a lycaenid butterfly, *Glaucopsyche lygdamus*. *Journal of Animal Ecology* 55:451-462.

Pratt, P.D. and J.E. Pilkington. In preparation. *Checklist of the butterflies of Windsor, Ontario*.

Pyle, R.M. 1981. *The Audubon Society field guide to North American butterflies*. Chanticleer Press, Inc., NY. 916 pp.

Riotte, J.C.E. 1967. New and corrected butterfly records for Ontario and for Canada. *Journal of the Lepidopterists' Society* 21:135-137.

Riotte, J.C.E. 1967. *Pieris virginiensis* in Ontario (Lepidoptera: Pieridae). *Proceedings of the Entomological Society of Ontario*, 98:27-29.

Riotte, J.C.E. 1970. *Checklist of Ontario skippers and butterflies*. Toronto Entomologists' Association, Occasional Publication #1. 4 pp.

Riotte, J.C.E. 1972. On the distribution of some skippers in Ontario. *Journal of Research on the Lepidoptera* 11:81-82.

Ross, A.M. 1873. *The butterflies and moths of Canada*. Rowsell and Hutchison, Toronto. iv + 93 pp.

Rothschild, L.W. and K. Jordan. 1906. A revision of the American papilios. *Novitates Zoologicae* 13:411-753 + plates IV-IX.

Saunders, W. 1880. Notes on some rare insects captured in Ontario during 1880. *Proceedings of the Entomological Society of Ontario* 11:40.

Saunders, W. 1884. Brief notes of a trip to Point Pelee, with additions to our list of Canadian butterflies. *Proceedings of the Entomological Society of Ontario* 15:30.

Saunders, H.S. 1903. Notes of captures. *Proceedings of the Entomological Society of Ontario* 34:90.

Savignano, D.A. 1987. *The association of* Lyaeides melissa samuelis *(Lepidoptera:Lycaenidae) the Karner Blue, with attendant ants*. A report submitted to the New York State Department of Environmental Conservation, Endangered Species Unit. 21 pp.

Schweitzer, D.F. 1984. *A report on the "Macro" Lepidoptera of the Pinery Provincial Park, Grand Bend, Ontario*. A report prepared for the Lambton Wildlife Fund and The Pinery Provincial Park. Unpublished. 24 pp.

Schweitzer, D.F. 1985. *A report on the status of the Karner Blue butterfly* Lycaeides melissa samuelis *in the province of Ontario*. Unpublished report to Ontario Ministry of Natural Resources, London. 18 pp.

Scoggan, H.J. 1978-1979. *The flora of Canada, parts 1-4*. National Museum of Natural Sciences, National Museums of Canada, Ottawa, Canada. 1711 pp.

Scott, J.A. 1986. *The butterflies of North America: A natural history and field guide*. Stanford University Press, Stanford, California. 583 pp.

Scudder, S.H. 1889. *The butterflies of the eastern United States and Canada*. Volumes I, II and III. Cambridge, MA. 1956 pp. + 89 plates and 4 maps.

Shapiro, A.M. 1969. New distributional data on three northeastern United States butterflies. *Journal of Lepidopterists' Society* 23:265-269.

Shapiro, A.M. 1974. Partitioning of resources among lupine-feeding Lepidoptera. *American Midland Naturalist* 91:243-248.

Shapiro, A.M. 1977. Evidence for two routes of post-pleistocene dispersal in *Poanes viator* (Hesperiidae). *Journal of Research on the Lepidoptera* 16:173-175.

Shapiro, A.M. and R.T. Cardé. 1970. Habitat selection and competition among sibling species of satyrid butterflies. *Evolution* 24:48-54.

Shull, E.M. 1987. *The butterflies of Indiana.* Indiana Academy of Science, Bloomington and Indianapolis. 262 pp.

Smith, J.B. 1903. *Checklist of Lepidoptera of boreal America.* American Entomological Society, Philadelphia. 15 pp.

Soper, J.H. 1956. Some families of restricted range in the Carolinian flora of Canada. *Transactions of the Royal Canadian Institute* 31:69-90.

Soper, J.H. and M.L. Heimburger. 1982. *Shrubs of Ontario.* The Royal Ontario Museum, Toronto. 495 pp.

Syme, P.D. 1958. The occurrence of the Silver-bordered Fritillary at Hamilton, Ontario. *Ontario Field Biologist* 12:27.

Syme, P.D. 1960. A new sulphur butterfly in Ontario. *Ontario Field Biologist* 14:31.

Syme, P.D. 1962. The Karner Blue Butterfly in Ontario. *Ontario Field Biologist* 16:34.

Thaler, G.R. and R.C. Plowright. 1973. An examination of the floristic zone concept with special reference to the northern limit of the Carolinian zone in southern Ontario. *Canadian Journal of Botany* 51:1765-1789.

Tietz, H.M. 1972. *An index to the described life histories, early stages and hosts of the macrolepidoptera of the continental United States and Canada. Volume I.* The Allyn Museum of Entomology, Sarasota, FL. 536 pp.

Tyler, H.A. 1975. *The swallowtail butterflies of North America.* Naturegraph Publishers, Inc., Healdsburg, CA. 192 pp.

Voss, E.G. 1972. *Michigan flora.* Part 1. Cranbrook Institute of Science Bulletin 55 and University of Michigan Herbarium. 488 pp.

Voss, E.G. 1985. *Michigan flora.* Part 2. Cranbrook Institute of Science Bulletin 59 and University of Michigan Herbarium. 724 pp.

Wagner, W.H. Jr. 1977. A distinctive dune form of the marbled white butterfly, *Euchloe olympia* (Lepidoptera: Pieridae) in the Great Lakes Area. *The Great Lakes Entomologist* 10:107-112.

Walker, E.M. 1907. Notes on captures. *Proceedings of the Entomological Society of Ontario* 38:118.

Walker, E.M. 1912. The faunal zones of Canada. *Proceedings of the Entomological Society of Ontario* 43:27-37.

Walker, E.M. and J. Macoun. 1901. A collecting trip in southwestern Ontario. *Proceedings of the Entomological Society of Ontario* 31:85-90.

Watkins, D.A. 1956. The breeding of *Euptoieta claudia* (Lepidoptera: Nymphalidae) in Ontario. *Ontario Field Biologist* 10:28.

Watkins, D.A. 1961. Collecting *Atrytone bimacula* and other interesting skippers in Ontario (Lepidoptera: Hesperiidae). *Ontario Field Biologist* 15:33.

Wild, W. 1939. The butterflies of the Niagara Fontier region and beginner's guide for collecting, rearing, and preserving them. *Bulletin of the Buffalo Society of Natural Sciences* 19(1):17-35.

Williams, C.B. 1930. *The migration of butterflies.* Oliver and Boyd, Edinburgh. 473 pp.

Williams, C.B. 1958. *Insect migration.* Collins, London. 235 pp.

Wormington, A. 1970. Butterflies of the Hamilton area and other interesting areas. *Wood Duck* 23:64-65 and 100-103.

Wormington, A. 1983. The butterflies of Point Pelee National Park, Ontario. *Ontario Field Biologist* 37(1):1-26.

The Status of Two Butterflies, Karner Blue (*Lycaeides melissa samuelis*) and Frosted Elfin (*Incisalia irus*), Restricted to Oak Savannah in Ontario

Laurence Packer

Department of Biology, York University
4700 Keele St., Downsview, Ontario M3J 1P3

Abstract. *The status in Ontario of two species of lepidoptera, Karner Blue and Frosted Elfin, was investigated. Both are restricted to two sites in the Carolinian Zone of Ontario – the Pinery-Port Franks area on Lake Huron south of Grand Bend, and the St. Williams Forestry Station and adjacent private land near Lake Erie, near the base of Long Point. Information is provided on the distribution and abundance, habitat requirements, general biology, and limiting factors of each species. A status of endangered in Ontario and Canada is proposed for Karner Blue and Frosted Elfin. Conservation recommendations are given on the maintenance of oak savannah habitat, critical for the perpetuation of these species in Canada.*

Introduction

Oak savannah is one of the most threatened vegetation types in North America. At the time of white settlement it covered at least 11,000,000 hectares of the American Midwest, yet only 113 relatively high quality sites comprising 2,607 hectares (0.02% of the original extent) could be located in a recent study (Nuzzo 1985). In Ontario we are fortunate in having a few areas where substantial tracts of high quality savannah persist. These include the Pinery-Port Franks area, Walpole Island Indian Reserve, Ojibway Prairie south of Windsor, Stone Road Alvar on Pelee Island, Long Point, Turkey Point, and a site adjacent to the St. Williams Forestry Station. As the extent of oak savannah habitat has declined, so of course have numerous associated species of specialized flora and fauna.

This paper documents the status of two species of lepidoptera, a group which continues to receive inadequate conservation oriented research. Less detailed comments on other rare insects are also included. Both main species are only known to occur in Ontario in the Pinery-Port Franks area and at St. Williams, sites which contain a large number of species which reach their northernmost distributional limits in the Carolinian forest of southern Ontario.

A detailed status report for the Karner Blue (Packer 1987a) and a status report which included treatments of Frosted Elfin and other rare lepidoptera (Packer 1987b) were submitted in 1987 by the author to the World Wildlife Fund and Ontario Ministry of Natural Resources. The following is a summary of these reports. A common approach in perpetuating these species is desirable; recommendations for their conservation have been combined and are presented at the end of the paper.

KARNER BLUE – *Lycaeides melissa samuelis*

Summary

The Karner Blue is undergoing a serious population decline throughout its range. It has been extirpated from many localities in the US and from four of the six places where it has been found in Canada. Of its two remaining localities in Ontario, its extirpation is imminent in one of them; a daily maximum of seven individuals was observed in the second generation at St. Williams, Haldimand-Norfolk RM, in 1986. The population at Pinery-Port Franks seems to be declining, although one small area has recently become very suitable for the species and its numbers here are increasing. The increase is unlikely to last because of successional changes within the habitat. Without active management at its current sites, the Karner Blue will become extirpated in Canada within 20 years. It may be possible to reintroduce the species into the Pinery. However, its habitat requirements are complex, involving its foodplant the Wild Lupine *(Lupinus perennis)*, ants which attend the larvae, and nectar sources for the adults. Of these, it will be most difficult to ensure the presence of a sufficient number of ants. For this reason, it is recommended that both the St. Williams and Port Franks sites be purchased or leased and managed for the Karner Blue while suitable habitat is provided within the Pinery. The latter may be expected to take several years to achieve, so action to ensure the butterflies' survival within its present locations is absolutely necessary.

Distribution

1. United States

Lycaeides melissa samuelis has been recorded from New Hampshire, Massachusetts, and all of the states bordering the Great Lakes (Konecny 1986). However, since 1975 it has been found in only 21 localities in the US and has disappeared from some of these within the past ten years. The Karner Blue is thought to have been extirpated in Massachusetts and Pennsylvania (Schweitzer 1985), Illinois (Konecny 1986), and possibly in Ohio (Schweitzer pers. comm. 1986). It is critically endangered in New Hampshire (Schweitzer 1985) and can be maintained in New York and Indiana only by deliberate habitat management (Schweitzer pers. comm. 1986). Its strongholds have been Michigan and Wisconsin. It has been recorded from 13 localities in the latter state (Kuehn 1983 in Konecny 1986); its status in the former is completely unknown.

2. Canada

At present the Karner Blue is known from only two sites in Canada, both in Ontario – St. Williams and Port Franks. It has been extirpated from four others – Orillia, London, Sarnia, and Toronto. Other records from Ontario, Manitoba, and Nova Scotia, are all based upon misidentifications (Hess 1983; Konecny 1986). It is highly unlikely that further populations will be discovered as its sole foodplant, *Lupinus perennis*, is also rare (Reznicek 1987), and searches of known stands of the Wild Lupine in Toronto, Walpole Island, and elsewhere, have failed to detect the presence of the butterfly.

Of the two extant populations in Ontario, that at St. Williams is extremely small and the habitat is rapidly becoming unsuitable. In 1984, the known St. Williams population was located within the boundaries of the forestry station and Schweitzer (1985) predicted that it would become extirpated within a few years.

By 1986 his prediction had proved to be true. In 1985 small numbers of the butterfly were found on an adjacent property. Surveys of aerial photographs of the surrounding area have shown that there is little chance of additional sites being discovered nearby.

In Lambton County, the *L. m. samuelis* population occurs as two demes (local or semi-isolated genetic populations) about 1.5 km apart at Port Franks. A core population exists with small satellite populations of the butterfly in tiny pockets in the immediate vicinity of this site. However these should probably not be considered as distinct populations and certainly have originated by emigration from the core. The second site may well have been colonised by the butterfly comparatively recently, probably also from the core (Schweitzer 1985). The latter population appears to be growing.

Protection

The Karner Blue is under review for listing under the US Endangered Species Act, having been rejected in 1978-79 because of the possibility of its not being rare in Michigan. It is officially recognized as endangered in New York and as threatened in Minnesota.

Loss of habitat is the most serious threat to the continued existence of healthy populations of this butterfly. Protection from such habitat loss is not provided for in any of the legislation to which the species has been subjected in the US. Thus, without active management of suitable sites, the laws protecting the species are unlikely to be effective in the long term. However, because of the small local populations that are typical of this species, extirpation by professional or amateur collectors should be considered a potential threat. In this regard the legislation could be useful, if enforced.

Population Sizes and Trends

The original St. Williams population has been known since at least as early as 1962, but became extirpated between 1984 and 1985 when the butterfly was discovered in an adjacent area (pers.comm. Kirk 1986 and Wynnia 1986). The Pinery population was first recorded in the 1930s (Hess 1981). At this time the species' range extended from the Port Franks area through to the northern edges of the Pinery PP. The last confirmed observation within the Pinery was made in 1980, despite searches within the Park boundaries and at the lupine sites along nearby roadsides since that date. In 1986 these areas were investigated during the peak of Karner Blue activity (both generations) by the author – none were seen. Lupines occur sporadically throughout this area (Hess 1981, 1983) but the butterfly is currently restricted to two sites at Port Franks.

In 1980, Hess (1981) estimated a population of 200-300 Karner Blues in the Port Franks area during a census of the first generation on June 12. All studies of this butterfly to date state that the second generation is much more numerous than the first. Consequently, this estimate seems to indicate a very high population level at this time. Crabe (1984) reports seeing 150-200 individuals at the main site on 21 July 1983, and 20-30 individuals at the separate second site. In 1984, the maximum daily total seen by Schweitzer (1985) was 109, in 1986 the comparable figure was 47. Surveys of the area by members of the T.E.A. in 1987 and 1988 (Hess 1988 and pers. comm.) suggest that this downward trend has continued with a maximum daily total of 40 individuals in 1987 and three for 1988 (It should be noted that comparatively few visits were made in 1988 and the peak abundance of the butterfly may have been missed). The estimates of Hess (1981) and Crabe (1984) could have included butterflies that were counted more than once, since none were individually marked. Nonetheless, a marked decline in numbers is indicated by these estimates.

Mark-release-recapture analyses were performed on the Lambton County demes by Schweitzer in 1984. Only the more numerous second generation was censused, during a two week period. In 1986 the author carried out mark-release-recapture estimates for both generations. Both of these studies treated three sites separately, the third site being the basal area of the dune adjacent to the main population. Results for these three sites are summarised in Table 1.

Table 1

Summary of Population Estimates for the Karner Blue Butterfly at Three Sites in Lambton County, Ontario in 1984 and 1986.

Year	1984		1986		1986	
Generation	2nd		1st		2nd	
Sex	male	female	male	female	male	female
Site A	300*	300*	130	125	210	235
Site B	100*	100*	55		120	90
Site C	20*	20*	33		136	125

* maximum upper limit estimates

In summary, rough population estimates from 1980 to 1988 are indicative of a sharp downward trend in Karner Blue numbers at its main site. The observed slight increase in Karner Blue numbers in Lambton County as a whole between 1984 and 1986, is due entirely to a rapid rise in suitability of the secondary site (perhaps resulting from partial clearing in anticipation of development); this improvement appears not to have lasted.

General Biology

1. Description

Lycaeides m. samuelis is a member of the Lepidopteran family Lycaenidae – the blues, coppers and hairstreaks. The blues form the subfamily Plebeiinae represented by seventeen species in eastern North America in nine genera.

In northeastern North America the two species of *Lycaeides* are the only blues with silvery spots on the underside of the hind wing. *Lycaeides argyrognomon* and *L. melissa* are difficult to distinguish and misidentifications have been common in the past. Dissection of the genitalia indicate that the two species are distinct. Colouration differences between the two are subtle; *L. m. melissa* can be distinguished by being less heavily dusted with fuscous above (♂); larger submarginal orange spots on the upper surface (♀); narrower marginal border to the fore wing (♂ and ♀); larger, brighter orange submarginal underside hind wing spots (♂ and ♀); and a more rounded hind wing (♂ and ♀).

There are four subspecies of *L. argyrognomon* in Eastern Canada, two of which are restricted to the Maritimes and Newfoundland. Only subspecies *nabokovi* is likely to be confused with *samuelis* in our area. Perhaps the easiest way to distinguish these two subspecies is the nature of the terminal line of the underside hind wing. In *L. m. samuelis* this is narrow but unbroken, in *L. a. nabokovi* it is broken into a series of small triangular spots (Masters 1972).

There are five subspecies of *L. melissa*; the Karner Blue is the most distinct (Nabokov 1949). The remaining four subspecies are western in distribution. Only the nominate subspecies – *L. m. melissa*, has a range that overlaps with that of *samuelis* in Wisconsin. Even here the two occupy different habitats with *L. m. melissa* being found in tall grass prairie and *samuelis* in pine barrens, pine prairies, and lakeshore dunes (Shapiro 1969). An additional difference is that the Karner Blue is restricted to the Wild Lupine as a foodplant (Opler 1984) whereas *L. m. melissa* feed upon a wide range of Leguminosae including *Lupinus*. These facts suggest that *L. m. samuelis* may deserve specific status as suggested by Schweitzer (1985).

2. Reproductive Biology

The Karner Blue is a bivoltine (i.e. has two generations a year) species. First generation adults are active in May and June, the second generation in July and August. The later developing second generation larvae are contemporary with the earlier emerging adults of this generation. Overwintering occurs in the egg stage.

Females lay their eggs on, or near, the larval foodplant. Cryan and Dirig (1978, in Konecny 1986) reported that first generation females lay their eggs on leaves and petioles of the foodplant. Oviposition behaviour of first generation Ontario Karner Blues was not studied. However, a detailed search was made for the eggs laid by second generation females in the third week of August 1986.

In August 1988, 82 Wild Lupine plants were searched for Karner eggs, which can be identified by their flattened, round shape, and surface sculpture characteristics. The state of health and position of the plants were recorded. By the time these observations were made, many of the plants had wilted and died back. The dead and dying plants were no less likely to have received an egg than were those still living. However, eggs were significantly more likely to be located on plants that were in comparatively shady places (Fisher's exact test, p = 0.012). All eggs noted were low down on the plants, usually lower than, or around, the position of the first leaf petiole. Some eggs were found attached to grass stems close to lupines.

Larvae of both sexes are extremely well camouflaged when on lupine plants, their colouration matching that of the lupine leaves very closely. Cryan and Dirig (1978, in Konecny 1986) state that pupation occurs with the larvae hanging from stems or twigs on or near the host plants. Careful searches were made of lupine plants just before and during the early stages of the emergence of the second brood. No pupae could be located. Two larvae were kept in captivity and both pupated underneath leaves in their petri dish containers. These observations suggest that in this population, Karner Blues may not pupate on the foodplant. They may pupate on the ground or under leaf litter nearby.

The sex ratio of adult Karner Blues is probably close to one to one. Although the estimates given in Table 1 are indicative of male biased ratios, this is a common phenomenon in mark-release-recapture analyses of Lepidoptera, thought to result from greater catchability of males.

3. Population Dynamics

The population trends of Lambton County Karner Blues indicate that a rapid increase in numbers is possible under good conditions. However, the dune base site appears to have a stationary population, whereas numbers at the main site may be decreasing. The population structure and dynamics of natural Karner Blue populations is probably one of large fluctuations in numbers following colonisation of newly suitable habitat after fires. Fires create early successional stage habitats favourable to growth of the larval foodplant. With successional change, numbers tend to dwindle gradually. The insect itself is not fire-resistant in any of its life history stages, and thus the phenomenon that makes the habitat particularly suitable for the species will actually result in its extermination on a small scale. Therefore, local dispersal is probably an important aspect of the population dynamics of this species. Where repeated mowing of the vegetation occurs at a time of year when the butterflies are not disturbed by the process, large populations may build up and persist indefinitely. Thus, active management may be quite successful in establishing healthy populations of the Karner Blue butterfly.

4. Sensitivity

Fire suppression has had an adverse effect upon the lupine population and perhaps also that of the ant species that tend Karner Blue larvae. Soil erosion by dirt bikes and other vehicles also poses a threat. However, the paths in the dunes around the primary site may help to provide intermediate levels of solar illumination, which seem to be suitable for the lupines. Shortage of nectar sources appears to have been a problem preventing successful colonisation of some otherwise suitable habitat in the St. Williams area.

Habitat

1. Habitat Requirements

There are three habitat requirements that appear to be absolutely necessary to the Karner Blue in Ontario. These are:

i)   adequate supplies of the larval foodplant – *Lupinus perennis,*

ii) adequate supplies of nectar sources for the adults,

iii) the presence of suitable ant species to protect the larvae.

i) *Lupinus perennis*

The Wild Lupine is a xerophytic species that is found on dry, sandy soils. It seems to grow best where it is in direct sunlight for between 40% and 80% of the day (Hess 1983). This legume is the only species of foodplant used by the Karner Blue (Opler 1984) and larvae of both generations feed upon it. The eggs of the butterfly are laid on, or near, the lupine plants.

ii) Nectar Sources

Tables 2 and 3 list the flower species that the Karner Blue butterflies were observed visiting in Port Franks in the first and second generations respectively. A wide range of flower species is visited, without any obvious colour or taxonomic preference. Some plants were visited more frequently than expected in terms of their relative abundance. The white flowers of sandwort were particularly attractive and at Site C large numbers of butterflies were found in a small dense patch of this plant even though suitable lupines for oviposition were at least 15 metres away.

Table 2

List of Nectar Sources Visited by First Generation Karner Blue Adults at Port Franks

Thyme-leaved Sandwort	*Arenaria serpyllifolia*
Lyre-Leaved Rock Cress	*Arabis lyrata*
Juneberry	*Amelanchier* sp.
Wild Lupine	*Lupinus perennis*
Wild Geranium	*Geranium maculatum*
Hairy Puccoon	*Lithospermum caroliniense*
Hawkweeds	*Hieracium* spp.

Table 3

List of Nectar Plants used by Second Generation Karner Blue Adults at Port Franks

Butterfly-weed	*Asclepias tuberosa*
Wild Bergamot	*Monarda fistulosa*
New Jersey Tea	*Ceanothus americanus*
New Jersey Tea	*C. herbaceus*
Black-eyed Susan	*Rudbeckia hirta*

iii) Attendant Ants

The myrmecophilous associations of Lycaenid butterflies have been well documented and are common within the group (reviewed by Pierce 1987). These associations range from facultative protection of the larvae by ants in return for secretions from glands on the surface of the larvae, to obligate feeding by the butterfly larvae upon ant broods within ant nests. Workers of four ant species were found associated with Karner Blue larvae near the Pinery PP. These species were *Camponotus pennsylvanicus*, *Formica exsectoides*, *Myrmica punctiventris* and *Aphaenogaster rudis*. The former species was the only one associating with the butterfly larvae at Site C and was not found at either of the two locations. At the main site, *F. exsectoides* was the most common attendant, apparently excluding the other, smaller species. There were several, very large and very old nests of this wood ant at this site and evidence of even older, now defunct nests. This indicates a long period of occupation of the site by this ant species. In the dune base areas, the smaller ant species predominated and no large *Formica* nests were found in the immediate vicinity. Interestingly, larvae attended by the smaller ant species were tended by a larger number of individual ants, whereas *Formica* normally attended the larvae solitarily (the mean number of ants per larva was 2.2 for the small ants and 1.3 for *Formica*).

Field censuses indicated that at most three percent of the later instar larvae were left unattended by ants. This is in marked contrast to the studies of ant attendance of Karner Blue larvae in two populations near Albany, New York (Savignano 1987). Savignano found that 24% of larvae were attended by ants at one site whereas the corresponding figure at the other locality was 54%. Eight different species of ant (in five genera) were found in association with Karner Blue larvae in New York. Collections of larvae and observations of disappearance rates were made at the New York localities but parasitism rates were generally too low for meaningful interpretation.

A short larval transfer experiment was performed in the Pinery PP region in 1986. Although sample sizes were necessarily small, there was an indication that larvae disappeared more rapidly in an area without ants.

It seems that ant attendance may be more important for Karner Blue survival in Ontario than it is in New York, although this should be verified by more intensive observations of larval survival in the presence and absence of ants. Perhaps the potential reduction in parasitism rates is more crucial in the more northern populations where climatic factors may have a greater effect upon butterfly numbers. It is worth noting that the wood ant population at the St. Williams Karner Blue site seems to have crashed recently – many old, defunct nests were found but no large active ones could be located.

2. Habitat Distribution

The Karner Blue is not found at all sites where lupine occurs. Possible reasons for this absence include: past or present inadequate numbers of the foodplant; absence of nectar sources at times when the adults are on the wing; and absence of sufficient numbers of ants that tend the larvae. It is also possible that not all of the current lupine sites are natural or that the butterfly has never been able to reach some of these areas, which are unlikely to have been contiguous even in the distant past.

3. Trend in Habitat Quality and Quantity, and Habitat Protection

The decline in Karner Blue population in North America is largely a result of habitat destruction by the encroachment of agriculture or residential or commercial development. In those areas where such destruction has not taken place, fire suppression has changed the ecology of previously suitable areas to the detriment of the butterfly. The planting of pine trees and suppression of fire in the Pinery PP must be considered as the most important causes of the decline of the Karner Blue in Lambton County. Fire is a natural part of many ecosystems and serves to maintain communities in an early successional stage. Once fire is suppressed, the plant species that require intermediate levels of shade, and those which cannot survive competition when the vegetation gets too dense, die out. For this reason, the lupine, upon which the Karner Blue depends, has become extremely localised in the Lambton County sites where both were once common. Furthermore, the habitat changes that have resulted from fire suppression have decreased the likelihood of successful reintroduction of the species.

The increased survival of larvae as a result of ant attendance indicates that ant population levels are a probable limiting factor, at least in Ontario. In the absence of ant attendance, the larvae are susceptible to higher levels of predation and parasitism. The larger of the two ant species observed tending the larvae was a member of the wood ant genus *Formica*. These ants may obtain up to 95% of their food from aphid honeydew secretion (pers. comm. Elmes 1986 and Breen 1986), a habit that probably preadapts them to attending and protecting Lycaenid larvae. Thus, the ants may require the presence of healthy aphid populations in addition to suitable nest sites. It should be noted that large wood ant nests are comparatively resistant to fire because of their depth. However, intense fires may result in the nest material itself catching fire, and this may burn slowly for several days after the surface fire has passed. Further research is needed to verify the relative importance of different ant species to the survival of Karner Blue larvae in Ontario.

Absence of suitable nectar sources can prevent the establishment of butterfly populations even in areas where ants and lupines are common. This is probably only a problem in the driest areas of suitable habitat, or those where the soil is extremely low in nutrients, a condition which the growth of lupines, with their nitrogen fixing root nodule bacteria, helps to prevent.

Because of the small isolated nature of Karner Blue populations, human disturbance during sensitive periods may be harmful. Collection or other disturbance of the adults may reduce survivorship and female oviposition rates. Disturbance during the period of larval feeding may result in increased predation and parasitism rates, because disturbed larvae drop off of their foodplant and have to be relocated by the ants.

Other insect species feed upon lupines. At the Pinery, augmentation of the small lupine population has been marred by an unknown species of insect that feeds upon the very small plants. Leaf mining Diptera and microlepidoptera, and a leaf rolling tortricid moth, also feed upon lupines in Lambton County. Presumably these are also rare species. The effects of these lupine feeders mentioned above (with the exception of the one that destroys the young plants) are likely to be small because the insects involved feed on only a small amount of each lupine plant. Indeed, the larvae of the Karner Blue itself seem to be the most damaging enemies of the lupine; small plants were observed to be completely destroyed by the feeding activity of one or more larvae. Thus, in extremely small localities where lupines are scarce, intraspecific competition is likely to be more important than interspecific factors listed above, again with the possible exception of the insect that consumes the young plant.

Evaluation and Proposed Status

The Karner Blue butterfly has undergone a global population decline as a result of habitat destruction. In many of its present localities it can be maintained only by active management. Its foodplant, the Wild Lupine, is itself a rare plant which is highly susceptible to habitat deterioration.

In Canada, two of the three sites where the species is found are slated for development, although this probably will not happen within the next ten years. There is a limited time period within which these localities have to be purchased and/or actively managed, or management plans implemented in the Pinery PP, and the species successfully reintroduced.

The proposed status for the Karner Blue butterfly in Ontario and Canada is **ENDANGERED**.

FROSTED ELFIN – *Incisalia irus*

Summary

The Frosted Elfin is probably the most endangered butterfly in Canada. It occurs only in an area of oak savannah in St. Williams and in suitable locations along nearby roadside verges. Its total population in Canada probably does not exceed 100 adults in any year: eight adults were observed in 1986.

This species relies upon the Wild Lupine as a larval foodplant and appears to be well adapted for exploiting small populations of the species. The males are territorial and defend patches of the foodplant.

Without immediate active management of its only locality, this species will become extirpated in Canada before the turn of the century. It is highly recommended that this site be purchased or leased and that the small areas where the lupine still grows be cleared of much of the competing vegetation. It seems important that this clearing be done so as to create small open patches. This situation seems to be preferred by this species. Such management would aid the survival of the endangered Karner Blue butterfly as well. Creation of small lupine stands on the St. Williams forestry station adjacent to the known Frosted Elfin site should be considered.

Distribution

1. United States

The Frosted Elfin butterfly is widely distributed in North America. It is found from southern Canada, south to Georgia and Alabama (Klots 1979). However, it is uncommon to rare throughout its range. In New England the species is sparsely distributed but can survive in very small patches of suitable habitat (Schweitzer 1986). It is normally more common than the Karner Blue in the US.

2. Canada

The Frosted Elfin has been found in the St. Williams area since the 1960s. It has always been uncommon even in its preferred habitat. Daniels (in Hess 1981) records seeing five individuals in an area of "1/2 square mile" in 1978, in 1979 12 were seen in an area of similar size. However, in 1977 Troubridge (in Hess 1981) recorded the species as being common in the area. In 1986 Mary Gartshore surveyed the only site where the species is known to persist. Seven individuals were found. Later in the year, Quimby Hess found an individual approximately half a mile from the main population.

The probability of this species being found in any other locality in Ontario is nil. Stands of the Wild Lupine are rare in the province (Reznicek 1987). The main sites have been carefully searched, and although this activity has been largely directed at the Karner Blue butterfly, it is unlikely that the distinctive behaviour of male *I. irus* could have been missed.

If this species was still present in the Port Franks area it would have been located during the course of the intensive field work that was carried out there by several researchers between 1984 and 1986. Although several other Elfin species were seen, *I. irus* was definitely absent.

Protection

This species is apparently not protected anywhere within its range.

Population Size and Trend

The area within which the Frosted Elfin occurs in St. Williams has been drastically reduced. Large numbers of pine trees have been planted in areas previously occupied by the butterfly. As the trees grew the lupines beneath them died out and the butterflies could no longer survive. Presently, the species survives on a small adjacent property and along the edges of the dirt roads that run alongside the forestry station.

The main site is an area of oak savannah which is becoming overgrown at an alarming pace. Lupine stands are found in several patches within the area but they are small and widely dispersed.

To summarize, the area inhabited by this species has been reduced over the years and is now extremely small. The population size is declining.

General Biology

1. Description

The Frosted Elfin is a dull brown butterfly with a slight variegated pattern on the underside, but of almost uniform colouration on the dorsal surface. It can be distinguished from other members of the genus *Incisalia* by the following combination of characteristics:

> basal half of underside hind wing dark – with no clear markings; outer half of underside hind wing with pale suffusion; outer margin of hind wing scalloped to form a slight tail; outer third of underside fore wing not noticeably paler than rest of wing.

2. Reproduction

The Frosted Elfin has one generation each year. The adults are on the wing in May and early June.

The males are quite clearly territorial (Gartshore pers. comm. 1986; Schweitzer 1986) and defend small clumps of lupine. This behaviour makes accurate censuses difficult because males without territories are extremely difficult to locate and the females are secretive.

The larvae develop in the flowers and developing seeds of the lupine plant. Pupation takes place underground near the foodplant.

Very little is known about other aspects of the reproductive biology of this species.

3. Movement

As with the Karner Blue, the natural habitat of the Frosted Elfin requires fire for adequate maintenance. Thus, in the absence of fire, the vegetation becomes too dense for the continued survival of the foodplant. Pupae are located sufficiently deeply in the soil to enable the butterfly to survive intense fires (Schweitzer pers. comm. 1987). It is probably more tolerant of denser vegetation than is the Karner Blue, as a result of the territorial behaviour of the male which is well suited to small patches of foodplant. However, it should be noted that observations of males at lupine patches may give a misleading picture of the real habitat requirements of this species. Territorial males are quite conspicuous and draw attention to the small lupine patches that they defend. The females are much more secretive but they may spend much of their time ovipositing upon lupines that are not necessarily in the same general location as the ones observed being defended by the males. The habitat preferences of females of this species should be studied. Schweitzer (1986) describes the species as capable of maintaining adequate populations where there are small weedy patches of lupine. Dispersal and exploitation of comparatively temporary habitat are likely components of this species' ecology.

4. Sensitivity

The Frosted Elfin is susceptible to habitat deterioration and loss as a result of human encroachment and fire suppression. Its extremely small population size in Ontario also makes it vulnerable to overcollecting and there is evidence that fairly large numbers (in comparison to its total population) have been collected from the St. Williams area from the 1960s to the present. Because of its early emergence this species can survive in areas where the lupines become overgrown late in the season. However, such overcrowding is eventually to the detriment of the foodplant.

Habitat

1. Habitat Requirements

The Frosted Elfin has been recorded to feed upon the Wild Lupine *(Lupinus perennis)* and Wild Indigo *(Baptisia tinctoria)*. It is not known whether it uses the latter foodplant in Ontario. However, all of the available records indicate an association with the lupine in the St. Williams area.

As described above, this species can survive in areas where the lupine population is divided into small pockets. It is this aspect of its biology that has enabled it to maintain itself in the St. Williams area at numbers approximating, now perhaps slightly exceeding, those of the Karner Blue in the same habitat.

2. Distribution

The Frosted Elfin is restricted to sites where its foodplant(s) grow. In the US these are pine barrens and some lakeshore dune systems, where the butterfly is found in association with the Karner Blue. The Frosted Elfin is less rare than the Karner Blue in the US (Schweitzer 1986). In Canada, the only known habitat is a dry oak savannah.

3. Trend in Quality of Critical Habitat

What little suitable habitat for this species that still remains is deteriorating quite quickly as a result of successional changes. The species is facing a total loss of suitable habitat in its only locality in Canada.

4. Habitat Protection

Almost all of the area inhabited by this species is on a single piece of privately owned land. A few patches of lupine which may support tiny numbers of the butterfly are found on the very edge of the St. Williams forestry station on the verge of a dirt road. It is highly unlikely that the latter are of sufficient total size for long-term survival of this species. Dispersal from the main site has probably been the way in which these isolated sites have been colonised.

The critical site will certainly not remain in suitable condition without active management, and this is required immediately if the species is to survive.

Limiting Factors

Loss of suitable habitat resulting from human activities within the St. Williams area has been the main reason for the diminished population of this species. The current main problem is deterioration of habitat as a result of succession.

Evaluation and Proposed Status

The Frosted Elfin is the most critically endangered butterfly species in Canada. The habitat in which the only remaining population is found is extremely rare in Ontario and natural succession here is threatening the species with extirpation. The species has been subjected to at least moderate levels of collecting in the past thirty years, the intensity of which has probably been sufficient to be detrimental.

The proposed status for this species in Ontario and Canada is **ENDANGERED.**

Conservation Recommendations

1. Habitat Protection and Management

i) Karner Blue

Although a 14 ha property now owned by Lambton Wildlife Incorporated encompasses the main Karner Blue population (Site A) in Lambton County, the remaining two populations are on private land. Although the chances of these areas being sold in the next few years seem small (Crabe pers. comm. 1986), successional changes in the habitat will render them less and less suitable for the Karner Blue as time passes. The purchased site will require careful observation to ensure its continued suitability for the Karner Blue. Low intensity management will be required to prevent the lupines from being crowded out by competing vegetation, and regular checks should be made on the availability of ants to attend Karner Blue larvae.

The complete demise of the Karner Blue in the St. Williams area must be considered imminent. There are a few remaining pockets of lupine growth, but these are fast becoming overcrowded with taller vegetation and it would appear that the wood ant population is also declining.

Active management of both areas will be necessary. In particular, the St. Williams site is unlikely to support the butterfly for more than one or two years without some clearing of the vegetation that is crowding out the lupine plants.

The Pinery PP remains the most likely site where large suitable areas could be produced and maintained indefinitely. Initially, a large amount of work is required to provide this habitat. Several areas within the park boundary will have to undergo a thinning of tree cover and burning of ground vegetation to provide suitable habitat for lupine growth. It is suggested that a network of such areas be provided such that it would be possible for the butterflies to disperse from one area to another. This habitat connectivity is known to increase the probability of population survival (Fahrig and Merriam 1985; Lefkovitch and Fahrig 1985).

Once the required management plans at the Pinery are implemented and the butterfly successfully reintroduced, the species may require only minimal further effort. Lupine planting will have to be followed by annual censuses of growth success and recruitment of the plant. Further research should reveal the habitat requirements of the ants that increase the survival rate of Karner Blue larvae. It is important that this latter research be performed soon because this may prove to be the most difficult aspect of the conservation program. This is because the social structure of ant colonies results in a long delay between the establishment of suitable conditions and the build up of large numbers of ant workers.

ii) Frosted Elfin

The best way to ensure the continued survival of the Frosted Elfin is to purchase, or at least lease, the area at St. Williams which it now occupies. As soon as this is done, an immediate alleviation of present habitat deterioration trends should be undertaken. Males of the Frosted Elfin seem to be highly territorial, and may benefit from the extremely fragmented lupine population in the area. Thus, any management for St. Williams should attempt to increase potential habitat by the selective scarification of small areas, separated from each other by a few metres of taller vegetation. Small scale tree felling and lupine seed planting should also be considered. Uprooting of competing vegetation immediately around surviving lupine patches should be done as soon as possible.

Involvement of a botanist familiar with the site should be considered crucial to ensure that the botanical rarities (of which there are many at the main site) are not adversely affected by implementation of management plans.

Introduction of the species into the Pinery PP may be possible in the distant future, but is not recommended until a healthy population has been established in the St. Williams area. It should be possible to reintroduce the species into the St. Williams Forest station if management plans currently being taken there to protect the Karner Blue are maintained and augmented.

Patrolling of purchased lands to prevent the collection of Frosted Elfin and Karner Blue should be undertaken.

2. Public Education Programs

The management proposals currently being implemented at the Pinery involve the use of fire to re-establish the natural ecology of the area. Fire is generally considered as undesirable and dangerous by the public. As a result of this reasonable fear, Park officials have been undertaking local education programs through newspaper articles, to inform the public of the necessity of this action. Visitors to the park are also informed of this.

Karner Blue conservation is being written about in Canadian nature magazines and it is hoped that some national (or at least Ontario-wide) CBC coverage can be obtained. The main problem that has to be avoided is making general knowledge of the exact location of the present Karner Blue sites. Because two of these are on private land to which the public has uncontrolled access, there are risks that large numbers of butterflies might be taken by unscrupulous collectors. Additionally, large numbers of naturalist visitors wishing to take photographs of the insect could damage the habitat.

An allied problem is that lupine plants are occasionally dug up by people for transplantation (which is unlikely to be successful). Public education on the undesirability of this is being undertaken by Pinery staff. Articles in appropriate magazines could also stress this problem and could provide information on where to obtain Wild Lupine seeds by mail order.

Public education efforts to preserve the Karner Blue in Ontario should also mention the Frosted Elfin. Moderately large numbers have been collected by Lepidopterists since the 1960s. Both species should be protected by the Endangered Species Act and collection should be prohibited by law. This course should be well advertised in the entomological literature to ensure that collectors in Ontario are aware of the species' legal status.

3. Further Research

i) Karner Blue

In the light of current knowledge concerning the biology of the Karner Blue, the following information will be required in order to ensure the successful implementation of a management plan for the species at the Pinery – Port Franks area.

a) Ant/Larva Interactions

At present, four species of ant appear to tend Karner Blue larvae in Ontario. A brief field experiment indicated that ant attendance increases the proportion of Karner Blue individuals that complete their development to the adult stage, as has been more firmly documented for other ant/Lycaenid interactions. A comparison of the effectiveness of the different ant species in defending the Karner Blue larvae is required. It seems possible that the smaller ant species makes up for any lack in defense capabilities by attending the larvae in larger numbers than the larger, more aggressive wood ant *Formica*. However, this remains to be demonstrated.

Because the larval transfer experiments performed during the course of this study resulted in the death and/or disappearance of a large proportion of the experimental Karner Blue larvae, it is recommended that further experiments be carried out only upon laboratory-reared larvae. These should be easily obtainable by capturing some old, worn, first generation females and placing them in suitable cages with living lupine foodplant for oviposition. The larvae should be allowed to develop until they reach the fourth instar before being subjected to field experimentation. Some should be placed in areas where only the smaller ants are known to occur, or where they are more common than *Formica* – Site B is recommended for this. Others should be placed on Lupines at Site A, the main population. A third experimental placing may be necessary at Site C to test the suitability of *Camponotus* as a defender of Karner Blue larvae against predation and/or parasitism. Methods should follow those of Pierce and Easteal (1986) as closely as possible.

Because the different ant species predominate in different areas where predation and parasitism pressures may also be expected to vary, it could be argued that the above experiment is confounded, and that variation in defense success should be analyzed within one area. This could be managed in a site where several attendant ant species are found (as with Site A) by placing a ring around the stem of the lupine such that only the smaller ants can get between the ring and stem. Tanglefoot should be placed over the ring so that the larger ants cannot get to the larvae by walking over the barrier.

b) Ant Biology

Whichever species of ant turns out to be best at defending the Karner Blue larvae, knowledge concerning its habitat requirements should be obtained. The wood ants are better understood in this regard and they may well be the more effective defenders. Some work has been done in Europe to manage wood ant populations and this literature should be consulted to ensure successful augmentation of wood ant populations in the areas of the Pinery that are designated as Karner Blue management sites. However, these ants are often heavily dependent upon one or a few species of aphids for the majority of their nourishment (they obtain honeydew secretions from the aphids, which they in turn protect). Thus, the preferred food source of these ants needs to be discovered. There are several extremely large wood ant nests at the main Port Franks population, with well marked trails traversed by thousands of workers. These should be followed and the tree species from which the ants are obtaining their aphid-secretion food discovered. Suitable aphid-bearing trees should be protected during thinning operations at the Pinery.

c) Lupine Growth and Lupine/Larva Interactions

Lupine seeds are being germinated with extremely high success rates by the Pinery PP staff and their associates. Currently, the main problem with sustained lupine growth is that the very young plants are consumed by an as yet unidentified (and yet to be captured) insect species. This needs to be prevented and several means may be envisaged to ensure this. Nonetheless, it is possible that some natural feeding inhibiting chemicals could be sprayed upon the small plants, such as a solution of onion and garlic extract, as used by organic home gardeners. This will wash off with time and so repeated application may be necessary. However, it is possible that the problem insect is only active for a brief period each year; if so, this would minimize the time expenditure in protecting the plants. Alternatively, cages or other barriers preventing access to the plants could be placed around them. These would have to be removed before the butterflies are reintroduced.

Once the successful early survival of lupines has been achieved, a field experiment should be carried out to determine the optimal conditions for their rapid growth and natural recruitment into the population. Detailed recommendations on methods are provided in the status report (Packer 1987a).

ii) Frosted Elfin

The species occurs in such small numbers that immediate habitat protection will have to take place to ensure that there will be any remaining individuals of this species left to study. Very little is known of its biology. However, it does seem well suited to the exploitation of small lupine patches. Three plants that are crowding out the remaining lupine patches should be partially cleared. Observations on the behaviour and oviposition site preferences of females should be performed.

4. Associated Species

It is important to stress that the habitats occupied by the butterflies described in this report are deserving of conservation because of the species assemblages that they harbour. In addition to these rare butterflies, several other extremely uncommon insect species were recorded out of the small proportion that it was possible to get identified. It should be noted that there are few insect taxa for which adequate keys are available and fewer people trained to be able to use them. Consequently, it will be many years before much of the insect survey material is adequately documented. Nonetheless, many interesting species have been identified. Pre-eminent among those already identified are the following:

a) The bee *Lasioglossum (Dialictus) pictum* – found on the edge of the younger dune systems within the Pinery PP. This represents the first Canadian record for this generally more southern species.

b) *Paralictus michiganensis* – a cleptoparasitic bee species. One female was caught in a malaise trap. This specimen represents only the second individual of this species ever caught.

c) *Perilampus rohweri* – this small parasitic wasp was found not uncommonly on the edge of the younger dunes, but previously, less than ten specimens had ever been caught anywhere in the world.

Additional rare lepidoptera species have been found in the area. Two of these are worthy of some detailed comments.

i) Dusted Skipper – *Atrytonopsis hianna*

The Dusted Skipper is a widespread but local and uncommon species in the US. It is found from New England south to Georgia and west to Nebraska. In Canada, the Dusted Skipper is known from Manitoba, Saskatchewan, and the Pinery PP area in Ontario. There are no historical records of this species elsewhere in Ontario. My observations indicate that the species is found in open dune areas and woodland clearings throughout the Pinery PP and in suitable areas at least as far south as Port Franks. There are old records as far north as Grand Bend. Currently, it occurs at low densities over a wide area and appears to have a long, drawn out period of emergence. It was found in all areas of suitable habitat that were investigated, from the outermost vegetated dune systems in the Pinery, to clearings made for ski trails and electricity lines.

The Ontario population of this species is well isolated from all of its other known sites. It cannot be stated with certainty that it does not occur in other parts of Ontario. Its supposed foodplant is not uncommon, but it definitely does not occur in some areas where the larval food is present.

It is a mystery why this species is not found in other good quality dunes where the supposed foodplant – Little Bluestem *(Andropogon scoparius)*, grows. Although it has undoubtedly undergone a reduction in habitat in recent decades, this trend is likely to be reversed by the implementation of management plans currently being undertaken at the Pinery.

The Dusted Skipper has one generation each year and the adults are to be found in May and June. The larvae are thought to feed upon Little Bluestem *(Andropogon scoparius)* (Campbell *et al.* 1986).

Observations made on this species in the field in 1986 indicate that it has a comparatively drawn out period of emergence. It was never found in large numbers, rather a few would be found whenever a search was made in the right habitat – vegetated dune areas, woodland clearings, etc.

Searches were made for the larvae; none were seen but remains of silk tents, commonly used by skipper larvae to hold the edges of foodplant leaves together, were found on large Little Bluestem plants. This species is known to make such tents (Heitzman and Heitzman 1974).

Like most butterflies of its family, the Dusted Skipper is a fast flier. It is likely that individuals cover quite a large area during their adult lives.

The proposed status for this species is RARE in Ontario and Canada.

ii) *Schinia gloriosa*

In 1984 an owlet moth *Schinia gloriosa* was discovered for the first time in Canada in the dune systems at the Pinery (Schweitzer 1984). In 1986 the species was caught at lights throughout the Park. Of note was its discovery in clearings inland from the dunes where comparatively small amounts of its foodplant *Liatris cylin-*

dracea were located. Suitable habitat was searched for the larvae in the following localities: Rondeau, Manitoulin Island, and Long Point (in the latter locality the foodplant could not be located). No definite sightings of the larvae were recorded. However, developing seed pods of the plant bearing signs of larval feeding similar to that seen for this species, were found at Rondeau, indicating the possibility of its presence. Nocturnal light trapping revealed no specimens of the adult at the largest *Liatris* stand in the Turkey Point area and a malaise trap set up near a smaller patch of this plant revealed no adults. The status of this species cannot be determined because several suitable areas remain to be checked for it. If it is shown that the species is restricted to the Pinery, it should, at least, be considered as **RARE** in Ontario and Canada.

Acknowledgements

This study would not have taken place if it were not for the financial support of the World Wildlife Fund and the Ontario Ministry of Natural Resources. The author is grateful to these bodies for this funding. A special thanks goes to Irene Bowman of the MNR.

The staff at the Pinery Provincial Park are thanked for their help and cooperation throughout the project and for providing accommodation at the park during 1986. I would particularly like to thank Terry Crabe for his help in guiding me around the Karner Blue sites, for facilitating contact with many authorities on the distribution and biology of the species, and for his help with contacts for lupine management programs.

The logistic support of Dr. D. C. Darling of the Royal Ontario Museum was extremely useful and ensured the smooth running of the research carried out at the Pinery and St. Williams.

The comments of Dr. D. F. Hardwick, Dr. Dale Schweitzer, Gary Allen, Donald Kirk, Mary Gartshore, Quimby Hess, Jim Hodgins, Mike Oldham, Dr. Paul Prevett, Phil Taylor, and Dolph Wynnia were extremely useful in compiling the information presented here.

I am grateful to Michelle Smith, Gordon Fuller and Gillian Sutcliffe for field assistance, I thank Dr. L. Gall for performing the computer analyses of the Karner Blue population data and Dr. A. Francouer for ant identifications.

References

Campbell, C. A., A. A. Bryant and D. P. Coulson. 1986. *Status, distribution and life history characteristics of some uncommon butterflies in the Carolinian forest zone.* A report prepared for the World Wildlife Fund of Canada. 125 pp.

Crabe, T.J. 1984. *Status of Lupinus perennis (Wild Lupine) and Lycaeides melissa samuelis Nabokov (Karner Blue) in the Pinery Provincial Park/Port Franks Area – 1983.* Unpublished.

Fahrig, L. and G. Merriam. 1985. Habitat connectivity and population survival. *Ecology* 66(19):1762-1768.

Gall, L. F. 1986. Measuring the size of lepidopteran populations. *J. Res. Lep.* 24:97-116.

Heitzman, J. R. and R. L. Heitzman. 1974. *Atrytonopsis hianna* biology and life cycle in the Ozarks. *J. Res. Lep.* 13:239-245.

Hess, Q.F. 1981. The status of *Plebejus melissa samuelis* Nabokov and the foodplant *Lupinus perennis* Linnaeus. *Toronto Ent. Assoc. Occas. Pub.* 12:9-24.

Hess, Q.F. 1983. The status of *Lycaeides melissa samuelis* Nabokov and its foodplant in Ontario in 1982. *Toronto Ent. Assoc. Occas. Pub.* 14:12-16.

Hess, Q.F. 1987. Butterflies of Ontario and summaries of Lepidoptera encountered in Ontario in 1986. *Toronto Ent. Assoc. Occas. Pub.* No. 18-87. 83 pp.

Hess, Q.F. 1988. Butterflies of Ontario and summaries of Lepidoptera encountered in Ontario in 1987. *Toronto Ent. Assoc. Occas. Pub.* No. 19-88. 82 pp.

Klots, A. B. 1979. *A field guide to the butterflies of eastern North America.* Houghton Mifflin Co. Boston, Mass. 349 pp.

Konecny, A. 1986. *A status report on the Karner Blue butterfly (Lycaeides melissa samuelis Nabokov) in Canada.* A report prepared for the Ontario Ministry of Natural Resources. 48 pp.

Lefkovitch, L. P. and L. Fahrig. 1985. Spatial characteristics of habitat patches and population survival. *Ecol. Mod.* 30:297-308.

Masters, J. H. 1972. A new subspecies of *Lycaeides argyrognomon* from the Eastern Canadian Forest Zone. *J. Lep. Soc.* 29:150-154.

Nabokov, V. 1949. The Nearctic forms of *Lycaeides* Hubner. *Psyche.* 50:87-99.

Nuzzo, V. A. 1986. Extent and status of midwest oak savannah: presettlement and 1985. *Natural Areas Journal* 6(2):6-36.

Opler, P. A. and G.O Krizek. 1984. *Butterflies east of the Great Plains.* John Hopkins Univ. Press, Baltimore. 294 pp.

Packer, L. 1987a. *Status report on the Karner Blue butterfly,* Lycaeides melissa samuelis *Nabokov, in Canada.* A report prepared for the World Wildlife Fund and the Ontario Ministry of Natural Resources, Wildlife Branch, Nongame Program. Unpublished. 66 pp.

Packer, L. 1987b. *Status report on some rare lepidopteran species in southern Ontario.* A report prepared for the World Wildlife Fund and the Ontario Ministry of Natural Resources, Wildlife Branch, Nongame Program. Unpublished. 38 pp.

Pierce, N.E. 1987. The evolution and biogeography of associations between lycaenid butterflies and ants. *Oxford Surveys in Evolutionary Biology* 4:89-116.

Pierce, N. E. and S. Easteal. 1986. The selective advantage of attendant ants for the larvae of a lycaenid butterfly, *Glaucopsyche lygdamus. J. Anim. Ecol.* 55:451-462.

Reznicek, R. R. 1987. *Lupinus perennis* L. Two pages in K.M. Pryer and G.W. Argus, eds. *Atlas of the rare vascular plants of Ontario.* Part 4. National Museum of Natural Sciences, Ottawa. (looseleaf).

Savignano, D.A. 1987. *The association of* Lycaeides melissa samuelis *(lepidoptera:Lycaenidae) the Karner Blue, with attendant ants.* A report submitted to the New York State Department of Environmental Conservation, Endangered Species Unit. 21 pp.

Schweitzer, D. F. 1984. *A report on the "Macro" Lepidoptera of the Pinery Provincial Park, Grand Bend, Ontario.* A report prepared for the Lambton Wildlife Fund and The Pinery Provincial Park. Unpublished. 24 pp.

Schweitzer, D. F. 1985. *A report on the status of the Karner Blue butterfly* Lycaeides melissa samuelis, *in the Province of Ontario.* A report prepared for the Ontario Ministry of Natural Resources. 18 pp.

Schweitzer, D. F. 1986. Review comments upon L. Packer "Biological and status investigations of some potentially endangered Lepidoptera species in southern Ontario".

Shapiro, A. M. 1969. New distributional data on three northeastern United States butterflies. *J. Lep. Soc.* 23:265-269.

American Lotus in bloom is unmistakable
– its massive leaves reach 60 cm (2 feet)
across, while its creamy-yellow, fragrant
flowers reach 25 cm (10 inches). A nationally rare species, it is restricted to only a
handful of marshes in Ontario.
Artist – Zile Zichmanis.

Historical Changes in the Unionidae (freshwater mussels) Fauna of the Sydenham River Watershed[1]

G.L. Mackie

Department of Zoology, University of Guelph
Guelph, Ontario N1G 2W1

Jane M. Topping

Invertebrate Division, National Museums of Canada
Ottawa, Ontario K1A OM8

Abstract. *Of 33 species of Unionidae (and their forms and subspecies) that have been reported from the Sydenham River drainage in southwestern Ontario since 1937, only 13 were found alive in 1985. None of the four species which are rare or endangered in Canada (Simpsonaias ambigua, Epioblasma rangiana, Villosa fabalis, Anodonta imbecillis) and which were once reported from the study area, were found alive in 1985. The diversity of Unionidae tends to increase downstream, but with significant variations. Conservation recommendations are provided.*

Introduction

The main objective of the present study was to determine what species of Unionidae presently exist in the Sydenham River in southwestern Ontario. The Sydenham River is the richest river in Canada for freshwater mussels (Clarke 1981). Thirty-three species have been recorded from the river and its drainage, with 29 reported by LaRocque & Oughton (1937), and 32 by Clarke (1973). Of the 33 species, four are confined (within Canada) to the Sydenham River drainage (Clarke 1976): *Anodonta imbecillis, Villosa fabalis, Simpsonaias ambigua,* and *Epioblasma rangiana. E. rangiana* is very rare throughout its range, and the Sydenham River population, although small, may have been the most extant healthy population in North America (Clarke 1976). In addition, *A. imbecillis, S. ambigua, V. fabalis,* and *E. rangiana* are endangered in Canada (Clarke 1976) and *S. ambigua* and *E. rangiana* are endangered and threatened in the US (Stansbery 1971; Bogan and Parmalee 1983).

Study Area

The Sydenham River drainage is part of the Lake St. Clair watershed (Figure 1). The river is situated in Kent and Lambton Counties in the southwestern part of Ontario and lies entirely within the Deciduous Forest Region (Carolinian Zone). The basin has an overall length of about 100 km, an average breadth of nearly 38 km, and a total drainage area of 2735 sq km (Department of Energy and Resources Management 1965). The main drainage systems are the Sydenham River and the

[1] An expanded version of this paper has appeared in *The Canadian Field-Naturalist* Volume 102, Number 4, pp. 617-626. Permission granted by Dr. Francis Cook, to print here, is gratefully acknowledged.

North Sydenham River, with the latter receiving two large tributaries, Black Creek and Bear Creek (Figure 1). Extensive land drainage systems (large ditches or canals and dykes) are common around most towns, especially Wallaceburg, which is situated in the lower reaches. The mean temperature, dissolved oxygen content, and water velocity during May to September at ten stations are provided in Table 1.

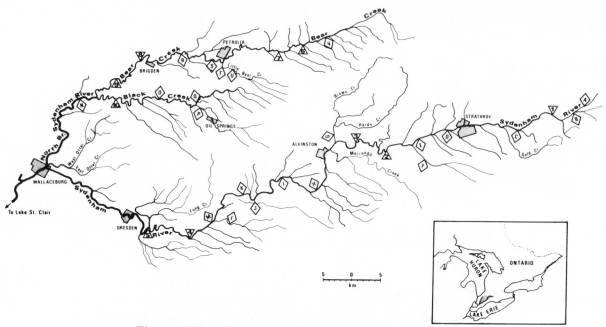

Figure 1. Map of study area showing locations of intensive (numbers) and extensive (letters) study stations. Inset shows location of study area between Lake Huron and Lake Erie.

Materials and Methods

We surveyed the species present at each of 22 stations in the study area (Figure 1, Stations A to V). The stations selected included those studied and reported by Clarke (1973), and new stations (Appendix). The new stations were selected according to their accessibility at approximately ten km intervals on each of the main rivers and some of their tributaries. Each station was visited once during August, 1985, and usually at least 60 person-minutes were spent looking for Unionidae at each station. The kinds and numbers of specimens of each species found were recorded for each station. Both living and dead shells (empty and gaping, or single valves) were collected, but because empty shells and valves can drift from upstream over several years, more emphasis was placed on living material when interpreting the results. A view box (a tall box, 20 cm square by 75 cm high, with a window on the bottom) was used to search for unionids in turbid reaches. Long-handled sieves with 0.32 mm mesh opening was used to sample the surficial sediments for unionids of smaller length classes.

At ten stations quantitative measurements of unionid densities and water quality measurements were taken and qualitative surveys of species present were conducted. Each station was visited four times at approximately four-week intervals from May 15 to September 1, 1985. The stations selected (Figure 1, Stations 1 to 10) included those studied and reported by Clarke (1973), those studied but reported only in his field notes, as well as four new stations that were known to contain Unionidae on the basis of exploratory surveys (Appendix). Stations one to five were on the main Sydenham River and Stations six to 10 were on the main tributaries of the North Sydenham River (Figure 1).

Before sampling the Unionidae at each station, water temperature (degrees C) and dissolved oxygen (mg/L) were measured using a YSI oxygen metre, model 27. Water velocity (cm/sec) was measured with a portable Marsh McBirney water current metre, model 201. All measurements were taken at mid-stream (Table 1).

Table 1

Some physical and chemical features of the water at the ten intensive study stations. Means are based on four samples taken at each station in May, June, July, and August/September.

Water Variables	Stations									
	1	2	3	4	5	6	7	8	9	10
Velocity, cm/sec	2.4	11.1	19.2	2.8	14.3	2.3	5.6	18.3	4.3	<0.5
Temperature, °C	18.2	17.6	18.5	20.7	20.7	21.8	21.0	21.5	17.7	18.4
Dis. Oxygen, mg/L	11.6	9.3	9.2	7.7	7.7	8.3	9.7	9.8	7.2	7.5

Results

Twenty-seven species were collected in the study area. Thirteen of these were found alive in the Sydenham River and 12 in the North Sydenham River and its two main tributaries, Black Creek and Bear Creek (Table 2). None of the rare, endangered, or threatened species (Table 2) were found alive in the study area.

Table 2

Unionidae collected in the "Lake St. Clair Drainage" (LaRoque & Oughton, 1937) and in the Sydenham River since 1963-1967. The 1963-1967 data are based on collections of living specimens and empty shells made by H.D. Athearn and Carol B. Stein who deposited records in the National Museums of Canada, Ottawa. The 1985 data are based on the present study; L = live specimens; D = dead specimens; – = species not found.

SPECIES	Lake St. Clair Drainage 1937	Sydenham River Main River 1963-67	1985	North 1985
Subfamily ANODONTINAE				
Alasmidonta marginata	x	x	D	–
Alasmidonta viridis	x	–	–	D
Anodonta g. grandis	x	x	L	L
Anodonta imbecillis ***	–	x	–	–
Anodontoides ferussacianus	x	x	L	L
Lasmigona complanata	–	x	L	L
Lasmigona compressa	x	x	D	D
Lasmigona costata	x	x	D	D
Simpsonaias ambigua *, ***	–	x	–	–
Strophitus u. undulatus	x	x	L	L
Subfamily AMBLEMINAE				
Amblema p. plicata	x	x	L	L
Cyclonaias tuberculata	x	x	L	–
Elliptio dilatata	x	x	D	D
Fusconaia flava	x	x	D	D
Pleurobema sintoxia	x	x	D	D
Quadrula p. pustulosa	x	x	L	L
Quadrula q. quadrula	x	x	L	L
Subfamily LAMPSILINAE				
Actinonaias ligamentina carinata	x	x	L	L
Epioblasma rangiana *, ***	–	x	D	–
Epioblasma triquetra	x	x	D	–
Lampsilis fasciola	x	x	–	D
Lampsilis ventricosa	x	x	D	D
Lampsilis radiata f. luteola	x	x	L	L
Lampsilis radiata siliquoidea *B	x	x	L	L
Leptodea fragilis	x	x	L	L
Ligumia recta	x	x	D	D
Obliquarua reflexa	x	–	–	–
Obovaria subrotunda	–	x	D	D
Obovaria olivaria	x	–	–	–
Potamilus alatus *D	x	x	L	L
Ptychobranchus fasciolaris	x	x	D	D
Truncilla truncata	x	x	L	L
Villosa fabalis **, ***	x	x	–	–
Villosa iris	x	x	–	–

*   Species listed by Stansbery (1971) as rare and endangered.

**   Species recommended by Jenkinson (1981) for list of endangered and threatened species.

***   Species listed by Clarke (1976) as endangered in Canada.

*B L. radiata siliquoidea = L. radiata f. luteola

*D Potamilus alatus = Proptera alata

The most common species were *A. plicata*, *A. g. grandis*, and *L. complanata*, being well represented at most stations in the study area (Table 3). *P. alatus*, *Leptodea fragilis*, and to some extent, *Quadrula q. quadrula*, *T. truncata*, and *Lasmigona costata* are common at some stations only.

Table 3

Mean numbers of living Unionidae found per unit effort (= 60 person minutes) at Stations 1 to 10. Complete names for species are given in Table 2.

| Species | Stations | | | | | | | | | |
	1	2	3	4	5	6	7	8	9	10
A. g. grandis	10	4	4	6	4	3	4	3	2	5
A. ferussacianus	–	–	–	–	–	1	–	–	–	–
L. complanata	–	2	–	1	–	6	1	18	21	9
S. u. undulatus	–	–	–	–	–	–	–	–	1	–
A. p. plicata	–	15	9	3	2	2	33	1	–	–
C. tuberculata	–	–	–	–	1	–	–	–	–	–
Q. p. pustulosa	–	2	–	–	3	–	–	–	–	–
Q. q. quadrula	–	–	–	–	8	–	–	–	5	1
A. l. carinata	–	–	–	–	2	1	–	–	1	–
L. r. f. luteola	–	2	–	–	–	4	–	–	1	–
L. fragilis	–	3	–	3	–	–	–	3	3	5
P. alatus	–	1	–	6	5	–	–	–	8	2
T. truncata	–	3	2	–	4	–	–	2	3	2

Species diversity of both live specimens and empty shells in the Sydenham River tends to increase for 85 km downstream, reaching a maximum approximately ten km southwest of Shetland, Ontario (Figure 2). However, significant variations within this 85 km reach are present.

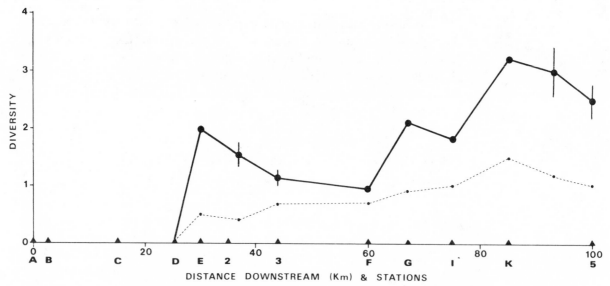

Figure 2. Variations in mean species diversity of alive and dead Unionidae in the Sydenham River. See Figure 1 for locations of stations. 95% confidence intervals (vertical bars) are calculable for numerical stations only (N = 4); only single estimates are possible for lettered stations.

Discussion

The Carolinian Zone of southwestern Ontario, one of the five most threatened natural regions in Canada, has about one-third of Canada's endangered, threatened, and rare species (World Wildlife Fund Canada 1984). Four species of Unionidae (*S. ambigua, A. imbecillis, V. fabalis* and *E. rangiana*) that are rare or endangered in Canada either no longer live in the Sydenham River watershed or are in such small densities that they were not found in this study. Moreover, of nine species restricted in Canada to the Lake St. Clair drainage (*Lampsilis fasciola, Obovaria subrotunda, Truncilla truncata, Obliquaria reflexa, Ptychobranchus fasciolaris, Alasmidonta viridis, Pleurobema sintoxia, Cyclonais tuberculata,* and *Quadrula p. pustulosa*) (Clarke 1981), only *T. truncata, C. tuberculata,* and *Q. p. pustulosa* were found alive in the Sydenham River watershed. Only *T. truncata* is common; *C. tuberculata* and *Q. p. pustulosa* are very rare in the study area. Over the past 50 years, 20 of the 33 species previously reported have either disappeared or are represented by empty shells only (Table 2).

The great variation in Unionidae diversity in the Sydenham River is no doubt attributable to changing substrate and water quality. Over the years an extensive agricultural drainage network, consisting of numerous canals and ditches, has been created to drain the predominantly agricultural land in the Sydenham River watershed. Deteriorating water quality with distance downstream is suggested by the diminishing dissolved oxygen values from the upstream to downstream stations in Table 1.

Conservation Recommendations

1. Since most unionids have an obligatory parasitic stage (called glochidia) on fish, and many are host-specific, the conservation programs recommended for fish should be used for Unionidae.

2. The most critical environmental requirements for Unionidae are (i) dissolved oxygen, (ii) substrate type, and (iii) water quality (particularly with respect to metal and organic pollution). Any activities which lower the dissolved oxygen levels, alter the substrate type, or increase loadings of metals (especially common non-essential metals such as Cd, Pb and Hg) or pesticides (especially organochlorines) and organic nutrients such as phosphates, must be curtailed.

3. The most common activities in the Sydenham watershed which would most likely cause such detrimental changes are agriculture and bridge and road construction. Farmers should keep fertilizers and pesticides away from the river and its tributaries and create strips of grass and forest lands adjacent to rivers to reduce runoff of pollutants and silt into the rivers. Bridge and road construction should not be permitted in areas with, or in areas immediately upstream of, high unionid diversity, because it increases silt loading. If bridge and road construction upstream of such areas is absolutely necessary, precautions should be made to reduce silt loading (e.g. building pools immediately downstream to catch silt). Industrial pollution is also a concern and any discharges of metals should not be permitted adjacent to the Sydenham River or its tributaries. The use of non-leaded fuels is highly recommended because lead is toxic to unionids. Remove and do not permit any further introductions of garbage, especially batteries, paint cans, plastics, or anything with cadmium or lead compounds, into the river or its tributaries.

Acknowledgments

This study was funded by World Wildlife Fund Canada and by the Natural Sciences and Engineering Research Council of Canada, Grant No. A9882. We are grateful to Mr. Robert Turland and Bruce Kilgour for collecting and measuring the Unionidae. They spent many hours learning the identifications of Unionidae before proceeding with the project, although most identifications were confirmed by one of the authors. Voucher specimens of all species collected are placed in the National Museums of Canada, NMC numbers 92763 to 92789, inclusive (including subspecies).

References

Bogan, A. E. and P. W. Parmalee. 1983. *Tennessee's Rare Wildlife. Vol. II: The mollusks.* Tennessee Wildlife Resources Agency, Nashville, TN. 123 p.

Clarke, A. H. 1973. On the distribution of Unionidae in the Sydenham River, southern Ontario, Canada. *Malacological Review* 6:63-64.

Clarke, A. H. 1976. The endangered molluscs of Canada. Pp. 148 -150 In: *Proceedings of a Symposium on Canada's threatened species and habitats*, May 20-24, 1976. Canadian Nature Federation and World Wildlife Fund.

Clarke, A. H. 1981. *The freshwater molluscs of Canada.* National Museums of Canada, Ottawa.

Department of Energy and Resources Management. 1965. *Sydenham Valley conservation report.* Ontario Department of Energy and Resources Management. 77 pp.

Jenkinson, J.J. 1981. Endangered or threatened aquatic mollusks of the Tennessee River system. *Bulletin of the American Malacological Union* 1981:43-45.

LaRocque, A. and J. Oughton. 1937. Preliminary account of the Unionidae of Ontario. *Canadian Journal of Research* (D)15:147-155.

Mackie G.L. and J.M. Topping. 1989. Historical changes in the unionid fauna of the Sydenham River Watershed and downstream changes in shell morphometrics of three common species. *Canadian Field-Naturalist* 102:617-626.

Stansbery, D. H. 1971. Rare and endangered freshwater mollusks in eastern United States. In: Jorgensen, S. E. and R. W. Sharp (eds.), *Proceedings of a symposium on rare and endangered mollusks (naiads) of the U. S. Fish and Wildlife Service*, U. S. Department of the Interior, 79 pp.

World Wildlife Fund Canada. 1984. *Annual Report.* World Wildlife Fund Canada, Toronto, Ontario. 40 pp.

Appendix

Relationship between study stations of Clarke (1973) and the present study (listed numerically and alphabetically according to present study).

Present Study	Clarke (1973)
2	1044
3	1045
4	1046
5	1049
6	1188 (Field notes)
8	1186 (Field notes)
A	1040
C	1041
H	1051 (Field notes)
J	1050 (Field notes)
K	552
S	1187 (Field notes)

The Madicolous Fauna of Southern Ontario, With Emphasis on the Niagara Escarpment

B.J. Sinclair

Department of Biology, Carleton University
Ottawa, Ontario K1S 5B6

Abstract. *Madicolous habitats, created by thin sheets of water trickling over various substrates, support a characteristic fauna. More than 70 species of arthropods are recorded from madicolous sites in southern Ontario. Thirteen of these species are restricted to the madicolous habitat. One new Canadian record,* Ochrotrichia confusa *(Morton) (Hydroptilidae), and one new Ontario record,* Tipula *(Pterelachisus)* perparvula Alexander *(Tipulidae), are reported. Examples of madicolous-restricted species, including the biology and geographical distribution of* Thaumalea americana Bezzi *(Thaumaleidae) are discussed. Several madicolous restricted species were found to be largely confined to the Niagara Escarpment.*

Introduction

The Niagara Escarpment is a range of habitats, each with its own characteristic and unusual flora and fauna. The Escarpment is a stronghold for a wealth of plants and animals, which are threatened elsewhere, yet still thrive within the natural areas of this cuesta.

Among aquatic habitats, the Niagara Escarpment possesses many ponds, streams, and springs. An additional aquatic habitat often seen on open rock cliff faces, but rarely examined, are seepages, or what are termed as madicolous habitats. Madicolous habitats (Latin verb madere: to ooze, trickle) are created by thin films (2 mm or less) of water flowing over various substrates (e.g. rock, mud, moss) (Vaillant 1956). Usually madicolous habitats are formed along the cliffs near waterfalls, escarpments, and roadcuts, fed by groundwater (Sinclair and Marshall 1986). The type of madicolous habitat is governed by the composition of its substrate. Many madicolous-restricted species are confined to a bare rock substrate, while other species prefer a thin film of mud or wet emergent mats of moss or watercress.

During 1985 and 1986, a survey was conducted on the madicolous habitats of eastern North America, with emphasis on the Niagara Escarpment and its affinities with the Appalachian Mountains. The purpose of this study was to create a species list, describe all new species or immature stages recognized, and examine faunal life cycles, biology, and geographical distribution.

This paper describes the madicolous habitat of southern Ontario, with an emphasis on the Niagara Escarpment. Several examples of madicolous-restricted insects, including *Thaumalea americana* Bezzi are discussed.

Materials and Methods

The insect fauna was sampled by picking the larvae directly from the substrate using forceps, sorting through filamentous algae, moss, and debris from seeps, or by using an aspirator to collect adult flies. A more efficient method was developed, simply known as "splash sampling". Splash sampling was used to flush organisms from the substrate by splashing water up onto the rock face, washing the organisms and debris down into a pan held below. From here the insects could be sorted into petri dishes and transported live back to the laboratory. The live immature insects were then reared to adult forms. Rearing was required to obtain positive species determination of the immature insects collected at the sites. Rearing also enabled positive larval-adult associations, which provided new information on the individual life stages of the madicolous insect species.

Using these sampling methods, a general survey of 68 madicolous sites in eastern North America was conducted, of which 40 sites were located in southern Ontario (Figure 1). Five of these sites, all in limestone regions, were sampled at

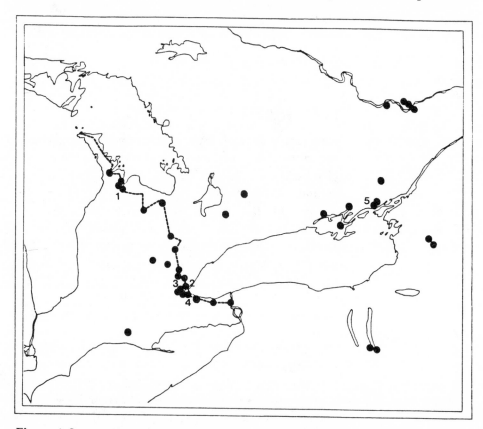

Figure 1: Survey sites of madicolous habitats of southern Ontario and adjacent New York.

●   Survey sites

----- Niagara Escarpment

Year-round survey sites:
1 Owen Sound
2 Dundas – Rock Chapel Sanctuary
3 Dundas – Webster's Falls
4 Hamilton
5 Kingston

three week intervals from April 1985 to April 1986. Four sites were located along the Niagara Escarpment, and included a uniform temperature (9 degrees C) madicolous spring at Owen Sound, a roadcut seepage in Hamilton, and two madicolous springs with fluctuating daily temperatures in Dundas. The other site, located at Kingston, was a roadcut spring-seepage with intermittent flow during the summer months.

Results and Discussion

In Ontario, approximately 70 species of arthropods were recorded from madicolous habitats (Table 1). From this total two-thirds were found to be Diptera (two-winged flies), and the immature stages of 14 species of Diptera were redescribed or described for the first time. Three species of Diptera from madicolous habitats along the Niagara Escarpment were recognized as new species.

A total of 13 species were recognized as being restricted to madicolous habitats, or what are usually termed eumadicoles (See Table 1 – Group A). Eumadicolous arthropods are not found in any other aquatic habitat. An additional 17 species of arthropods were found most commonly in madicolous habitats (See Table 1 – Group B), however these species are able to survive in areas of increased water volume; for example springs and saturated mats of moss and algae. The classification system utilized above and in Table 1 follows the categories defined by Vaillant (1956) for European madicolous fauna.

The most widespread and often collected madicolous species include *Euparyphus* spp. (Stratiomyidae), *Limonia humidicola*, *L. simulans* (Tipulidae) and *Orthocladius (Eudactyocladius)* sp. (Chironomidae). Within the Niagara Escarpment region, the most often collected madicolous species include *Cymbiodyta blanchardi* (Hydrophilidae), *Limonia* spp., *Pericoma slossonae* (Psychodidae), *Euparyphus* spp., *Thaumalea americana* (Thaumaleidae) and *Orthocladius (Eudactylocladius)* sp. Generally, the immature stages of madicolous-restricted species are direct air-breathers with spiracles located dorsally on a dorsoventrally flattened body, and have reduced prehensile organs (Thienemann 1909, Bertrand 1948).

Some of the more common madicolous species of the Niagara Escarpment region are discussed briefly below. Following this review, the eumadicolous species, *Thaumalea americana* is examined at length.

Ochrotrichia confusa (Morton) (Trichoptera: Hydroptilidae). This species is a micro-caddisfly and prior to this study was believed to be common in the Appalachian Mountains (Vaillant 1984). This caddisfly is restricted to madicolous habitats and represents a new Canadian record. They were found in five sites in southern Ontario, of which four sites were located along the Niagara Escarpment corridor.

Cymbiodyta blanchardi Horn (Coleoptera: Hydrophilidae). Adults and larvae were most commonly found in the madicolous zone of springs, roadcut seeps, and small streams. This species was the most common hydrophilid beetle collected from madicolous sites of southern Ontario.

Tipula (Pterelachisus) perparvula Alex. (Diptera: Tipulidae). This cranefly was previously known only from Manitoba and its larval habitat was unknown (Alexander 1926). The species represents a new Ontario record, known only from the Niagara Escarpment. The larvae were collected from algal mats and thin layers of mud and debris at the edge of cascading springs and roadcut seeps.

Table I: The madicolous fauna in southern Ontario. (Group A: Eumadicolous; Group B: Tychomadicolous 'madicoles preferentielles'; Group C: Tychomadicolous 'madicoles occasionnelles'; Group D: Tychomadicolous 'madicoles hotes' (Valliant 1955)).

Species	Group
Turbellaria	
Planarians	C
Hirudinea	
Dina parva Moore	D
Malacostraca	
Gammarus pseudolimnaeus Bousfield	C
Collembola	
Tomocerus minor (Lubbock)	D
Plecoptera	
Soyedina vallicularia (Wu)	C
Nemoura trispinosa Claassen	C
Hemiptera	
Microvelia americana (Uhler)	C
Saldula pallipes (Fabricius)	C
S. saltatoria (Linneaus)	C
Trichoptera	
Ochrotrichia confusa (Morton)	A
Lepidostoma sommermanae Ross	C
Rhyacophila sp. (*invaria* group)	C
Neophylax aniqua Ross	C
Pseudostenophylax sparsus (Banks)	C
Coleoptera	
Carabidae	
Bembidion spp.	D
Agonum sp.	D
Dytiscidae	
Hydroporus pseudovilis Young	C
Hydraenidae	
Hydraena angulicollis Notman	C
Ochthebius kaszabi Janssens	C
Hydrophilidae	
Cymbiodyta blanchardi Horn	B
Laccobius spangleri Malcolm	B
Anacaena limbata (Fabricius)	C
Staphylinidae	D
Diptera	
Tipulidae	
Tipula (Pterelachisus) perparvula Alex.	B
Limonia simulans (Walker)	A
L. (Dicranomyia) humidicola (O.S.)	A
L. (Dicranomyia) stulta (O.S.)	B
L. (Geranomyia) diversa (O.S.)	B
L. (Geranomyia) canadensis (Westw.)	B
Dactylolabis hudsonica Alex.	A
D. montana (O.S.)	A
Pedicia (s.s.) albivitta Walker	C
Dicranota (Rhaphidolabis) sp.	C
Psychodidae	
Pericoma slossonae (Williston)	A
P. kincaidi Quate	C
Threticus bicolor (Banks)	A
Dixidae	
Dixa similis Johannsen	B

Species	Group
Thaumaleidae	
Thaumalea americana Bezzi	A
Ceratopogonidae	
Atrichopogon sp.	A
Dasyhelea sp. Thomsen	B
Chironomidae	
Parochlus kiefferi (Garrett)	C
Diamesa nivoriunda (Fitch)	C
Pseudokiefferiella sp.	B
Orthocladius (Eudactylocladius) sp.	B
Metriocnemus sp.	B
Parametriocnemus lundbecki (Johannsen)	C
Paratrichocladius nitedellus (Malloch)	C
Eukiefferiella claripennis (Lundbeck)	C
Chaetocladius stamfordi (Johannsen)	C
Limnophyes fumosus (Johannsen)	C
Thienemanniella sp.	C
Tokunagaia sp.	C
Hudsonimyia sp.	B
Microspectra nigripila (Johannsen)	C
Stratiomyidae	
Euparyphus (s.s.) *stigmaticalis* Loew	A
E. (Aochletus) brevicornis Loew	A
Caloparyphus greylockensis (Johnson)	B
C. tetraspilus (Loew)	C
Odontomyia (Odontomyiina) sp.	C
Empididae	
Clinocera lineata Loew	B
C. fuscipennis Loew	B
C. maculata Loew	C
Clinocera sp.	B
Dolichopodidae	
Liancalus genualis Loew	A
Muscidae	
Lispoides aequifrons (Stein)	C
Spilogona torreyae (Johannsen)	C
Tachinidae	
Chaetostigmoptera angulicornis (Curran)	parasitoid
Ephydridae *Scatella* sp.	C
Hymenoptera	
Ichneumonidae	
Phygadeuon sp.	parasitoid
Araneae	
Erigone atra Blackwell	D
Eperigone tridentata (Emerton)	D
Pirata sp.	D
Acari	
Trichothyas (Lundbladia) musciola (Mitchell)	A
Tyrrellia circularis Koenike	B
Panisopsis (Marshallothyas) aspos (Cook)	C
Pergamasus septentrionalis (Oudemans)	D
Calyptostoma sp.	D
Gastropoda	
Limnaea (Fossaria) obrussa Say	C

Dactylolabis montana (O.S.) (Diptera: Tipulidae). The larvae of this species was previously unknown. This cranefly was found in seeps along the Niagara Escarpment and roadcuts of the Kingston area, which dried up for periods of several weeks during the summer.

Pericoma slossonae (Williston) (Diptera: Psychodidae). The larval habitat of this species of moth fly was also previously unknown. This species was generally limited in distribution to Ontario and New York State, and is especially common along the Niagara Escarpment.

Euparyphus (Aochletus) brevicornis Loew (Diptera: Stratiomyidae). This soldier fly species is widely distributed in eastern North America and especially common in roadcut seeps along the Escarpment. The brightly coloured black and yellow banded adult is common in Ontario from late June to mid-August. The puparium of this species is parasitized by the Ichneumonid Wasp *Ceratophygeuon pechumani* Townes (*Pygadeuon* in Table 1).

Thaumalea americana Bezzi (Diptera: Thaumaleidae). There are four species of this family known from eastern North America, of which only T. americana is recorded from Ontario. Larvae of this species are restricted to the bare rock substrate of madicolous habitats.

In southern Ontario, larvae were collected from uniform temperature springs (9 degrees C) and in seeps with annual temperature ranges of 2-20 degrees C. This wide thermal tolerance is unusual for thaumaleids which are generally reported as coldwater stenotherms (Vaillant 1954,1956). There are however, two species of *Thaumalea* known from localities with temperatures greater than 18 degrees C, but these species were intolerant of near freezing water temperatures (Vaillant 1954, Andersson 1967). Larvae of thaumaleids feed on diatoms scraped from the rock surface.

Adults are generally weak fliers and look similar to black flies, but do not bite. The flight period in southern Ontario is from late April to October, with peak activity from May to August.

The wide thermal tolerance has enabled *T. americana* to disperse throughout the hilly and mountainous regions of eastern North America, exploiting the numerous closely spaced madicolous habitats. Prior to this study, the species was positively recorded from Ontario and Quebec, south to West Virginia and Virginia (Stone 1964). The range of *T. americana* has now been extended southwards with new records from North Carolina, Tennessee, Alabama, and Georgia (Fig. 2).

Figure 2: Geographical distribution of *Thaumalea americana*

     In southern Ontario, *T. americana* was previously known from three localities: Owen Sound, Orangeville, and Niagara Falls. It is now recorded from numerous sites along the Niagara Escarpment, with outlying localities in the limestone regions of Rockwood and Elora. Elsewhere in Ontario this species is known only from a recently discovered site in Ottawa (Fig.3).

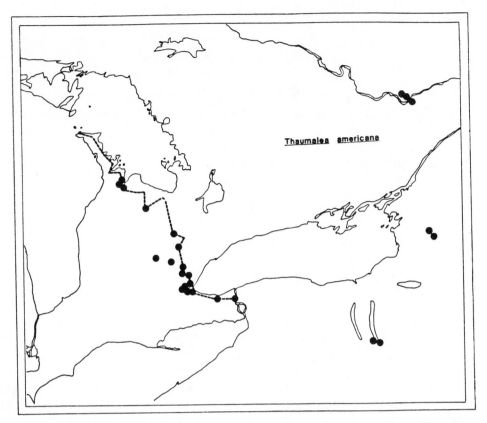

Figure 3: Geographical distribution of *Thaumalea americana* in southern Ontario and adjacent New York.

----- Niagara Escarpmen

Summary

This first comprehensive study of madicolous habitats of North America provided many new larval-adult associations and previously unrecognized taxa. The study also yielded new information on the life stages, biology, and geographical distribution on a wide variety of insect species. More than 70 species of arthropods were collected from madicolous habitats. Thirteen species were classified as being restricted to madicolous habitats and three new species of Diptera were found from sites on the Niagara Escarpment. Many species were particularly abundant along the Escarpment compared to other areas of Ontario; for example, *Thaumalea americana*.

Conservation Recommendations

1. The Niagara Escarpment supports a diversity of habitats as well as geological features. Large areas have remained in their natural state, providing refuge for many rare species. The Niagara Escarpment Commission, through years of public hearings, implementation of landuse controls, acquisition of land, and the formation of parks, has attempted to preserve this last refuge for not just rare species but also habitats, by establishing a "unique environmental corridor" through southern Ontario. This survey of madicolous habitats was a first

study of habitat-restricted insects along the Escarpment. Several species were found to be particularly abundant along the Escarpment compared to other regions of Ontario. For this reason, the madicolous habitat should be added to the list of habitats that deserve attention in the continuing efforts to preserve the diversity of the Niagara Escarpment.

2. For any alterations or exploitation proposed for the Escarpment, such as a Hydro station at Webster's Falls (proposal has recently been withdrawn), impact studies should address not only rare or endangered species but entire habitats. For example, a hydro station at a waterfalls could possibly affect groundwater levels and destroy neighbouring madicolous habitats.

3. Further studies on madicolous restricted species are still necessary and the possibility of new discoveries from the Niagara Escarpment region remain.

Acknowledgements

I would like to thank my supervisor, Dr. S.A. Marshall (University of Guelph), who suggested this project and provided advice and support on numerous occasions. I am also greatly indebted to Dr. D.R. Oliver (Biosystematics Research Centre, Ottawa) for his thought provoking discussions concerning the madicolous and freshwater spring habitats.

I gratefully acknowledge the financial support of a Natural Sciences and Engineering Research Council (NSERC) Postgraduate Scholarship and a World Wildlife Fund grant to S.A. Marshall (Carolinian Canada Project).

References

Alexander, C.P. 1926. Undescribed species of crane-flies from the U.S. and Canada. Part II. (Diptera, Tipulidae) *Insec. Inscrit. Menst.* 14:114-122.

Andersson, H. 1967. Faunistic, ecological and taxonomic notes on Icelandic Diptera. *Opuscula Ent.* 32:101-120.

Bertrand, H. 1948. Les insectes hygropetriques. *L'Entomologiste* 4:86-100.

Sinclair, B.J. and S.A. Marshall. 1986. The madicolous fauna in southern Ontario. *Proc. Ent. Soc. Ont.* 117:9-14.

Stone, A. 1964. Guide to the insects of Connecticut. Part VI. The Diptera or true flies of Connecticut. Ninth Fascicle. Family Thaumaleidae. *Bull. Conn. St. Geol. Nat. Hist. Surv.* 97:119-122.

Thienemann, A. 1909. *Orphnephila testacea* Macq. Ein Beitrag zur Kenntnis der fauna hygropetrica. *Ann. Biol. lac.* 4:58-87.

Vaillant, F. 1954. Nouvelle contribution à l'étude des Thaumaleidae (Diptera). *L'Entomologiste* 10:94-97.

Vaillant, F. 1956. Recherches sur la faune madicole (hygropetrique s.l.) de France, de Corse et d'Afrique du Nord. *Mem. Mus. natn. Hist. nat., Paris* A 11:1-258.

Vaillant, F. 1984. The Hydroptilid larvae living on dripping rocks. pp.407-412 *in* J.C. Morse (Ed.), *Proc. 4th Int. Symp. Trichoptera*. Clemson, S.C. 1983. Publ. Dr. W. Junk (Hague). 486pp.

Reintroductions

The Tiger Salamander is a member of
Ontario's herpetofauna, based on one
specimen collected by P.A. Taverner at
Point Pelee National Park in 1915.
Artist – The late E.B.S. Logier
(a preliminary sketch from 1928).

Bald Eagle Reintroductions near Cayuga, Ontario

Bruce W. Duncan

Hamilton Region Conservation Authority
838 Mineral Springs Road, Ancaster, Ontario L9G 3L3

Abstract. *Two Bald Eagles* (Haliaeetus leucocephalus) *were hacked[1] at Taquanyah Conservation Area near Cayuga (ten km north of Lake Erie in the Regional Municipality of Haldimand-Norfolk) in both 1986 and 1987 by the Hamilton Naturalists' Club in cooperation with World Wildlife Fund Canada (WWF), Ontario Ministry of Natural Resources (MNR), and Grand River Conservation Authority (GRCA). These introductions, in conjunction with those by the Canadian Wildlife Service (CWS) at Long Point National Wildlife Area, were an attempt to increase the small Bald Eagle population found along the north shore of Lake Erie.*

Background

The Bald Eagle is listed as an endangered species under the Endangered Species Act of Ontario and is found in extremely low numbers in the south of the province (Bortolotti 1987). McKeating (1985) mapped known nest sites in southern Ontario for 1983 and showed only seven. In northwestern Ontario, they are much more plentiful (Grier 1985) and the Lake of the Woods population has been used as the source of young Bald Eagles for the Long Point and Taquanyah releases.

There are several reasons for this disparity in numbers from south to north. Before settlement by Europeans, Bald Eagles were probably as plentiful in southern Ontario, especially along the shorelines of larger lakes, as in northwestern Ontario (McKeating 1985). However, habitat changes caused by forest clearing for agriculture and shooting by settlers started the decline in numbers during the 1830s. After 1945, a very rapid drop in the population resulted from serious reproductive problems caused by DDT poisoning. By the time DDT use was banned in Canada in 1970, and the US in 1973, only three nests were still active along the Lake Erie north shore. Apparently, the northwestern Ontario birds, nesting in a non-agricultural area and wintering along the Mississippi River, did not experience DDT-induced reproductive problems. Their numbers stayed fairly high.

1986 Summary

In March 1986, the MNR contacted the Hamilton Naturalists' Club about hacking two Bald Eagles which could be taken from nests at Lake of the Woods in addition to the six taken annually for CWS's reintroductions at Long Point. These extra two would not significantly reduce the numbers in the northwestern Ontario population. The Hamilton Naturalists' Club agreed to participate, with funding from MNR, WWF, and GRCA. Ontario Hydro donated five poles, erected them, and placed the 2 m X 2 m X 1.7 m cage atop them in May 1986. The cage was at about nine metres height.

---

[1] Hacking is the controlled release of young raptors during the period of development from fledging to independence.

In June, George Melvin of Brock University's Biology Department was hired to feed and monitor the eaglets for 12 weeks. On June 20, 1986, the two Bald Eagles arrived at Taquanyah after a flight provided free of charge by Air Canada. They were placed in the hack box, and thawed smelt were dropped down the food tube. These were readily eaten. The food tube extended down from the plywood back wall of the cage and allowed food to be dropped without the eaglets seeing the caretaker. It was important that as little contact as possible with humans be permitted. All food drops were done quietly and with the caretaker out of sight of the birds. Every four to five days, however, uneaten and decaying food, along with soiled nest material, was removed from the hack box in full view of the birds. These cleanouts were essential for hygiene and were done as quietly and quickly as possible to minimize disturbance.

There were virtually no problems with the 1986 eaglets during the seven weeks they were in the hack tower, other than two sets of people crossing the cordon (about 250-300 m around the tower) and walking under the cage. They were quickly asked to leave.

On August 2, both eaglets were caught at 2230 hours, hooded, and taken to the Nature Centre. Here, a small radio transmitter was affixed to the tail and a numbered grey wingtag placed on the wing of each bird. They were returned to the tower as quickly as possible (about one hour later) and normal daily feeding was resumed. Neither bird showed any outward sign of stress or discomfort following this operation.

On Tuesday, August 5, at 0440 hours, the cage door was opened so that at dawn the eaglets were free to leave. They were about 13-14 weeks old at this time and had been exercising vigorously for two to three weeks. Normal fledging occurs at 11 to 13 weeks.

Both birds left the cage and perched on the branches provided at the front of the tower. This was at 0605 to 0610 hours. They exercised here but returned periodically to the cage to feed. At 0840 hours the male slipped from a perch while exercising and flew to a nearby tree. The female followed at 1015 hours.

For the next seven days, the eagles flew from tree to tree, moving further from the tower and taking longer and more skilful flights as time passed. They were tracked by staff and volunteers using radio receivers and binoculars. On August 11, both birds returned to Taquanyah Conservation Area and spent the night. On August 12, at 1130 hours, the female soared to about 300 metres height then glided north out of sight. We had no more radio or visual contact with her. On August 13, the male flew up from a barn to the northwest of Taquanyah and also disappeared.

On September 4, we were informed by the Quebec Ministère du Loisir, du Chasse et de la Pêche, that the male had been shot near Lac St. Jean, Québec. He had apparently been seen in a roofless chicken coop at a farm and was shot with a .22 calibre rifle by a 12 year old girl. The female eagle has not been reported since August 12, 1986.

There were some problems in the 1986 hack that we attempted to solve for the 1987 release:

1. Shooting of the male. The eaglets had occasionally been fed day-old chicks in addition to fish, quail, and rats while in the hack box. This would be discontinued.

2. The question of whether both birds had fed in the seven days after fledging when they were being tracked and observed by staff and volunteers. A pat-

terned hack board and buzzer would be used in 1987 to attempt classical conditioning to the food.

3. Possible disturbance due to attaching the radio transmitters. This operation would be done several days earlier in 1987.

1987 Summary

On June 19, 1987, the eaglets arrived at Taquanyah and were immediately placed in the cage. One eaglet was about ten days younger than the other but this proved not to be a problem. He, in fact, was so much more aggressive than the female that he appeared to bully her about food regularly. There were no problems at all in 1987 while the eaglets were in the hack box. Both fed well and exercised (although not as much as the 1986 birds) as fledging approached. During each weekly cleanout, a Hamilton Naturalists' Club photographer took slides and videotape footage of the birds for publicity. This added no stress to the weekly cleanouts.

The eaglets were caught and had radio transmitters and wingtags attached on July 29. They appeared undisturbed the next morning. Release was scheduled for August 4, but a forecast of high winds prompted a delay to August 6. The door was opened in the early morning dark and shortly after dawn, both birds had moved out onto the front perches. They did not fly until over two days later, preferring instead to feed from inside the cage and from another patterned hackboard on the roof.

When they did fly, they returned at least every two days to the tower to feed. The eagles remained in radio range until November 4 when the male left and November 7 when the female left. These dates are within the approximate time period for eagles from northwestern Ontario to begin their southward migration (for example, see Evans 1987).

We were surprised to see the female back on December 14 to 16. The weather until then had been very mild, perhaps providing some explanation of why she had not continued further south. This return after almost six weeks absence showed that she had been able to feed and care for herself during that time. She appeared strong and healthy.

We were unable to test our classical conditioning hackboard and buzzer since the eagles never strayed far from Taquanyah during their early flight period and always returned to the tower to feed. From December 16, 1987 to the time of writing (September, 1988), we have had no reports of the 1987 eagles.

Conclusions

We feel that the program, in spite of the shooting of the 1986 male, has been successful. There were no problems with the birds when under direct care and all were strong and healthy at release. When subsequently encountered after release, they were also in good condition. Even the 1986 male was found to be in good physical condition when autopsied. In addition, the Taquanyah Bald Eagle releases showed that successful reintroductions can be made at quite public areas. Our eagle tower was located only 500 to 600 metres from a swimming area used by a dozen or more people daily and at the eastern edge of a multiple-use conservation area. A restricted area was roped and signed allowing the tower to have a buffer zone of 250 to 300 metres but we depended upon the good will of people not to cross the cordon.

There was an excellent public response to the introductions with over 120 volunteers assisting in 1986 and 1987 and about 1200 visitors coming specifically to see the eagles from a distance during the two summers. Publicity was effective and improved the image of eagles, other raptors, and endangered species in the area.

Conservation Recommendations

We are recommending no release at Taquanyah Conservation Area in 1988 for the following reasons:

1. There are currently five "wild" nests along the north shore of Lake Erie. From 1983 to 1987, 34 young Bald Eagles have been hacked at Long Point and Taquanyah, both Lake Erie north shore areas. More eagle releases may not be necessary here.

2. The CWS has introduced 30 eagles in five years at Long Point and is now pausing to evaluate the success of the program. The Taquanyah program has been considered unofficially an adjunct to the Long Point program.

3. The release of only two eagles at Taquanyah in 1988 would probably be inadequate since mortality is between 50 and 60% in the first year and 10 to 15% thereafter.

4. If more than two eagles were to be released, extra expenses would be involved: expansion of the hack tower would require cooperation from Ontario Hydro; more radio transmitters would be required; extra food and perhaps staff would be necessary. There are drawbacks to more than two eagles being released at Taquanyah: the enlarged hack tower might be used only one year; tracking six eagles would be extremely difficult; a larger restricted area in the Conservation Area might be required, particularly when the birds fledge, and would probably conflict with other uses by the public.

I think that it would be more beneficial to increase the Bald Eagle population in the other portion of southern Ontario where there are still "wild" nests: the Rideau Lakes area. If there is a suitable location, along with interested and competent people, I would recommend releases there to add to the two nesting pairs.

Acknowledgements

This project was largely financed through the World Wildlife Fund and the Ontario Ministry of Natural Resources. The approximate total costs were $9000 in 1986 (including the tower), and about $7000 in 1987. WWF contributed $2500 in each year. We are grateful to them and to the MNR for their support.

References

Bortolotti, G.R. 1987. Bald Eagle account. Pp. 110-111 in: *Atlas of the breeding birds of Ontario*. M.D. Cadman, P.F.J. Eagles, and F.M. Helleiner, eds. University of Waterloo Press. Waterloo, Ontario. 617 pp.

Evans, M. 1987. Report from the Overlook. Pp. 5-9 in: *Hawk Ridge Nature Reserve Annual Report, 1986*. Duluth Audubon Society, Duluth, Minnesota.

Grier, J. 1985. Status of Bald Eagles nesting in northwestern Ontario. Pp. 49-51 in: *The Bald Eagle in Canada: Proceedings of Bald Eagle Days*. 1983. J. M. Gerrard and T. M. Ingram, eds. Eagle Foundation. Apple River, Illinois.

McKeating, G. 1985. Charles Broley: Eagles then and now in southern Ontario. Pp. 25-34 in: *The Bald Eagle in Canada: Proceedings of Bald Eagle Days*. 1983. J. M. Gerrard and T. M. Ingram, eds. Eagle Foundation. Apple River, Illinois.

One of our most beautiful native plants, Goat's-rue is restricted in Canada to a few populations centred around Turkey Point on Lake Erie. The oak savannahs and woodlands here provide its required sandy, open habitat.
Artist – Steve Varga.

A Reintroduction Plan for Trumpeter Swans in Ontario

Harry G. Lumsden   Ontario Ministry of Natural Resources
Wildlife Research Section, Maple, Ontario L0J 1E0

Abstract. *The ten year objective of this plan is to reestablish a self-sustaining wild population of Trumpeter Swans in southern Ontario, and eventually in the Hudson Bay Lowlands. The trumpeters will be used to replace the feral Mute Swans which were introduced from Europe. When no longer needed as foster-parents, the Mute Swans will be returned to captivity and placed in zoos and private institutions.*

The reintroduction of Trumpeter Swans will enhance Ontario's natural heritage, restore diversity to Ontario's wetland communities, and provide opportunities for the people of Ontario to view and hear one of the most spectacular waterfowl species in the world.

Methods will include fostering trumpeters on feral Mute Swans in southern Ontario by placing eggs in their nests. Eggs will be provided by aviculturists and cooperators who care for Trumpeter pairs owned by the project. Wild caught trumpeters will be released at suitable sites.

Purpose

This plan outlines the objectives, strategies, and tactics for the reintroduction of Trumpeter Swans in Ontario. Although some of the techniques for use have been developed, we have much to learn about handling Trumpeter Swans. Many of the strategies and tactics outlined must be regarded as experimental. This is a long-term plan subject to annual assessment in the light of results and a major review at five-year intervals.

Background

Trumpeter Swans were present in considerable numbers in southern Ontario in what is now agricultural land (Shea 1868, Thwaites 1903, Biggar 1929, Lajeunesse 1960). They disappeared as summer residents so early in the settlement process that no record of breeding survives.

In the Hudson Bay Lowlands, evidence of the presence of Trumpeter Swans is contained in the accounts of fur traders (Tyrell 1931, Rich and Johnson 1954, Williams and Glover 1969) and from bones found in archaeological sites at Fort Albany (Baldwin 1967) and near Hawley Lake (Savage, pers. comm.). On the Quebec side of James Bay, Barnston (1860) reported that a considerable number of swans hatched in the Eastmain area. It is likely that they bred throughout the Hudson Bay Lowlands of Ontario and into Manitoba (Lumsden 1984).

Indians had difficulty killing large birds (Wrong and Langton 1939) and particularly swans (Lumsden 1984) with bows and arrows. When they received guns through trade in the mid-1600s, all this changed. They shot large numbers of trumpeters for the trade in swan skins and killed many more for subsistence (Hearne

1795). The extinction of Trumpeter Swans in Ontario was accomplished in a relatively short time, caused by unrestricted killing during migration and on their wintering grounds in the Atlantic states.

While we have lost many large marshes to drainage in southern Ontario, many suitable areas for swans remain. In northern Ontario, the muskeg survives in its pristine condition. There seem to be no habitat barriers to the reintroduction of Trumpeter Swans in Ontario.

Mute Swans, native to Eurasia, escaped from captivity and bred as wild birds in 1910 on the Hudson River near the Atlantic coast (Hindman 1982) and in the 1920s in Michigan. In Ontario, the earliest feral breeding record was in 1958 (Peck 1966). Mute Swans have spread to eleven states on the Atlantic coast, where there are now 5,300 birds, plus 1,500 in Michigan, and 115 in Ontario.

Most of the states which have an established population of Mute Swans either have control programs (five states) or are contemplating control. Mute Swans live in high densities, consume large quantities of aquatic vegetation (329 g dry weight, 3.8 kg wet weight per bird per day, Willey 1968) and uproot much more than they eat. They are aggressive to other waterfowl and sometimes kill ducklings. We have many records of Canada Goose and some Mallard nests being disrupted by Mute Swans in Ontario. It would be desirable to replace Mute Swans with trumpeters in southern Ontario. In the west, Trumpeter Swans occur in much lower breeding densities than do Mute Swans in southern Ontario, and hence should have a lesser impact on submerged vegetation. They are less aggressive toward other waterfowl species. Territory size in trumpeters is seldom smaller than 23 ha (Banko 1960) but Mute Swan territories have ranged in size from as small as 0.4 ha near Hamburg, West Germany (Peters 1931) to 4.8 ha in Rhode Island (Willey 1968). The density at Cranberry Marsh, Ontario, was one breeding pair per 4.0 ha in 1984.

Trumpeter Swans were reintroduced to a number of refuges and managed areas in the US by transferring full- or half-grown cygnets. In Canada, restoration to Elk Island National Park was attempted by fostering captive-hatched cygnets on wild caught trumpeters.

Experimental release of trumpeters by fostering under Mute Swans was started in Ontario in 1982. From 1982 to 1984, 32 eggs were received from Grande Prairie, Alberta, with the help of the Canadian Wildlife Service (CWS) and the Alberta Division of Fish and Wildlife. Eighteen of these eggs were used for restoration. From these, two cygnets reached the flying stage in each of 1982, 1983, and 1984. From eggs of captive pairs in 1985 to 1987, five cygnets reached flying stage. In the spring of 1988, five of these cygnets were known to be alive.

Two eggs in 1984 and seven eggs in 1985 were donated by aviculturists, but none resulted in cygnets surviving.

Objectives

Ten Year Objectives

1. To establish 15 breeding pairs of Trumpeter Swans in southern Ontario by fostering under Mute Swans and using all other available techniques.

2. To prevent increase of feral Mute Swans by taking their eggs.

Long Term Objectives

1. To establish a self-sustaining wild population of Trumpeter Swans in both southern Ontario and the Hudson Bay Lowlands.

2. To remove all feral Mute Swans from southern Ontario to captivity in zoos and parks.

3. To provide additional viewing opportunities to the people of Ontario.

4. To restore an element of diversity to Ontario's wetland communities.

Reintroduction Strategies for Southern Ontario

1. The Fostering Technique
Since 1982, we have been testing Mute Swan ability to foster raise trumpeters. We conclude that if precautions are taken, Mute Swans nesting on the northwest shore of Lake Ontario can successfully foster raise trumpeters. This is accomplished by putting trumpeter eggs into Mute Swan nests. The precautions needed, and techniques used, are listed below under tactics.

2. Choice of Stock
Three isolated breeding stocks of Trumpeters Swans exist in North America. They are located in the tri-state area of Montana, Idaho, and Wyoming, centred on the Red Rock Lakes, in the Grande Prairie region of Alberta, and in Alaska, with a few pairs scattered in the Yukon, British Columbia, and the Northwest Territories.

The eastern stock of trumpeters in southern Ontario occupied a very different type of habitat to those surviving in the west. To provide as much genetic diversity as possible to increase the probability of success, it would be desirable to use stock from all three breeding populations.

The Hudson Bay Lowlands boreal habitat is similar to that in parts of Alaska. We should use the northern boreal stock for restoration there.

3. Numbers of Eggs
We estimate that we will need a minimum of 50 eggs per year to exploit fully the fostering approach to restoration of Trumpeter Swans in southern Ontario. These must now come from captive pairs owned by the program or as gifts from aviculturists.

4. Sites
Since the main effort at restoration is to be through the fostering technique, eggs will be placed in Mute Swan nests where they occur on the northwest shores of Lake Ontario between Bowmanville and Hamilton. The highest density of Mute Swans and the best quality habitat is located in Cranberry Marsh south of Whitby. Mute Swans have been successful in raising cygnets in other marshes and these pairs will also be used as foster parents when more eggs are available.

5. Turtle Control
Of the trumpeter cygnets hatched by Mute Swans at Cranberry Marsh, ten have disappeared. It is likely that most were taken by Snapping Turtles. Control of Snapping Turtles was started in Cranberry Marsh in 1985. This control project will be continued as long as necessary in future years.

6. Number of Years

Trumpeter Swans are long-lived birds which do not breed until they are three, or more usually four years old. It will be necessary to persist with the fostering program using 50 eggs per year, for at least ten years.

7. Release of Stock

Captive pinioned trumpeters raised by their own parents could be used for restoration. If released on selected marshes where there is adequate natural food and supervision, they can be permitted to raise cygnets which are allowed to fly free. Artificial feeding should not be done in summer. Preferably the birds should be wintered on their breeding marsh with artificial food, and the progeny allowed to pioneer into neighbouring marshes upon being driven out in spring by their parents.

At present, shortage of adult stock precludes this approach.

8. Breeder-Loan Arrangements

For success, the fostering technique will depend on an adequate supply of trumpeter eggs. Some aviculturists have already promised eggs for the program. Four pairs of trumpeters are now available for placement with cooperators who will provide eggs for the fostering program.

9. Transplanting Techniques

There is a possibility that the CWS might be able to supply wild-caught trumpeters from Comox, British Columbia, for the Ontario restoration program. Trapping wild trumpeters on the Pacific coast and releasing them wing-clipped on a suitable marsh has not been tried yet in southern Ontario. Conventional wisdom suggests that, on regaining the power of flight, the birds would return to their original home range. However this did not happen when three families of trumpeters were moved from LaCreek National Wildlife Refuge, South Dakota, to Mingo National Wildlife Refuge, Missouri; survivors of these broods remained at Mingo. We can expect that some trumpeters at least will remain at the release site if arrangements are made to winter them there. Failure to provide wintering facilities would probably result in scattering of the birds and possibly failure to return. The installation of an aerolater or bubbler in deep water, to maintain open water, would be essential for wintering swans. Food would also have to be provided.

On an experimental basis we suggest that 20 Trumpeter Swans be used for a release in southern Ontario. A suitable site might be at Long Point on Lake Erie, the location where the last wild Trumpeter Swan of which we have record was shot in 1886.

10. Conventional Stocking

An often suggested technique is to raise trumpeters in captivity and release them to the wild. This technique will not be used. Artificial propagation in incubators and brooders results in birds which are hyper-aggressive toward humans. The absence of natural brood care probably results in birds which are incompetent parents, as experience with geese has shown. We have evidence that trumpeters raised artificially in captivity are not able immediately to feed themselves on natural foods, and need time to learn.

Reintroduction Strategies for the Hudson Bay Lowlands

In the Partidge River drainage and the Nettichi and Kinoje drainages near Moosonee, there are extensive areas of rich fen suitable for Trumpeter Swans. Wild caught stock which have used similar habitats in their own boreal breeding grounds would be the most suitable for release in the Hudson Bay Lowlands.

Agreement in principle with the relevant Indian bands would be a prerequisite for this kind of project. It would be necessary also to have the whole-hearted cooperation of the trapline owner where the swans were released.

Swans caught in January in British Columbia would have to be held in captivity until 20 April to 1 May (breakup dates vary in the Lowlands) before transport and release in the north. This project is not likely to be successful unless a minimum of 50 swans were released during the first year. Depending on survival migration and return, additional larger plantings of birds might be tried in a second and third year.

It would be best to delay this project until we have gained experience with trapping, shipping, and handling wild trumpeters for release in southern Ontario.

Marking and Tracking Trumpeter Swans

An important part of the program will be the follow-up to find out what happens to the released trumpeters. This will present problems because some may migrate long distances and others may wander unpredictably. All will be marked with either patagium tags or neck collars. These markers will be adequate for tracking local movements.

The use of telemetry will entail considerable expense and may not be satisfactory if swans leave the Province on migration. We do not have the resources to search for birds in the US.

Specifications for a satisfactory transmitter would include:

– Life of 24 months
– Range 50 km
– Weight 300 g
– Loop antenna contained within the unit
– On-off switch to have the transmitter run during daylight hours four days out of 20.

Such a system will need design work and could cost a minimum of $10,000 for ten units. An additional cost will be flying time. This will involve about 1,600 km of flying or about eight hours air time. At current Ministry rates (1985) this would cost about $680 per search. A minimum of three searches per year would be needed.

The use of telemetry should be deferred until we have more experience with a larger number of swans marked with patagium tags.

Public Involvement

Because Trumpeter Swans are migratory birds, it has been necessary to get the approval of authorities in the US and Canada for the reintroduction to Ontario. Both the Atlantic and Mississippi Flyway Councils have endorsed Ontario's plan to restore the Trumpeter Swan to its former range in the province.

The reestablishment of Trumpeter Swans in Ontario has received the endorsement of the Federation of Ontario Naturalists and the Ontario Federation of Anglers and Hunters.

The public will be encouraged to continue to help with all aspects of this program, and will be kept informed of progress and developments through periodic news releases and circulated reports.

Conservation Recommendations

Mute Swans can foster-raise trumpeters if the following precautions are taken:

1. Mute Swans will usually lay a second clutch if the first is removed immediately upon completion. Trumpeters lay about three weeks later than mutes, but their cycles can be synchronized by removing the mutes' first clutch.

2. Trumpeter eggs must be collected for shipping in the second half of incubation and preferably five to eight days before hatching. Eggs from captive trumpeters kept near fostering areas can be collected fresh. Many pairs will then lay a second clutch which can also be used.

3. For shipment, eggs should be packed point down to avoid damage to the air cells, and placed in well ventilated containers.

4. We have had problems with some embryos which seemed to be too weak to pip the shell. All eggs should be candled on receipt and the outline of the air cell drawn on the egg with a pencil. Close to hatching, this cell extends down one side of the egg. It is at the end of this extension that the beak and egg tooth of the embryo is located. If necessary, the shell can be cracked with a knife at that point to assist pipping.

5. Mute Swans do not have to incubate for the usual 34 to 36 days for normal parental behaviour to develop. We have not seen abnormal behaviour, and pairs have successfully hatched trumpeter cygnets after incubation which lasted 16, 17, 24, 38, and 58 days.

6. Trumpeter cygnets start to click about three days and call about two days before hatching. It is important that eggs spend this full period under the foster parents. Failure to do so results in loose family bonds and increased hazards to overly independent cygnets.

7. Mute Swan foster fathers are aggressive toward and sometimes attack trumpeter cygnets when they first leave the nest. Trumpeter cygnets may be too white for acceptance by mute males. Dying the dorsal surfaces of the cygnets brown on hatching eliminates this problem.

We now know what to do to make fostering of trumpeter cygnets on Mute Swans a success. We have developed means of increasing the number of eggs laid by captive pairs so that it is not unreasonable to expect to get 15 to 20 eggs from each pair, each year.

What we shall need to make restoration of trumpeters a success, is persistence in the use of every technique available. We must not expect instant success. Trumpeter Swans are in short supply, they have a relatively low reproductive rate, low survival in their earlier years, and they do not normally mature until they are four years old. At Grande Prairie, Alberta, only 60% of the wild cygnets that hatch, survive to fly, and only 43% of those survive to the end of their first year (CWS data). If Ontario trumpeters survive at the same rate, we can expect that only two or three of every ten cygnets that hatch will survive to one year old.

To date, our overall success rate has not been as good as the wild birds, however, annual results have been variable. In our best year (1986), when 12 cygnets hatched we could expect that three might survive to one year old. Four are now in their second year. There have been other years when none survived to one year old.

Unless release of wild caught trumpeters speedily establishes a breeding population, we must expect a further ten or 12 years of effort before we can expect success. This will require funding at a rate of about $21,000 per year. The Ontario Ministry of Natural Resources (MNR) is currently approaching the Federation of Ontario Naturalists to sponsor the program, and will contribute $5,000 per year toward the costs. Thus the project will need an additional $16,000 per year to do a reasonable job. The program cannot function without one person hired for four months, and provision of a truck on which boats can be carried.

Acknowledgements

The World Wildlife Fund provided a grant in 1984 to subsidize helicopter rental to pick up eggs in Alberta, and set aside $10,000 for the restoration program in 1987, $5,000 of which was donated by Canada Life Assurance Co. The total costs of the program since 1982 have been $20,000 to $28,000 per year (this does not include supervision and administration costs). The majority of this amount has been paid by MNR and used to cover the use of a truck for four months and salaries of two or three assistants.

On a volunteer basis, many naturalists have reported the numbers of marked swans and have helped with finding Mute Swan nests. They have also helped to drive, trap, and mark Mute Swans and trumpeter cygnets on Cranberry Marsh.

References

Banko, W.E. 1960. *The Trumpeter Swan*. U.S. Dept. of the Interior. 63:214.

Baldwin, D. 1967. *Archaeological newsletter*. New Series No. 26, Royal Ontario Museum, University of Toronto. 4pp.

Barnston, G. 1860. Recollections of swans and of Hudson's Bay. *Ibis* 2:253-259.

Biggar, H.P. (ed.) 1929. *The work of Samuel de Champlain 1615-1618*. Champlain Society Publication No. 3, Toronto. 418pp.

Hearne, S. 1795. *A journey from Prince of Wales Fort in Hudson's Bay to the northern ocean*. R. Glover (ed.) (1958). MacMillan Co. of Canada. 301pp.

Hindman, L.J. 1982. Feral mute swan population status and problems in the Atlantic Flyway with special reference to Maryland's population. *Trumpeter Swan Society, Conference* 8:4-7.

Lajeunesse, E.J. 1960. *The Windsor border region*. University of Toronto Press. 374pp.

Lumsden, H.G. 1984. The pre-settlement breeding distribution of Trumpeter Swans *Cygnus buccinator* and Tundra Swans *C. columbianus* in eastern Canada. *Can. Field Nat.* 98(4):415-424.

Peck, G.K. 1966. First published breeding record of Mute Swan in Ontario. Ont. *Field Biol.* 20:43.

Peters, N. 1931. *Jahre Britstatistik und Entwicklung der Hamburger Alsterschwan*. Abk. naturw. Ver. Hamburg 23.

Rich, E.E. and A.M. Johnson. 1949. *James Isham's observations on Hudson's Bay, 1743*. Champlain Society No. 12. 352pp.

Rich, E.E. and A.M. Johnson. 1954. *Moose Fort Journals, 1783-1785*. Hudson Bay Record Society Vol. 17, London. 392pp.

Shea, J.G. 1868. *Land of the Hurons*. J. Munsell Co., Albany, N.Y.

Thwaites, R.G. 1903. *A new discovery of a vast country in America by Father Louis Hennepin*. Jesuit Relations and Allied Documents. A.C. Mclung & Co., Chicago. 711pp.

Tyrell, J.B. 1931. *Documents relating to the early history of Hudson Bay*. Champlain Society Pub. No. 18. Toronto. 419pp.

Willey, C.H. 1968. The ecological significance of the Mute Swan in Rhode Island. *Proc. Northeast Fish and Wildlife Conf.*, Bedford, N.H. 23pp.

Willey, C.H. and B.F. Halla. 1972. *Mute swans of Rhode Island*. Wildlife Pamphlet No. 8, Rhode Island Dept. of Nat. Resources. 47pp.

Williams, G. and R. Glover. 1969. *Andrew Graham's observations on Hudson's Bay 1769-1791*. Hudson's Bay Record Society, Vol. 27. 423pp.

Wrong, G.M. and H.H. Langton. 1939. *The long journey to the country of the Hurons*. Champlain Society Publication No. 25., University of Toronto Press, Toronto. 411pp.

Wild Turkey Reintroduction

Dave Reid

Ontario Ministry of Natural Resources
Simcoe, Ontario N3Y 4T2

Abstract. *Wild Turkeys formerly occupied most of southern Ontario south of the Canadian Shield. Unregulated hunting and habitat destruction led to the demise of the Wild Turkey from most of its former range in the 1800s. The last documented Wild Turkey sighting in Ontario occurred in the first decade of this century. Early attempts at restoration involved release of large numbers of game farm turkeys and were unsuccessful.*

Beginning in 1984, releases of Wild Turkeys trapped in the wild from several midwest and northeastern states has led to the successful re-establishment of this game bird to six locations in southern Ontario. Preliminary results of research conducted at one of these locations, the Simcoe area, are presented, as well as seven conservation recommendations to ensure the continued success of the Wild Turkey restoration in Ontario.

Introduction

As the district biologist with the Ministry of Natural Resources, Simcoe District, I've had a close association with the Wild Turkey reintroduction in our district. This paper will present a brief history, touch on the research that was partially funded by the World Wildlife Fund, summarize the current population status, and conclude with seven recommended conservation steps.

Wild Turkeys belong to the same group of birds as pheasant, quail, and grouse. They are the largest gamebirds in North America – adult gobblers may weigh over 12 kg (27 lbs). They are a very stream-lined bird, metallic bronze in colouration. Though primarily a ground-dwelling bird, Wild Turkeys are capable of strong flight for short distances (Ontario Ministry of Natural Resources and Ontario Federation of Anglers and Hunters 1986).

Male Turkeys can be distinguished from females by a number of unique features including: head adornments (wattles, caruncles, snood); less feathering on a more colourful head (red, white, and blue); black tipped body feathers vs. buff tipped feathers of the hen; the presence of a bony projection or spur on the lower part of each leg; the presence of a long, bristle-like feather, known as a beard, hanging from the centre of the breast (hens rarely have this beard); and the distinctive "gobble" call made by males to attract females during the spring breeding season (Ontario Ministry of Natural Resources and Ontario Federation of Anglers and Hunters 1986).

Figure 1 shows the former range of the Wild Turkey in North America. There were once six subspecies in North America, the variety native to Ontario being the Eastern variety *(Meleagris gallopavo silvestris)*. The Wild Turkey disappeared from most of eastern North America in the 1800s, primarily due to unregulated, and market hunting, but also due to habitat destruction that occurred with the settlement of the Europeans, clearing of the land and logging. The species was virtually extirpated in Ontario by the late 1800s, with the last documented sightings occurring in the first decade of this century.

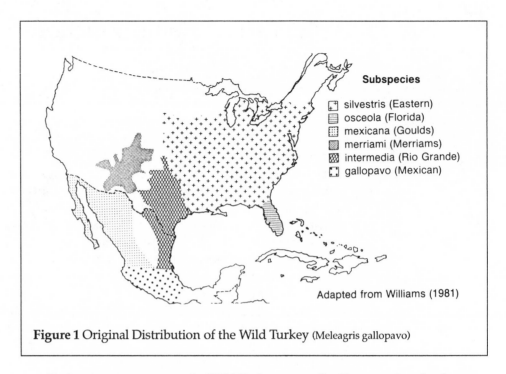

Figure 1 Original Distribution of the Wild Turkey (Meleagris gallopavo)

Early attempts to restore the Wild Turkey to much of its range involved game farm birds. Because of the wild , high-strung nature of the Wild Turkeys, they were crossed with domestic turkeys to provide a game farm wild turkey that could successfully be reared in captivity. The release of hundreds of thousands of game-farm birds throughout the early 1900s was largely unsuccessful in restoring the Wild Turkey to its former range.

What really changed things to the benefit of the Wild Turkey was the development of the technique of cannon or rocket netting of wild birds and transferring these into new areas. This occurred around late 1940s and early 1950s and has resulted in the resurrection of the Wild Turkey throughout most of its original range, and in fact, out beyond its former range to the western United States.

Methods

The first release of trapped Wild Turkeys in Ontario occurred in the first week of March 1984, when 27 birds from Missouris' Ozark Mountains were released in the Simcoe area. Subsequent releases there included 14 birds from southern Iowa in 1985, and 15 more birds, also from southern Iowa, in 1986, for a total release of 56 birds over three years. This was largely a cooperative project involving the Ontario Federation of Anglers and Hunters, the local fish and game clubs, the Ministry of Natural Resources, and, to a lesser extent, the Federation of Ontario Naturalists. The Wild Turkeys that we received in Simcoe were traded for River Otters to Missouri. River Otters also went in a tripartite trade to Nebraska for the turkeys from Iowa, and some of the birds that came from Iowa were in return for some Canada Geese that we had given them in previous years.

Simcoe is not the only area in Ontario where Wild Turkeys have been reintroduced. Figure 2 illustrates the southern boundary of the Canadian Shield, which approximates the historic maximum northern range of the Wild Turkey in Ontario, and six sites where the birds have been released. About 100 Wild Turkeys from northern Michigan were released in the Napanee area (Site 2) in 1984 and 1985, in

trade for some Ontario moose. In 1986, 102 Wild Turkeys were released at three
sites in Central Ontario – in the Alliston area (Site 3), the Glen Morris area near
Cambridge (Site 4), and in Short Hills Provincial Park near St. Catharines (Site 5).
The Central Ontario birds came primarily from New York, in trade for Ontario
Hungarian Partridge, but also included a gift of birds from Vermont. The sixth
release, occurred in the Lindsay area in 1987, a result of a gift of 22 Wild Turkeys
from the state of New Jersey.

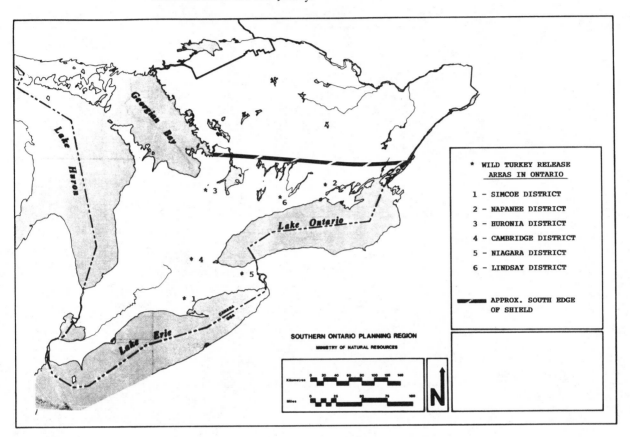

Figure 2: Wild Turkey Release Areas in Ontario

Most of the birds in the first two Simcoe releases had radio transmitters
mounted on them. They had individual frequencies so individual birds could be
monitored. The radios were strapped on the birds' back with the antennae running
down the tail. The radio telemetry through triangulation enabled studies of habitat
utilization, nesting locations, and success and mortality rates and causes.

Findings

Unfortunately, one of the things we found in the initial release was a high level of
infertility. I think the first year there were about 54 eggs in four nests that didn't
hatch because the hens never got bred. This was believed to be a consequence of
one of the most severe storms we had right at the onset of the release and also the
fact that the hens were released about a week apart from the males. Wild Turkeys
normally flock separately in the winter, so that when you are able to trap them you
usually get one sex or the other.

Table 1 indicates the extent of the nesting problems in the first two releases. Infertility was also a problem in the second year, 1985. That year, the males did not arrive until late in the day and we made the mistake of releasing them that day, rather than holding them for release the next day. Apparently, turkeys may roost on the ground instead of roosting in trees when released into a new area late in the day. Although the toms released in 1985 did not carry radios, one was found dead within 100 metres of the release site, apparently killed by a fox. Mortality of the toms released in 1985 may have resulted in the infertile clutches that year.

Table 1

Nest Fate of Wild Turkey Hens Released in the Simcoe Area of Southern Ontario

Year	Approx. Date of 1st Egg	Dist. from Release (km)	Clutch Size	Nest Fate
1984	May 7	2	?	hatched, June 19
	May 8	2	?	hatched, June 16
	May 10	25	14	infertile
	May 11	20	12	infertile
	May 17	25	14	infertile
	May 18	30	14	infertile
	June 1	8	10	destroyed
1985	May 2	30	12	hatched, June 8
	May 7	2	9	hatched, June 14
	May 10	25	12	infertile
	May 11	20	15	infertile
	May 28	5	7	infertile

Radio telemetry enabled us to locate dead birds and inspect the birds and kill locations for clues as to the causes of mortality. Table 2 summarizes preliminary causes of mortality in 1984 and 1985. Transport and handling shock was a direct cause of mortality on at least four birds, and may have indirectly led to some of the other mortality. Mammalian predators are fox, coyote and domestic dogs. The Great Horned Owl is the primary avian predator. One bird was road-killed and a nesting hen was run over by a tractor cultivator.

Table 2

Cause of Mortality of Wild Turkeys Released in the Simcoe Area of Southern Ontario in 1984 and 1985

Number	Probable Cause of Mortality
9	mammalian predator
4	transport and handling shock
3	avian predator
2	human, accidental
1	starvation

Confining these high strung birds for a relatively long time (over 48 hours) between capture and release was felt to increase the risk of mortality due to transport and handling shock. A shorter time period of 24 hours or less would minimize stress from transport and handling on the birds. Also, the release of the males at the same time as the females would increase the chances of breeding and reduce the risk of infertility.

For the third release in 1986 we pursued many different transportation methods to shorten the time between capture and release, and ensure the males were released at the same time as the females. Air transport by commercial, chartered, and MNR planes, could not be coordinated due to the nature of turkey trapping (you can never be sure what time of day and on which day birds might be captured), and the need to have all the birds certified free of poultry diseases before they could cross the border. What we chose to do in 1986 was send three people down by truck to southern Iowa to learn about their trap and transfer methods, participate in the actual capture of the birds for Ontario, and immediately drive back to Ontario, stopping off briefly at Michigan's Rose Lake Wildlife Research Centre to have the birds disease tested before crossing the border. Thus, in February 1986, we were successfully able to simultaneously release ten hens and five toms in Ontario within 24 hours of when they were captured in Iowa. We also learned a lot from the Iowa Conservation Commission about trap and transfer methods, and from the Michigan Department of Natural Resources about blood sampling and disease testing procedures.

The 1986 release was the best of the three releases made in the Simcoe area because the weather was milder, the birds appeared to be less stressed and in better shape upon release, and the hens and toms were released simultaneously. The Simcoe flock has grown quickly since 1986 from an estimated population of 80 birds, including those released in 1986, to the present spring population of between 600 and 800 birds.

In 1987 we had over 50 brood observations and the birds are now spread out over a 1000 km square area. The range and the approximate numbers are determined each spring with help of volunteers who run gobbling surveys.

Public observations were very important to help keep track of occupied range and reproductive success. Not everything reported in the initial years was a Wild Turkey, as several reports of Guinea Fowl, Muscovy Ducks, and Turkey Vultures, were submitted as Wild Turkey sightings. Free ranging game farm turkeys were identified by enquiring about the behaviour of the bird observed. While it is often possible to approach game farm turkeys quite closely, the typical behaviour of truly wild turkeys is to flush or run at distances of 200 metres or more from the observer, immediately upon seeing the person.

Conservation Recommendations

1. Initiate an aggressive trap and transfer program to spread the existing birds out so that we have Wild Turkeys throughout southern Ontario.

2. Continue the public involvement aspect. We've had cooperation from local fish and game clubs in posting release sites to identify them as Wild Turkey Release Areas. These clubs have also been of assistance in conducting turkey surveys, and in advertising a $250 reward offered by the Ontario Federation of Anglers and Hunters for information leading to the arrest and conviction of anyone

harassing or killing a Wild Turkey at or near a release site. This is an important step in the success of the reintroductions.

3. Control free-ranging game farm birds because of the genetic threat to initial releases and because of the threat of disease to the successful establishment of a wild population.

4. Protect the habitat that we have remaining, through plan review, and lobbying for more, or better, tree-cutting bylaws.

5. Educate land owners on habitat needs of the Wild Turkey, for example on good forest management practices, to ensure that the habitat that we have is protected and retained for the future.

6. Stepped up enforcement against poaching.

7. And lastly, controlled hunting. I interpret conservation to be the wise use of a resource and I think its important that we make good use of our Wild Turkey resource. In May of 1987 Ontario had its first spring hunt, in the Napanee area, where hunter numbers were controlled by lottery draw. It was for gobblers only and since there are normally a surplus of gobblers in the population for breeding purposes, it had no adverse effect on the turkey population's growth potential. A mandatory training seminar was attended by all involved, and mandatory checking of the relatively small number of birds harvested (63) was required to provide biological information.

Conclusion

As Ontario's Wild Turkey resource grows, moving further away from extirpation, to the point of becoming common and mundane, don't lose interest in this magnificent game bird simply because it is no longer rare and unusual.

Acknowledgements

Tables 1 and 2 are compiled from data generated by Joe Weaver while a Master's student at the University of Western Ontario. Joe and his thesis supervisor, Dr. Davison Ankney, were involved in radio telemetry studies of the 1984 and 1985 releases in the Simcoe area.

References

Ontario Ministry of Natural Resources and Ontario Federation of Anglers and Hunters. 1986. *The Wild Turkey*. Queen's Printer, Ontario. (pamphlet).

Williams, L.E., Jr. 1981. *The book of the Wild Turkey*. Winchester Press, Oklahoma.

A Mass Hack of Peregrine Falcons by the Peninsula Field Naturalists

Cathy A. Sanderson
Mary Ellen Foley*
Cathy Vandenbogerd

* 32 Maplewood Drive
St. Catharines, Ontario L2M 3P1

Abstract. *In 1987, 15 Peregrine Falcons (subspecies* anatum*) were successfully fledged from three 'hack' sites in the Niagara Region by the Peninsula Field Naturalists, in cooperation with the World Wildlife Fund and Ontario Ministry of Natural Resources. This effort is part of an ongoing Peregrine Falcon Release Project, the purpose of which is to re-establish one or more nesting pairs of peregrines in Ontario.*

Introduction

The Peregrine Falcon *(Falco peregrinus)* is probably one of the most well-known endangered species in North America. In the early part of this century, admiration of this bird was limited to a few apparently eccentric bird watchers and a small community of falconers. However, after it reached near-extirpation in North America in the early 1970s, the plight of this majestic raptor captured the public's imagination. Programmes initiated to restore the peregrine to its earlier numbers by a means called 'hacking' (by Cornell University in 1972, and by The Ontario Ministry of Natural Resources in 1977) brought the peregrine more fame, and more fans.

Results, however, in the form of returning Peregrine Falcons, were mediocre in Canada, including Ontario. To try to co-ordinate and standardize efforts, a National Peregrine Recovery Team was formed in 1986, and one of its first recommendations was the 'mass hack' – the release of a large number of birds in the same area in the same year.

The 1986 Peregrine Falcon Release by The Peninsula Field Naturalists at Brock University in St. Catharines was the first in Canada ever undertaken by a private club. Four birds were released. One, a male, returned, and was sighted in Toronto in September, 1987. The next year, the club was asked to release fifteen falcons in the Niagara region in keeping with the initiatives of the Recovery Team. This the club agreed to, although not without some trepidation. The release preparations, the release itself, and the results, are described in the pages that follow.

Methodology

The methods used during this mass hack were based on the procedures developed by The Peregrine Fund (Sherrod *et al.* 1982), and unless otherwise stated, are those described in Foley (1987).

1. Sites

After an extensive search of the Niagara Peninsula, three sites were chosen and permission was obtained for their use. The sites were selected with several criteria in mind. Each had to be a prominent building of at least four storeys in height. The buildings needed a large, hazard-free roof for the fledgling falcons to use for flight practice and orientation. The building had to be secure and safe from intrusions or theft. Each site needed a large, safe area surrounding the building for the falcons' early flights. The site also had to be well away from highways or roads with heavy, fast traffic; from industrial or other chimneys that cannot be covered; and at least 1.5 km away from nests of Great Horned Owls (*Bubo virginianus*). Finally, in case of a return by a peregrine from the previous year's hack (which might put the new fledglings at risk), we needed a stand-by site which was at least 15 km away from the 1986 site.

The first site was the roof of the Shaw Festival Theatre in Niagara-on-the-Lake. The roof of the Schmon Tower of Brock University (the previous year's site) was the second choice. The third was the roof of E.L. Crossley Secondary School in Fonthill. A description of each site and its advantages and disadvantages follows.

The Shaw Festival Theatre is located on the edge of the small town of Niagara-on-the-Lake, Ontario. The building has two roof levels, one of approximately six storeys, and the lower level where the hack box was placed, of approximately four storeys. The hack box and blind were placed against a wall and faced southwest, overlooking a large open parkland on two sides of the building. The building had a night alarm system. No large highway, no Great Horned Owls, and no dangerous chimneys were nearby. Particularly important was the fact that the theatre was much more than 15 km away from the 1986 site.

The theatre also had several unique disadvantages. Access to the roof by hack attendants was difficult and included crossing the stage, mounting a spiral staircase, and negotiating a catwalk over the stage, other staircases, and a wooden ladder. This route was impossible for transfer of the materials needed to construct the hack box, and all supplies were hoisted up the exterior wall of the building. Moreover, construction and access of attendants had to be scheduled with regard to rehearsals and performances. Tourists were a concern, with the town receiving approximately one million visitors each year.

The Schmon tower at Brock University fulfilled the requirement of height (14 storeys), security (campus police and controlled access), and safe surroundings (extensive grounds surrounded by farmland). The University is located south of St. Catharines on the edge of the Niagara Escarpment, making the tower a prominent landmark. The hack box was located on the roof of the tower and was reached through a ventilation window in the penthouse. Fortunately, elevators were available up to the thirteenth floor. A highway approximately a kilometre away was too far away, we hoped, to be a major concern.

E.L. Crossley Secondary School is situated on the highest point of land in the Niagara Peninsula and the roof itself is five storeys high. Security was met at this site by lack of activity at the school during the summer and an alarm system linked to the police. The school is located in the farmland surrounding the small town of Fonthill, providing a relatively safe flying area for the fledglings. A busy road approximately 100 meters in front of the school proved not to be a hazard.

2. Hack Box Features
Several features of the hack boxes were important. In all cases, the approach of humans was concealed from birds in the box and on the roof by the use of blinds behind and around the sides of the hack boxes, which enclosed the roof access. At the Shaw site, a ladder was partially covered to hide humans approaching the blind. The blinds allowed the birds to be fed and observed without disturbing them or associating humans with food.

A sliding door was added to the standard hack box design suggested by The Peregrine Fund (Sherrod *et al.* 1982). The door could be closed from the blind, locking the falcons behind the hide with a minimum of disturbance. This door was used when cleaning was needed in the hack box, and on the morning of release while the front of the box was removed.

The front of each hack box (the bars and protective screening) was removable as a single unit. This saved time and disturbance on the morning of release.

Several 7 x 15 cm pieces of one-way glass were used to observe the birds within the hack box and after release. Wide-angle peep-holes that are found in doors had been tried, but they were inadequate for identification purposes.

Since it was intended to release the birds before they could fly well, many branches were provided as perches on the roof of the blind and nearby. The birds were provided with a gravel-covered balcony extending in front of and around one side of the hack box, which was raised one metre from roof level. There were also branches on the balcony. A narrow carpet-covered ramp extended from the balcony to the roof level to assist birds returning to the hack box. This ramp was used as a perch and a sleeping place, as well as for access to the balcony of the hack box.

Just before the arrival of the Shaw peregrines, and too late to rectify the damage, it was discovered that the builder had not made the hack box to conform to Cornell specifications. It was short by more than 30 cm in length and several cm in width. Little as this may seem, it added up to significant loss of area, a particularly serious problem since the box was to house six peregrines rather than the more usual four.

3. Other Features

One of the features that made caring for the birds much easier was a closed circuit television system at each site. At Brock and Shaw there were colour cameras, with pan-and-tilt controls. The focal length of the lens was also easily controlled. At these sites a VCR was attached to the colour monitor, capable of recording over a twelve-hour period. This system allowed continual observation of the birds both in and out of the box, with no disturbance. The monitor was situated where the public and staff could observe the birds. At Brock, a second monitor was installed in a more peaceful location for the falcon caretakers. At Crossley, a fixed camera and a black and white monitor were installed.

To provide almost continuous observation of the fledglings while they were learning to fly, volunteers were used as observers in addition to regular staff. Critical days were divided into blocks of three hours and volunteers were scheduled to surround the release site. People from the Hamilton Naturalists' Club, The Niagara Falls Nature Club, Buffalo Ornithological Society, and our club, The Peninsula Field Naturalists, volunteered their time, many of them more than once, to watch the falcons. There was always regular staff nearby in case of emergency, and observers at each site were in contact by walkie-talkie.

At Shaw, the local media were very enthusiastic about the project. A press conference was held when the falcons arrived and the media were kept informed of major events at all sites. To capitalize on the opportunity for public education, names were given to the falcons. The names chosen were those of local historical figures, which gave the birds an individuality and appeal which the public and staff appreciated.

Results and Discussion

The falcons arrived in two shipments from the Canadian Wildlife Services facility in Wainwright, Alberta, on June 28 and July 14. The first six birds went to Niagara-on-the-Lake because this site was 26 km from the nearest of the other two sites. This was done to prevent the better flying, older birds from harassing the birds which were to be released later at the other sites. Brock and Crossley were only 18 km apart, and since the birds in the second shipment were very close in age, the males were placed at Brock and the more slowly developing females at Crossley. The 26 km between the Shaw birds and the younger birds effectively separated them, while the 18 km distance did not prevent the two younger groups from meeting.

On release day (July 10 at Shaw, July 22 at Brock, July 26 at Crossley), preparations started before dawn in the hopes of catching the falcons sleeping on their hide. At the first two sites, birds were coaxed back and the sliding door closed, but at Crossley, the birds (all four) would not retreat. A blanket was held in front of the hack box while the front panel was removed.

1. Shaw Festival Theatre

On being released, the falcons spent varying amounts of time exploring the roof, feeding, and exercising. The first bird at Shaw was "0T0 ("Larry")", who went to the centre of town and stayed there overnight. The three females had difficulties, some of which we feel were caused by lack of exercise and muscle-building while in the box. "1C8 ("Mrs Pat")" flew to a neighbouring hospital roof (two storeys), and in attempting to leave it (she had been frightened by a power lawn mower), crashed to the ground. Over the next few hours, she made a few attempts to get airborne, but got progressively weaker and more stressed. Late in the day, she was finally captured and returned to the hack box, where she was confined in the hide until morning. After re-release she had no further difficulties (Dehydration may have exacerbated "Mrs. Pat's" problems; we had been advised not to provide water in the hack box because the birds would sit in it and soften their feathers, but the days following release were very hot. Based on this experience, we think water should be available in the hack box in a narrow dish the falcons cannot sit in).

"2C0 ("Kay")" was found walking in the parking lot of the theatre at dusk and was easily recaptured. She appeared to have been in a minor collision, probably caused by poor landing techniques. She was confined overnight in the hide and released the next morning. That day, she still appeared lethargic and so was recaptured and sent to her namesake, Katherine McKeever, of the Owl Rehabilitation Research Foundation, for examination. No injuries were found, and she was returned and released. From this point on, she had no further problems. It is possible that her poor flying skills and lethargy were caused by the close confinement of the hack box.

"1T1 ("Newark")" also ended up on the ground several days after she started to fly, as a result of misjudging a landing and hitting a wall. After several hours on the ground she flew on her own.

The falcons' flying abilities increased without further incident. The birds were often seen at Fort Niagara, in New York State, approximately two km from the release site. All the birds began hunting at a normal age.

2. Brock University

The release of the five males at Brock University went without incident and they rapidly became proficient flyers. A minimal crew stayed on at Brock, and the rest moved on to Crossley.

3. E.L. Crossley Secondary School

As previously noted, the actual release at Crossley was different from other releases. However, this did not appear to have been detrimental to the falcons and all flew normally. One week after release, "3C6 ("Emily")" tried to fly too soon after a heavy rain and landed in the parking lot. Once dry, she flew away.

4. Behaviour

Interesting behaviour was observed at all sites. The most disturbing was at Shaw while the birds were still in the hack box. The birds had a poor appetite, were lethargic, and did relatively little of the wing-pumping which is so crucial to strong flight after release (this was particularly true of the females). "0T9 ("George")" spent a good deal of the time in the back of the hide, and "Kay" often slept with her head up the chute, or as far out of the bars as she could push it. We now believe this was because the box was too crowded, particularly for a six-bird hack. We think this was the cause of the females' difficulties in early flight. None of the Crossley females, who were in a large box, and whose first flights were within a day in age of the Shaw females, had comparable problems.

At Crossley, two of the falcons were seen hunting together through an orchard with one bird flying below the trees, and the other above and behind, in an apparent ploy to flush, then capture the flushed birds. In another instance, a falcon appeared to use a parked van as a cover to approach small birds.

With only 18 km separating Brock and Crossley, it was expected that the birds would meet. The first observed meeting occurred at Crossley, eleven days after the females had been released. At this time all four females were on the roof or circling the school, when a fifth falcon flew approximately 100 m from the building, heading towards Brock. The Crossley birds screamed loudly, but did not chase or flee. The fifth falcon continued towards Brock. The second observed meeting occurred at Brock, when a feeding falcon suddenly began to scream and mantle his food (to protect it). The camera was pivoted, and there on the roof of the blind, was "3C6 ("Emily")", from Crossley.

All the falcons dispersed normally, after showing evidence of hunting for themselves. Food was left out for a few weeks after the birds' last appearance.

After the birds at Brock had dispersed, "2T1 ("Tom Longboat")" returned, after an absence of several days, and he remained to feed once a day until September 22.

5. Post-Dispersal Results

On August 23, 28 days after her release, "3C6 ("Emily")" was seen for the last time, feeding on the roof of Crossley. On August 29, she was found dead in southwestern Michigan. Autopsy results have not yet been received, but she appeared to have a broken wing and leg, indicating a collision.

In February, 1988, a female peregrine was found in Toledo, Ohio. This bird was identified as "3C7 ("Nellie McClung")", released from E.L.Crossley. She was paired with an unidentified male, with whom she eventually mated, and produced two chicks in mid-May, 1988. It is interesting to note that this female was less than one year old when she hatched her chicks.

On July 11, 1988, The Hamilton Naturalists' Club released six falcons in a similar project at Mohawk College in Hamilton. Six days after release, there were seven falcons at the site. The new bird was identified as "2T1 ("Tom Longboat")", released from Brock the previous summer. Tom spent several weeks near the College, and appeared almost daily to eat quail. In early September, Tom was observed in the Dundas Marsh, and was seen capturing and partially eating a Lesser Golden-plover *(Pluvialis dominica)*.

On September 17, 1988, two Wainwright-hacked birds, a male and a female, appeared in downtown Toronto. The female was identified as "1C8 ("Mrs. Patrick Campbell")", released from Shaw. As of this writing, both birds are still there, and the male is still unidentified.

Conservation Recommendations

1. All peregrine releases, regardless of where they take place, should proceed according to the methodology developed by Cornell University and the Peregrine Fund, who have had far more success in their results than any Canadian efforts.

2. The dimensions of the hack box should be carefully monitored to conform to Cornell specifications. There should never be more than six birds hacked in one box.

3. All would-be peregrine release groups should read The Peregrine Fund's hacking manual (Sherrod *et al.*) before attempting to hack. Problems that arise which are not covered by the manual should be dealt with by consulting one of the experts at The Peregrine Fund itself.

4. In choosing an appropriate hack site, the safety of the birds should be the primary consideration. For example, what were once traditional peregrine eyries are now, with the growth and development of vegetation over the years, prime habitat for Great Horned Owls. As for the selection of general area, it has become clear that peregrines do not necessarily return to the area (or even country!) in which they were hacked. Hence choice of area to hack in once again becomes a matter of what is safest and best for the birds, rather than which area wants or needs to have peregrines nesting there.

5. Just as the Peregrine Recovery Team meets once a year to discuss broader strategy, so the people who actually do the hacking should also meet yearly. There is an urgent need for consultation and discussion of failures and successes, so that mistakes are not repeated again and again, as is happening now.

6. Similarly, there is an urgent need for an education programme in raptor identification and biology at the district levels of the MNR, who deal most often with the public. Local MNR staff in several areas of Ontario have identified Red-tailed Hawks, American Kestrels, and even Herring Gulls, as Peregrine Falcons. Moreover, when a peregrine was found seriously injured in southwestern Ontario in 1988, district staff failed to see any urgency in getting it into experienced veterinary hands.

7. Finally, there is a pressing need for a large flight cage to be built (perhaps at the University of Guelph, or at the Owl Foundation) for recovery and release training of raptors such as the one mentioned above, so that there will not be a need to send them out of the province.

Acknowledgements

The following people or companies donated either financial support, material goods, use of their property for hack sites, time and labour, or invaluable advice:

Canadian Wildlife Service staff at Wainwright, Alberta
Doug Hagen, Ministry of Natural Resources
Dave Euler, Ministry of Natural Resources
Jim Weaver, Marty Gilroy, and other members of the Peregrine Fund
World Wildlife Fund, Canada
Gordon and Diana Bellerby
Brock University, St. Catharines
Canada Trust
John and Margaret Cooper
E.L. Crossley Secondary School
Fonthill Building Centre
Vince Goldsworthy
Imperial Oil Limited
The John Howard Society
Niagara Glass Limited
The Owl Rehabilitation Research Foundation
Panasonic
Peninsula Upholstery
Penner Building Centre
Al Plosz
Quebec and Ontario Paper Company
Shaw Festival Centre
Security Information Services
Sunlife Assurance Company of Canada
T.C.G. Materials

Special thanks are due to hack site attendants, who devoted long, long hours and much care to the falcons: Bob Curry, Martin McNicoll, Iva Peprna, Ian Rabenda, Cathy Sanderson, and Cathy Vandenbogerd. We would also like to thank The Niagara Falls Nature Club, The Hamilton Naturalists' Club, The Buffalo Ornithological Society, and all the people of St. Catharines and the Niagara Region, Toronto, Burlington, Hamilton, and New York State, who came out in such numbers to help us watch the falcons while they were at risk.

References

Sherrod, S.K., W.R. Heinrich, W.A. Burnham, J.H. Barclay and T.J. Cade. 1982. *Hacking, a method for releasing Peregrine Falcons and other birds of prey*. The Peregrine Fund, Ithaca, New York.

Foley, M.E. 1987. Peregrine Falcon Release in the Niagara Peninsula. *The Wood Duck* 40(5):78-79.

Appendix 1: Peregrine Falcons Hacked in 1987 in Niagara Region

Name	Sex	Colour Band	Fish & Wildlife Band	Hatch Date	Release Site	Date Released	Date of First Flight	Age (in days) of First Flight	Time to return to box after First Flight	Age (in days) at Dispersal	Date last seen at Release Site
Larry McKeever	M	0T0	686-03955	May 31	SHAW	July 10	July 10	40	23 1/2 hrs	88	Aug. 27
George Bernard Falcon	M	0T9	986-03954	May 31	SHAW	July 10	July 12	42	immediately	82	Aug. 21
Mrs. Patrick Campbell	F	1C8	987-45405	May 31	SHAW	July 10	July 13	43	had to be rescued	80	Aug. 19
Kay McKeever	F	2C0	987-45409	June 3	SHAW	July 10	July 15	42	3 1/2 hrs	65	Aug. 7
Newark	F	1T1	987-45411	June 3	SHAW	July 10	July 16	43	immediately	79	Aug. 21
Penner	M	1T0	686-03957	June 3	SHAW	July 10	July 13	40	32 hours	77	Aug. 19
Billy Bishop	M	2T4	686-03964	June 12	BROCK	July 22	July 22	40	30 hours	59	Aug. 10
Adam Beck	M	2T3	816-81005	June 12	BROCK	July 22	July 23	41	12 hours	82	Sept. 2
Sam McGee	M	2T2	686-03965	June 12	BROCK	July 22	July 22	40	24 hours	80	Aug. 31
Tom Longboat	M	2T1	816-34127	June 13	BROCK	July 22	July 24	41	2 hours	100	Sept. 22
Ernest Thompson Seton	M	1T5	816-34126	June 12	BROCK	July 22	July 24	42	4 1/2 hours	60	Aug. 11
Lucy Maude Montgomery	F	3C5	987-45425	June 12	CROSSLEY	July 26	July 26	44	immediately	70	Aug. 21
Emily Carr	F	3C6	987-45430	June 14	CROSSLEY	July 26	July 28	44	immediately	70	Aug. 23
Nellie McClung	F	3C7	987-45429	June 13	CROSSLEY	July 26	July 26	43	24 hours	72	Aug. 24
Mrs. Dexter D'Everardo	F	3C8	987-45422	June 12	CROSSLEY	July 26	July 27	45	2 hours	72	Aug. 23

Summary

An extremely rare bird in Canada, the
King Rail breeds only in large, Great Lakes
marshes in Ontario, such as those at
Walpole Island, Rondeau, Long Point, and
Oshawa. Declines noted in Ontario and
through its eastern US range are probably
the result of declining North American
wetlands.
Artist – Ron Ridout.

Goals for a Conservation Data Centre for Ontario

George Francis

Department of Environment and Resource Studies
University of Waterloo
Waterloo, Ontario N2L 3G1

Abstract. *A number of large atlas projects have been collecting valuable information on the fauna and flora of Ontario. The effectiveness and success of natural heritage protection and management is crucially dependent upon such field studies. There is a need for the systematic storage, screening and application of ecological information. A strategy for the management of such information is proposed. This would include: a conservation data unit, a trust fund and networks of field volunteers.*

Introduction

It would be helpful to go back to 1986 when the Ontario Breeding Bird Atlas project was drawing to a successful conclusion. The field work was over, the data files were being finalized, and the text for the book was being written and reviewed. Informal discussions among various people addressed the question of what might be done next, in part to build on the successful experience of this major volunteer-based project. The Management Committee for the breeding bird atlas sponsored a meeting of Waterloo in April 1986 in which about two dozen people from across the province discussed some possibilities. At least three main themes emerged at this meeting and during other discussions held from time to time in 1986.

First, there should be other atlas projects. Although birds are undoubtedly the best known among our fauna and flora in Ontario, the breeding bird atlas provided new insights into the distributions of a number of species. For other animals or plants, atlassing should provide even more new information and understanding. The Ontario Herpetofaunal Summary was then under way entirely as a volunteer endeavour, and its first two years yielded a lot of interesting records. Perhaps it could be developed into a major atlas project. A follow-up project to monitor more closely the rare species of birds was also raised at that time, and led directly to the proposal for the Ontario Rare Breeding Birds project outlined by Mike Cadman in this book. Along with this, it might have been worthwhile trying to develop a Register of Ornithological Sites, similar to one developed in the U.K. This would bring yet another set of criteria to bear on identifying areas for conservation purposes. Generally, the botanists in these discussions remained sceptical of atlas projects. So far as we could see this was more on grounds of feasibility than desirability. There are a number of difficult plant taxa that make reliance on field reports by volunteer observers problematic.

Second, we need to get a better handle on who's protecting what, where and how. Pulling together such information "by hand" from multiple and diffused sources for any bioregion in the province is a long, slow process. The identification sub-committee for the Carolinian Canada project reviewed a large number of consultations in order to short-list 38 priority sites from among the 1000 or so for which some information was available. Similarly, the equivalent of at least a year's work went into compiling information to determine that some 123 areas along the Canadian side of the Great Lakes are under formal categories of protection administered by different government agencies, and another 209 sites have been flagged by systematic surveys done at various times over the past 25 years (starting with the International Biological Program surveys), but for which no follow-up actions were taken. The Nature Conservancy of Canada (NCC) and the Canadian Council on Ecological Areas (CCEA) had been talking about developing a registry of protected areas in Canada, but the Conservancy didn't have the wherewithal to proceed at the time. CCEA has since embarked upon compilations of summary review sheets for ecological reserves or their equivalents (such as Areas of Natural and Scientific Interest in Ontario). This is beginning to show the considerable progress that is now being made in a number of provinces towards establishing ecological reserves, but the Register deals with just this one formal category of protected area.

Third, an information exchange system ought to be developed that would link field surveys and research with natural heritage area planning and management and involve a number of organizations and groups. The research component of Carolinian Canada was a good precedent, since it pointed out how much still has to be found out about the basic ecology of "non-game species" of animals, and plants other than trees of commercial importance. Much more of this kind of effort should underlie planning and management decisions for conservation. Perhaps some ongoing publication should be considered, such as a re-utilized and re-oriented version of "The Ontario Field Biologist".

These discussions also led to three main conclusions at that time. First the funding for new atlas projects would be hard to obtain until the final project from the breeding bird atlas was published to show the kinds of results to be expected. Second, while individual initiatives to launch various field surveys or research are welcome, some means have to be found to put field surveys, and ecological or other research relating to natural heritage areas on a sound and continuing basis. And third, these kinds of endeavours should be rooted in and involve the main constituency of organizations that could both contribute to and benefit from them. That constituency is the Ontario Natural Heritage League.

A Data Centre and the Natural Heritage League

During 1987, further talks among people affiliated with member organizations of the Natural Heritage League led to raising the issues at the League's annual meeting. A representative from The United States Nature Conservancy was the invited luncheon speaker and he described the conservation data bases maintained by the Conservancy and how they are used to develop State Natural Heritage Programs. A panel discussion on the theme of "Getting the Knowledge We Need for Natural Heritage Planning and Management" pointed out some opportunities for closer cooperation among groups in Ontario, and by implication, the wasted effort or ineffective use of conservation funds should this cooperation be resisted or ignored. This led to a resolution calling upon the Coordinating Committee for the League to look into the issue and report back. Some months later, the Coordinating Committee appointed a small working group on conservation data to help with this. Table 1 is a summary of the situation as perceived by the working group by mid 1988.

Table 1

Management Information for the Natural Heritage League

Statement from the Working Group on Conservation Data to the Coordinating Committee of the Natural Heritage League, July 1988

The Situation

The effectiveness and success of natural heritage protection and management is crucially dependent on ecological field studies. They identify what needs to be protected and the management guidelines for protecting it. The organization of a shared information system and the strengthening of field studies on a continuing basis has become essential for the ONHL. Without this, there will be severe limits to what the League and its members can achieve, since they will not have the essential knowledge to support their commitments to conservation.

What's To Be Done?

The management information for the ONHL should include:

1. A **conservation data unit** that provides interactive networking among existing data bases and is compatible with various Geographic Information Systems used for land use or resource planning.

2. A **trust fund** or comparable funding support for ecological surveys and specific field studies on a regular and continuing basis.

3. **Networks** of field volunteers for data gathering and site monitoring.

The **Conservation Data Unit** would be organized as a co-operative venture among members of the League. It would link up and further develop as necessary three computerized data bases:

- "atlas" and related field survey data on the occurrences of natural communities and species of animals and plants in Ontario

- registries of who is protecting what, where, and how

- a reference and referral system for research on natural heritage planning and management and ecological field studies relevant to this.

Meanwhile, the Nature Conservancy of Canada had decided to adopt the U.S. Conservancy's "Biological and Conservation Data System" to establish a "Canadian National Conservation Data Centre" based in Toronto. It would help coordinate the development of provincial information systems and provide computer links across Canada and to the U.S. system. NCC, with help from the U.S. Nature Conservancy, would raise funds to get the information system up and running, but it would also negotiate an agreement with the appropriate provincial government agencies to take over responsibility for maintaining the provincial systems and keeping them up to date. This was the procedure followed in the United States to develop the State Natural Heritage Programs.

During the past years, the NCC has entered into discussions with each of the provinces. The progress in this regard is outlined in the paper by Phil Hoose and Susan Crispin. The working group on conservation data convened by the League's Coordinating Committee has held two sessions to go over the technical and administrative details of this particular information system. As a result, the group recommended the following in mid-September 1988 (Table 2).

The Coordinating Committee agreed to the first four points, and deferred a decision concerning the fifth until some more details could be brought forward. NCC has since received $25,000 from the Steering Committee of Carolinian Canada to proceed with point 2 in Table 2.

Table 2

Conclusions of the Working Group on Conservation Data submitted to the Coordinating Committee of the Natural Heritage League on 15 September 1988

1. NCC would like to receive an endorsement in principle for its initiative to introduce TNC's "Biological and Conservation Data System" (BCD) into Ontario.

2. MNR and others in the working group would like to have the NCC apply to the BCD system first to Carolinian Canada as a kind of pilot project to test its capabilities as a management information system.

3. NCC should also examine ways to interface the BCD system with the provincial topographical data base (GIS) being developed by MNR.

4. NCC should work closely with League members to develop an accepted classification of natural communities, and start by assessing the applicability of the classifications developed by the natural heritage programs in the neighbouring Great Lake States to the Great Lakes region of Ontario.

5. The CC/NHL should take up related issues concerning:

   a) strengthening support for atlas field surveys to collect information of the occurrences of plants and animals in Ontario;

   b) development of a bibliographic reference or referral system on the planning and management of natural heritage areas in Ontario, including field research in conservation biology that has management implications; and

   c) developing the ecological and environmental monitoring functions in selected natural heritage areas.

The NCC's initiative here goes a long way towards meeting the needs and opportunities identified a few years ago. The design specifications for the Biological and Conservation Data System focus on tracking ecosystem occurrences as defined by classifications of natural communities (habitat and distinctive plant species) and lists of plants and animals that are endangered, threatened, rare, or otherwise of special interest. The classifications and lists are drawn up separately for each State and Province. The status of each species ("score cards") in terms of relative rarity or endangerment is recorded with reference to its total range, national status, and its status in each State/Province in which it occurs. Other components of ecosystem occurrences can also be added, such as geological and/or geomorphological areas of interest, or sites of special wildlife significance such as bat caves. Basic descriptive information is stored for each site having a significant ecosystem occurrence, including ownerships, management actions or management needs. Bibliographic references and the names of contact people are also maintained with reference to each site or occurrence. The system adopted by NCC is a 6th generation software ("Advanced Revelation") that has been developed and tested for over 15 years in the United States. It is extremely versatile, user friendly and Geographical Information System compatible. In addition to this computerized information system, the State Natural Heritage Programs maintain sets of topographical maps which record the locations of ecosystem occurrences as well as manual files with selected background documents concerning them. The same will be done in Canada.

Because of the Conservancies' focus on conservation of biotic diversity, they do not maintain complete atlas data bases *per se,* although they welcome atlas data on the particular species of interest. In Ontario, NCC has drawn upon the breeding bird atlas data, and its is a co-sponsor of the Rare Breeding Bird Monitoring project. Atlas data are of particular use for studies relating to over-all landscape diversity, and they will be increasingly valuable for use in the emerging field of landscape ecology. We still, however, have to find ways to put all of this on a sound continuing basis in Ontario if we are indeed to get the knowledge we need for conservation.

Dryland Blueberry (*Vaccinium pallidum*),
is restricted to the Carolinian Zone in
Canada, with the exception of populations
in eastern Ontario near the St. Lawrence
River. It prefers dry, sandy openings in oak
or pine woods.
Artist – Steve Varga.

The Status of Natural Heritage Data Centres in Canada

Phil Hoose

The Nature Conservancy
1815 N. Lynn Street
Arlington, VA 22209
U.S.A.

Susan Crispin

Nature Conservancy of Canada
794A Broadview Avenue
Toronto, Ontario M4K 2P7

Abstract. *Since 1986, the Nature Conservancy of Canada has been developing a Canadian Natural Conservation Data Centre. The Centre uses the methodology developed by the U.S. Nature Conservancy for the State Natural Heritage Programs. The goal is to develop a Conservation Data Centre in each province. A grant from the Carolinian Canada project has been used to develop a data system for the Carolinian Life Zone.*

Project Overview

In 1986, the Nature Conservancy of Canada (NCC) set out to establish a Canadian National Conservation Data Centre (CNCDC), using the State Natural Heritage Programs methodology developed by the U.S. Nature Conservancy. The NCC did so because it needed a way to organize data on thousands of natural areas throughout Canada and to establish conservation priorities.

Without such a tool, the NCC had no objective basis for deciding how to spend land acquisition dollars that are very hard to raise. It seemed impossible to choose protection targets from among the thousands of important areas that scientists had identified over the years, including Natural Sites of Canadian Significance, Natural Areas of Canadian Significance, International Biosphere sites, Areas of Natural and Scientific Interest and Ramsar Convention Wetlands.

The NCC's goal is to establish a data centre in each province and to link them, through the computer technology, to a national coordinating centre in Toronto. These centres can in turn be linked to compatible data centres in each of the states and in nine Latin America nations, to form a network that will cover most of the hemisphere. This is a great advantage, since biota acknowledge no jurisdictional boundaries (a particular Piping plover doesn't know or care if it's in Ontario or in Michigan).

Each centre will offer mapped and computerized occurrence information on the plants, animals, ecosystems and important natural areas of each province. The rarer the natural element, the more information that will be managed. It will be possible, by activating the relevant portions of the network, to determine the exact status of a particular species or community (i.e., how many known occurrences are there throughout its range, how many are protected, which populations or examples are the biggest and best, which are the worse, to what degree are they protected, what constitutes a good occurrence, who owns them, if they are targeted for protection by a conservation agency).

NCC's goal from the outset is to place each provincial data centre within a government ministry, sharing the costs at first and then arranging for the government to employ the staff and fund the program at a negotiated date. Of the 49 state programs in the United States, all were started this way and 33 have transferred into full public custody and funding.

With such a data base, public agencies can use the information to evaluate public land policies, choose acquisition priorities, and review development proposals which require licences or permits. Industry can use the data centres for facilities planning. The data is mapped, and in many places is linked to a Geographical Information System.

Below is a province by province summary of the status of the NCC's efforts to place conservation data centres:

1. British Columbia: Contact between the NCC and the Ministry of Environment has been made. The Ministry is awaiting approval of an internal budget to fund a CDC for the province.

2. Alberta: The Canadian Petroleum Association, needing data for facilities siting, has agreed to provide substantial funding. A decision was taken in April 1990 to establish an Alberta CDC within the Department of Forestry, Lands and Wildlife.

3. Saskatchewan: Contact between the NCC and the Department of Environment and Public Safety have been made. A proposal is under consideration.

4. Ontario: The Carolinian Canada project awarded a grant of $25,000 to NCC to develop a data system, using the CNCDC methodology, for organizing data on the sites and protection activities within the region. In response to interest generated by the NCC the Ministry of Natural Resources formed a task force in early 1990 to formerly evaluate the desirability of establishing a CDC for all of Ontario.

5. Quebec: The Quebec centre started operations in July, 1988, housed within the Ministry of the Environment. Maps have been provided and manuals translated into French. A contract calls for the ministry to take over the program in 1991, with NCC-ministry cost sharing until then. The NCC has already raised much of its required portion. Three biologists have been hired and data is being entered. A $25,000 grant from the Canadian Wildlife Service has allowed workers to place an early emphasis on entering CWS data on the St. Lawrence valley.

6. New Brunswick: Contracts between the NCC and the New Brunswick Department of Natural Resources have been made. A proposal is under consideration.

7. Nova Scotia: Contact between the NCC and the Department of Education, Nova Scotia Museum, have been made. A proposal is under consideration.

8. Great Lakes Data Centre Network: A major grant from the Joyce Foundation of Chicago has been received. It is funding networking of natural heritage data centres in Quebec and Ontario with those of the eight states bordering the Great Lakes: Minnesota, Wisconsin, Illinois, Indiana, Michigan, Ohio, New York and Pennsylvania. This data will be used to develop basin wide priorities for species and natural area protection.

9. National Coordination Centre: Two $50,000 grants from the C.S. Mott Foundation of Michigan have enabled the NCC to assign the director of the

heritage program in Michigan to Canada. Sue Crispin has been providing technical support to the provincial centres and demonstrating the data system to potential users. The Youth Employment Services program also provided assistance for the Carolinian Canada project. George Argus and Kathleen Pryer of the National Museum have completed their effort to rank – in terms of relative endangerment – all the rare vascular plants of Canada.

Data Management System

The Natural Heritage Data Centres (or Conservation Data Centres) are more than just data bases; they represent a comprehensive information management technology developed specifically for natural heritage data. This technology is the result of nearly 20 years of research, development and testing by the U.S. Nature Conservancy (TNC). Heritage Data Centres have now been implemented by TNC in 49 U.S. states and seven Latin American nations.

The computer software which The Nature Conservancy has developed for Heritage Data Centres is now in its sixth generation, using Advanced Revelation, an extremely powerful, yet user-friendly, database management program. Some advantages over DBASE III (which was used previously) include variable length fields, files that remain continuously open, automatic reindexing, extensive on-line user help, a highly menu-driven format, and multiple option fields throughout, enabling customization of the records to national and provincial needs.

Superimposed on Advanced Revelation is an extensive applications software package which was just released by The Nature Conservancy, called "Biological Conservation Data System" (BCD). It is being provided free of charge to heritage programs and major cooperating agencies and organizations – like the Nature Conservancy of Canada – under special agreements. This software is new and is not yet in general use among the U.S. heritage data centres. However, since the Canadian programs are just starting, we have been given immediate access to this current technology.

The heritage database, under BCD, is a system of eight inter-related files:

1. **Element File**: defines the species, communities, and other features of conservation interest in a state, province, or nation. There are several types of element files:

   EGT = Element Global Tracking
   – identifies elements using an international coding system
   – records global/national/provincial names; national or provincial names can conform to local usage, with international communication still possible because of codes
   – records status ranks at global/national/provincial levels (see below under Element Ranks)
   – provides legal and administrative status listings; COSEWIC will be added in an option field

   EGR = Element Global Ranking
   – Element ranks constitute the backbone of the heritage data system, allowing prioritization of different types of features at multiple levels: Global, National, and Provincial. These ranks are used in concert with and in support of legal status designations like Endangered, Threatened, etc., and enable a working prioritization that includes species not yet formally designated, as well as

communities and other types of features that don't normally receive "endangerment" type designations.

VCA/PCA = Vertebrate and Plant Characterization Abstracts
– Contain information on species biology, ecology, distribution, behaviour, taxonomy, management, and information sources. These are completed for all species in the province, not just rare ones. A community characterization abstract is under development.

2. **Element Occurrence File:** Forms the main body of the data system, containing detailed data on individual occurrences of priority elements. Features of this file include:
   – importation of basic element data from ET, enabling "single-point data entry";
   – many location parameters for data retrieval; enables direct uploading to geographic information systems and many other applications;
   – text fields expandable to about 20 pages;
   – numerous optional fields for built-in flexibility and adaptability; in Ontario, these will be used for map square, Ontario Base Map (OBM) number, Universal Transverse Mercator (UTM) easting & northing, lot, concession, COSEWIC status, MNR administrative regions and districts.

3. **Managed Area File:** contains records on areas in some sort of conservation ownership (public or private), on which elements often can be readily protected. Cross-references by code to the Element Occurrence and Site files.

4. **Source Abstract File:** a computerized bibliography of all information sources used in populating the various database files. Cross-referenced by codes to all other types of records.

5. **Contacts File:** an electronic rolodex, with individual and organizational contacts coded in the same fashion as source references.

6. **Actions File:** a "tickler" file to schedule, track, and prompt conservation activities.

7. **Sites File:** contains information and tracks the status of areas targeted for protection; cross-referenced to Element Occurrence and Managed Area files.

8. **Tracts File:** contains information on the disposition of ownership tracts within sites targeted for protection.

By using just one key, a person can easily view records that are linked by codes for elements, managed areas, and sites. The desired record can then be selected and brought up on the screen like one piece of paper being laid over another. This can be done repeatedly to create a whole "stack" of related records for data input, updating, or retrieval. The previous records are then recalled by using one key stroke.

Among BCD's other valuable built-in features is a library of standard reports used by heritage programs. Available pre-formatted reports include element occurrence listings, map legends, provincial element lists, and a prioritized summary of provincial elements and their occurrences called the Natural Diversity

Scorecard. The Easywriter function released in Advanced Revelation version 1.1 makes it easy to construct specialized report format to meet other needs as they arise.

Another feature built-in to the Tools menu of the program is an export function which simplifies downloading data to DBASE III files used by many cooperators and to ASCII files for uploading to a GIS. Conversely, data in various existing databases such as the Ontario Rare Breeding Bird Project, Ontario Herpetofaunal Survey, and MNR Regional Endangered Species mapping project can be imported into BCD along with data from a myriad of other sources to create a single, integrated database. Such a data source is capable of providing a comprehensive synthesis of all natural heritage data for a province, and it can be linked to national and global initiatives.

The BCD software is undergoing constant testing, evaluation and enhancement by staff at The Nature Conservancy in Arlington, Virginia. These enhancements are being provided to heritage programs through controlled releases approximately every six months.

As time goes on, the National Conservation Data Centre in Toronto will be able to provide increasing support to the provincial programs. In addition to being a clearing house for codes and ranks of all Canadian species and communities, national staff will help coordinate identification and conservation of nationally significant elements and, in concert with The Nature Conservancy (U.S.), of continentally and global significant elements.

Pictured here are two provincial rarities, the Giant Swallowtail butterfly, and one of its larval food plants, the Hop-tree. Both species are restricted in Canada to the Carolinian forest, with the exception of a few records for Giant Swallowtail slightly to the north of this zone.
Artist – Steve Varga.

Implications of the Carolinian Canada Research

Paul F. J. Eagles

Department of Recreation and Leisure Studies
University of Waterloo
Waterloo, Ontario N2L 3G1

Introduction

Carolinian is a nickname that has stuck. It refers to the rich, deciduous forests of extreme south western Ontario. This is an area of short, mild winters and long, hot summers. Many early botanists observed that a number of plants that had their southern geographical limits in the Carolina states had their northern limit in this part of Ontario, and hence the nickname. The name may not be familiar to readers of this volume from outside Ontario. The name Carolinian Canada was consciously chosen for this particular conservation program because of its connotations of the south and of the exotic. This was seen to be important to the long term political profile goals of the program.

The research outlined in this book portrays a rich assortment of findings, ideas and people. In this paper, I have undertaken to draw out some of the conclusions that are woven through the various studies. In order to do this a series of categories have been utilized.

The Issue of Scale

The papers reveal a classic issue in the development of conservation objectives: the issue of scale. There are papers that deal with provincial, life zone, county, site and species conservation efforts.

The Carolinian Life Zone is a regional climatic and vegetation zone within Ontario. Six papers address conservation issues over the entire life zone.

The status of 231 species of rare plants that are found in the Carolinian is documented by Mike Oldham. This important paper, for the first time, contains a thorough review of the status of these plants.

John Ambrose and Peter Kevan provide insight into the population and reproductive biology of 10 of these rare plant species that occur in the Carolinian.

Mike Oldham, in his second paper, documents the program under way to improve our knowledge of the distribution, abundance and ecology of the herpetofauna in Ontario. This is a province wide program, but the information on the Carolinian can be easily drawn out of the computer data base.

Craig Campbell, Daryl Coulson and Andrew Bryant document the status of 63 species of butterflies that are found in the Carolinian. This landmark paper provides a preliminary, yet important, look at the status of each species.

Mike Cadman discusses the methods now being used to document the continuing status of each of the species of birds that were found to be rare during the research for the Atlas of Breeding Birds of Ontario. This project is province wide in scope, but the information of the birds in the Carolinian area is available from the central database.

Stewart Hilts and Tom Moull report on the innovative program to contact the landowners in the 38 Carolinian Canada sites. With each of the special conservation sites the landowners are being contacted, told about the ecological significance of their lands and asked to cooperate in voluntary conservation.

The county is an highly visible political unit. Many land use planning decisions are made within the context of country or regional governments. Many people have a degree of attachment to this political level. And a number of papers in this proceedings outlines conservation efforts at the county level.

Steven Varga and Gary Allen outline the work under way to document the status of plants in each of the counties in the Carolinian Life Zone. They reveal an intriguing cadre of keen volunteer botanists who are spending much of their leisure time in recording the plants in their favorite county.

Rose Klinkenberg, Jane Bowles and Michelle Kanter report on their work to document the natural sites within Kent and Elgin Counties. Michael Bradstreet reports on the work to document the natural sites within the Haldimand-Norfolk Region. In the last decade, documentation of the environmentally sensitive areas of counties has been undertaken by dedicated conservationists such as these.

Work is also being done within individual natural sites.

Inventory work on Sassafras Woods, within the City of Burlington, has been undertaken by Catherine Lindsay. Documentation, such as this, is an important first step for the development of a management plan.

Gerry Mackie and Jane Topping undertook research within the Sydenham River Watershed. Even with the prominence of watershed-based Conservation Authorites in Ontario, studies of the fauna in entire river basins are still few in number.

Allen Woodliffe and Gary Allen report on their work within the Walpole Island Indian Reserve. They reveal this site as being probably the most significant long grass prairie in North America.

Research is also under way on individual species. Many papers report on such efforts.

The population ecology of the Tulip Tree is discussed by Kevin Kavanagh. Laurence Packer discusses the Karner Blue and the Frosted Elfin butterflies. Mark Stabb and Paul Aird assess the status and ecological requirements of the Southern Flying Squirrel. Cathy Sanderson, Mary Ellen Foley and Cathy Vanderbogerd outline Peregrine Falcon release work. Harry Lumsden, Dave Reid and Bruce Duncan discuss the reintroduction efforts in regards to the Trumpeter Swan, Wild Turkey and Bald Eagle, respectively.

It is clear from these papers that a conservation strategy must involve efforts at each of the five levels of scale: provincial, life zone, county, site and species. Conservation policy, record keeping, cooperation, and research must be designed with each level of scale in mind. Government agencies, scientists and conservation volunteers must be prepared to deal with many scales of activity.

The World Wildlife Fund research program, that underlays this publication, did not make a conscious effort to deal with scale; but the research community did. The various funding applications from this community covered the range of scales, as if some grand plan was in place. Maybe it was.

Habitat Change and Species Endangerment

Paper after paper references the ongoing, insidious loss of natural habitat in the Carolinian life zone. This loss occurs in all habitat types and species groups, but a few are particularly hard hit.

During the natural areas study of Kent and Elgin counties in 1985 and 1986 the researchers observed significant natural sites being destroyed. Rose Klinkenberg, Jane Bowles and Michelle Kanter reported that; "Several sites or portions of sites in Kent County were clearcut or lost to agriculture during the survey. These include parts of Skunk's Misery and Moraviantown Complexes, a prairie site on Prince Albert Sideroad Prairie in Chatham, a sandplain woodlot south of Thamesville, and the Thamesville Moor."

Craig Campbell, Daryl Coulson and Andrew Bryant report that 22 of the 63 taxa of butterflies that are largely restricted to the Carolinian, are extirpated, endangered, threatened or vulnerable. This is 35% of the species surveyed by these authors! Of these 22 species at risk, 13; "are largely dependent on savannah habitat (oak, oak-pine, Common Hackberry-Chinquapin Oak-Blue Ash or Red Cedar)." They go on to document a number of important savannah sites for butterflies, in Ontario's Carolinian zone, which no longer exist. Nor can we rely on the United States to protect this important community type. Laurence Packer points out that of the oak savannah that covered vast tracts of the midwest at the time of European settlement, only .02% remained by 1985.

Gerry Mackie and Jane Topping document that in the Sydenham watershed there appears to be only 13 species of freshwater mussels left, of the 33 species previously documented. This is a loss of 60% of the species! The loss appears to be due to water quality reductions caused by agricultural operations.

Mike Oldham points out that 36 species of plants are possibly extirpated from the Carolinian Life Zone and consequently from the country. In addition, "30 species are known from a single site, 31 species are known from two sites and 40 species are known from between three and five sites." Therefore 43% of the rare Carolinian plants are in a very precarious position.

These three studies dealing with butterflies, mussels and plants show clearly that many species are on the verge of extinction within the life zone and therefore within Canada.

The studies also point out that a species-by-species conservation plan is needed. And conservation action must be timely. Many of the remaining species are on the verge of Canadian extinction.

Conservation Genetics and Island Biogeography

Many authors point out that the remaining natural sites are often small and isolated. This results in potentially serious problems for the individuals and species that still exist in these sites.

Individual plants that remain, may be too isolated for effective cross pollination to occur. John Ambrose and Peter Kevan show that some Kentucky Coffee Trees have few fruit, probably due to a lack of effective pollination because of long distances to other trees.

The isolation of small populations may result in species inbreeding. Craig Campbell, Daryl Coulson and Andrew Bryant raise this as an issue with many of the rare butterflies that are now restricted to small patches of isolated habitat.

It is clear that it is virtually impossible for many species to migrate normally. The long stretches of farmland are a daunting barrier to the movement of seeds, juveniles, roots or other plant structures that are used for dispersal.

However, Brad Bricker and Richard Reader point out that woody species can survive for long periods in small woodlots. Their studies point out that the species richness of woody plants was as high for small woods, as for larger ones. This finding may be caused by the relaxation effect, the gradual loss of species in a habitat fragment due to isolation effects. This effect takes a very long time in southern Ontario woodlands. This is a positive finding since it gives conservationists time to develop appropriate protection strategies.

The Need for Detailed Biological Knowledge

The development of management and conservation policy for a species is dependent upon information. The most basic data required are simply presence or absence. After this, an idea of the general habitat requirements of the species is useful. However, if some species or habitat intervention is necessary then much more knowledge is required.

Laurence Packer discusses the biology of two endangered species of butterfly, the Karner Blue and the Frosted Elfin. His elegant and comprehensive description of the state of knowledge of these species provides a basis for the management actions. The understanding of the three way symbiosis between the Karner Blue, various species of Wood Ants and the Wild Lupine is important. A lack of such understanding would probably doom any site manipulation to failure.

The Karner Blue occurs in Canada only at Port Franks and near St. Williams Forestry Station. The key habitat at both sites has now been acquired with Carolinian Canada funding. The Port Franks site is owned and managed by Lambton Wildlife Incorporated, a local naturalist group. The St. Williams site has been added to the holdings of the Ministry of Natural Resources Forestry Station and management action is under way. Dr. Packer's research findings are key to all of the management activities.

Kevin Kavanagh outlines a thorough review of the reproductive biology of the Tulip Tree. His findings prove to be quite valuable in the case where introduction of the species is contemplated. In addition, he makes important recommendations in regards to forestry practices with this species.

These two studies are good examples of the vital significance of field biological studies of important species. They show that such studies would be valuable on each and every rare species in the Carolinian life zone if site manipulation is anticipated.

Allan Anderson's research into the reproductive biology of the native orchids shows the significance of carefully controlled laboratory studies as well. His work is quite significant in the fact that he was able to germinate several species of wild orchid for the first time in the lab. This breakthrough points towards the artificial propagation of many species of rare plants, something that was heretofore impossible.

Brad Sinclair's paper on the madicolous fauna is a unique contribution. It discusses a special and poorly known habitat, sheets of water over rock or soil. The research found that 13 species of arthropods have at least part of their life cycle restricted to this habitat. The paper shows that even in southern Ontario, there are suites of habitats and species that are virtually unknown.

Habitat and Species Management

The research findings reveal that noninterventionist site management is not the ideal conservation approach in most situations. Author after author points out that active species, site and habitat management is necessary. Some of the approaches are outlined below

Reintroductions

The purposeful introduction of a species in order to augment a low population or to reintroduce an extirpated species is a valid conservation objective. The reintroduction of the Trumpeter Swan, the Wild Turkey, the Peregrine Falcon, and the Bald Eagle are all outlined in papers in this volume. Each of these programs were assisted with Carolinian Canada funds.

The Wild Turkey reintroduction has been very successful. The populations are healthy and spreading. The success of the Bald Eagle and Peregrine Falcon reintroductions is difficult to assess, but most observers feel that the visible increase in observations of individuals of these species is due, in part, to the population augmentation by the reintroduction program. It appears to be too early to assess the Trumpeter Swan program. The heavy mortality of the young and the lack of breeding success of the maturing individuals does not bode well for this approach. Recently, the release of adult birds, rather than young, has been considered (Lumsden, pers. comm.).

Mark Stabb and Paul Aird recommend that the Southern Flying Squirrel be reintroduced in to areas where it has been extirpated. They suggest that Point Pelee National Park is an ideal candidate for this effort.

Craig Campbell, Daryl Coulson and Andrew Bryant suggest that the extirpated Regal Fritillary be reintroduced to Ontario. They suggest that; "the meadows at Spooky Hollow and Turkey Point, or the oak openings at Skunk's Misery, would provide suitable conditions for such an experiment."

The most novel reintroduction suggestions have been provided by Allan Anderson. His landmark work on the germination and growth of native orchids has given him sufficient confidence to suggest that field reintroductions be attempted. His reintroduction proposals have several parts. He suggests that some plants be placed into; "botanic gardens and publicly owned reserves where photographers and naturalists can photograph and view some of these rare species without disturbing their natural habitats." This would presumably provide opportunity for environmental education on the plants as well as a safety valve for the application of naturalist leisure activity. He suggests that his methods can be passed onto commercial horticultural enterprises so that they can raise and sell the plants. This would hopefully; "supply the wildflower enthusiasts without resorting to the deplorable practice of digging large number of plants from the wild." And Anderson suggests that new natural areas for orchids be established through the purchase and reclamation of farm land. Such sites would; "allow natural regeneration and planting experiments with orchids and prairie species."

Anderson has suggested that a new, Carolinian prairie community be established on a suitable site. This site would be an active location for reproductive, biological and reintroduction studies. It might be best conducted through a interuniversity and government agency cooperative agreement. It is a proposal with considerable merit. It is one that could complement, but never replace, conservation of native wildflowers in natural areas.

John Ambrose and Peter Kevan have a number of reintroduction recommendations in regards to the 10 species of rare Carolinian plants that they dealt with. They suggest that; "a comprehensive program for reintroduction and population enhancement needs to be addressed." This hints at the need for rare plant nurseries that can grow the stock and make it available to conservation agencies and to private land owners. There is such a market now but there is no one fulfilling it.

Cathy Sanderson, Mary Ellen Foley and Cathy Vandenbogerd document the complexity of release programs. It is a complicated activity. There are considerable biological, administrative, fund raising and public relations implications in such a program.

Habitat Manipulation

Many of the rare species are critically endangered. Many require active habitat management if they are to continue to survive.

Laurence Packer points out that habitat manipulation is necessary for both the Karner Blue and the Frosted Elfin populations. The Karner Blue populations appear to be declining as; "successional changes in the habitat will render them less and less suitable for the Karner Blue as time passes." He recommends that "low intensity management will be required to prevent the lupines from being crowded out by competing vegetation". In regards to the Frosted Elfin at St. Williams, management should; "attempt to increase potential habitat by the selective scarification of small areas, separated from each other by a few metres of taller vegetation. Small scale tree felling and lupine seed planting should also be considered. Uprooting of competing vegetation immediately around surviving lupine patches should be done as soon as possible."

Craig Campbell, Daryl Coulson and Andrew Bryant also call for habitat management. They point out that many of the best savannah sites are on park lands but that; "nearly all are in serious need of successional management." This suggests that open habitats have become grown over with woody growth and that this growth should be removed for butterfly population enhancement.

In both of the butterfly papers, there are calls for selective, but carefully thought through ecosystem manipulations. The case is strongly made that the lack of such actions will probably doom the local butterfly populations.

When an endangered species is being enhanced, other commoner species may be reduced in numbers. However this reduction is usually trivial in amount given the numbers of the common species. Such an issue occurs with the Trumpeter Swan reintroductions. There is a very high mortality of cygnets due to snapping turtle predation. Harry Lumsden reports that; "Control of Snapping Turtles was started in Cranberry Marsh in 1985". This control of competing or predatory species is an important but potentially controversial aspect of any habitat management effort.

Mark Stabb and Paul Aird make some recommendations for the enhancement of Southern Flying Squirrel populations. These include: retention of trees with nesting holes and the provision of nest boxes.

Cooperation and Voluntarism

The Carolinian Canada project has been a large cooperative effort. Hundreds of individuals have been involved. Many government agencies, conservation groups, land owners and private citizens have been active.

The affiliation of the authors of the papers in this book show the wide range of organizations that were involved. Examples include: the Ministry of Natural Resources, University of Toronto, York University, University of Guelph, Carleton University, University of Waterloo, National Museums of Canada, Grand River Conservation Authority, Norfolk Field Naturalists, and Long Point Bird Observatory. And importantly, a number of authors were not employed or associated with any such agency. They did their work independently.

The study of the Southern Flying Squirrels thanked three individuals by name and; "dozens of other individuals who contributed information to this study." The Ontario Herpetofaunal Summary had records from over 1,700 participants as of January 1989. The report on the release of Peregrine Falcons in the Niagara Region thanked 14 people by name, 18 companies or agencies, members of three naturalist clubs and the citizens of four cities, one region and one state! The rebuilding of the Long Point Bird Observatory monitoring station, at the tip of Long Point, was made possible by volunters from the Bird Observatory and the St. Thomas Field Naturalists, as outlined by George Wallace.

Volunteers helped collect seeds of endangered plants, surveyed the locations of rare breeding birds, monitored the populations of butterflies, built hack platforms for eagles, input plant records into computer data bases, and did many other such activities.

These are examples of the types of cooperative and volunteer effort that went into the projects.

It is obvious that this conservation program has been a broadly-based activity. This is a very positive happening, since political and protection action will only occur if a sufficient number of citizens are concerned and make those concerns known.

Environmental Education

Several authors call for increased levels of environmental education.

The work involved with documenting the herpetofauna of Ontario has revealed the poor standing of many of these creatures in the public eye. The report states that; "Increased emphasis on amphibians and reptiles in interpretive activities would help improve their public image."

The research by Brock Fenton and his colleagues on bats has shown the need for conservation education. The report lists several conservation recommendations, concluding that; "The first and most important is changing the public's attitude towards bats."

The landowner contact program has a strong environmental education component. The landowners are informed about the ecological significance of their lands and asked to assist with its conservation.

The undertaking of the various projects and studies outlined in this document appears to have had a considerable conservation education component, more by accident than intent. Thousands of people learned more about the environment due to their involvement with these activities.

At present, there is no Carolinian Canada education program. The education that has occurred has been an artifact of other activities.

Conservation Data Centre

This compendium of research findings highlights the need for one, central operation for the storage of conservation data.

Papers reported on two large, formal data collection efforts; the rare breeding birds of Ontario and the herpetofauna of Ontario. Papers reported on two large, informal data collection efforts; the county level plant record schemes and the Carolinian rare plant records. Each of these four efforts are proceeding independently and in an uncoordinated fashion. For example, a number of county plant recorders are developing computer data bases. It is almost certain that each system is using different file structure, programs and computer operating systems.

Michael Bradstreet, when looking back onto the Haldimand-Norfolk natural areas inventory, comments that; "we must establish procedures for monitoring the population levels of rare, threatened, and endangered species throughout the Carolinian Zone." Mike Oldham, when commenting on the herpetofaunal inventory, comments that; "Ontario desperately needs a Conservation Data Centre where computerized records and detailed mapping of rare species and vegetation community information can be gathered and stored. At present this type of information is being assembled by a wide variety of individuals and agencies, with little standardization and exchange of information." I can not agree more.

What would such a centre do? It would keep records so that the following questions could be answered with the best information available.

1) How many individuals are there?

2) Where are they?

3) What is their long-term prognosis on each site?

4) On which species should protection and restoration effort be concentrated?

George Francis outlines in detail the goals for a Conservation Data Centre for Ontario. He discusses a proposal for such a Centre.

Fortunately, the Nature Conservancy of Canada has started the development of a Conservation Data Centre for Canada. The details of such a centre are outlined by Phil Hoose and Susan Crispin in their paper.

The Carolinian Canada program provided some of the funding for a data base for the Carolinian Life Zone in Canada. Each species of plant and animal is assessed according to it global, provincial and regional status. Each known station for each special species is documented. All records are computerized. The Carolinian Canada Conservation Data Base is nearing completion of its first phase. When completed, it is to be made available to all interested parties, probably through the auspices of the Ministry of Natural Resources.

The proposed Conservation Data Centre for Ontario is of vital significance if natural heritage conservation is to be placed upon a systematic and scientific basis. The paper by Mike Oldham shows, for plants, the importance of thorough records for the assessment of species significance based upon distribution and rarity. A Conservation Data Centre extends this concept to all species and communities. It is a very worthwhile effort.

Carolinian Canada Program Future

The research and other conservation projects outlined in this document add considerably to our knowledge. Every paper has important, long-term implications for conservation action.

Appendix 1 provides a summary of the action taken on each of the 38 Carolinian Canada sites.

Many species and their habitats are on the verge of extinction within Canada. Such extirpation can not be allowed to happen. There is now sufficient knowledge to develop a species by species conservation program. Such a program can look at the following conservation options.

1) Determination of species significance using the Conservation Data Base.

2) Species protection in situ.

3) Continuous monitoring of each natural site for each critical species.

4) Research into reproduction biology of critical species.

5) Population enhancement through artificial breeding, release, and reintroduction.

6) Habitat enhancement.

7) Re-creation of natural communities through the reclamation of derelict sites.

8) Creation of "nurseries" for the propagation of rare plant species.

9) Environmental education with landowners, general naturalist community, school children and general public.

10) Development of cooperative arrangements between all interested groups and agencies.

It is clear that such activities must be continued into the indefinite future. Therefore, an effort should be made to continue the Carolinian Canada program.

Any future program should build upon the findings of the papers found in this book. Any future program should build upon the large reservoir of good will, knowledge and sense of cooperation that is so evident in the conservation efforts to date.

Appendix

Carolinian Canada Site Protection Summary

The Carolinian Canada program operated under a memorandum of agreement amongst a variety of groups until 1990. This program provided grants for such activities as landowner contact and land acquisition. This program was separate from the research effort, largely funded by the World Wildlife Fund and the Ontario Heritage Foundation, that is the subject of this book.

Many authors in the book referenced the 38 Carolinian Canada sites. These sites were first identified as priorities in 1984 (Eagles and Beechey). Subsequent to that time the Carolinian Canada program amended the list somewhat with the addition of two sites (Ojibway Prairie Remnants and St. Williams Dwarf Oak Forest, also known as the Manester Property) and the replacement of some sites by alternative of higher levels of significance.

In order to provide an up-to-date status report on the 38 sites this chart has been included in this book. This information in the chart is taken from Nicholson (1990) and as amended to May 1990.

This chart contains several columns. Each column is discussed in turn. Column 1 contains the name of the Carolinian Canada Site. Column 2 contains the name of the lead agency that has assumed a leadership role in regards to that site. Typically the lead agencies are Conservation Authorities, often in cooperation with a Ministry of Natural Resources District office. For example, Beverly Swamp has four lead agencies, the Halton Region Conservation Authority (HRCA), the Hamilton Conservation Authority (HaRCA), the Grand River Conservation Authority (GRCA), and the Cambridge District of MNR (Cam.). Column 3 has three pieces of information: the total area of the site, the area in public ownership, and the area in private ownership. Column 4 has three pieces of information: the number of private landowners on the site, the number of private landowners contacted by the program, and the percent of the private land where the owner was contacted. Column 5 contains information on the number of private landowners who agreed to conserve their land and the percentage of private land thereby conserved. Column 6 contains the area of the site acquired by the program. Column 7 has the overall percentage of the site protected by acquisition or by private cooperation.

Program Comments

(The following material is taken directly from Nicholson 1990.)

The following table provides highlights of site protection for the 38 Carolinian Canada sites as reported by the participating lead agencies in January 1990. There were 16 respondents out of 16 questionnaires sent to each of the lead agencies involved.

Note: MNR data, and that obtained from the OHF are not necessarily consistent with that obtained from lead agencies due to incomplete reporting by lead agency respondents.

For each site, the following data are provided:

- total area, publicly-owned and privately-owned area
- details of landowner contact, including number of private landowners, number contacted at least once (assumed to be in an in-person visit in the last three years) by either the Guelph Project team or lead agencies, and the percentage of privately-owned area owned by those contacted
- number of landowners with National Heritage Stewardship Award agreements, and the percentage of privately-owned land owned by these awardees
- area within site purchased through the Carolinian Canada program
- the percentage of total area protected through either public ownership or National Heritage Stewardship Awards

Lead agencies are abbreviated as follows:

Conservation Authorities

ABCA	Ausable-Bayfield
CCCA	Catfish Creek
ERCA	Essex Region
GRCA	Grand River
HRCA	Halton Region
HaRCA	Hamilton Region
LPRCA	Long Point Region
LTVCA	Lower Thames Valley
MTRCA	Metropolitan Toronto and Region
NPCA	Niagara Peninsula
SCRCA	St. Clair Region
UTRCA	Upper Thames River

Ministry of Natural Resources District Offices

Aylmer	Aylmer District
Cam.	Cambridge District
Chatham	Chatham District
Niagara	Niagara District
Simcoe	Simcoe District

Others

Oakville	Town of Oakville
Windsor	City of Windsor
FON	Federation of Ontario Naturalists
St.WFS	St. Williams Forestry Station
Six Nations	Six Nations Band Council
Walpole Island	Walpole Island

References

Eagles, P.F.J. and T.J. Beechey. 1984. Critical Unprotected Natural Areas in the Carolinian Life Zone of Canada. World Wildlife Fund, Toronto. 402 pp.

Nicholson, J.P. 1990. An Evaluation of the Carolinian Canada Program Steering Committee of Carolinian Canada. 83 pp.

Appendix I: Carolinian Canada Site Protection – Summary

Site	Lead Agency	Site Area (ha)			Private Landowner Contact			NHSA Agreements		Carolinian Canada Acquisition	Protected Area
		Total	Public	Private	# of Landowners	# Contacted at Least Once	% Private Area	#	% Private Area	(ha)	% Total Area
Ausable River Valley	ABCA	1159	326	833	47	41	96	29	74	28	81
Beverly Swamp	HRCA/GRCA HaRCA/Cam.	1943	828	1115	114	65	80	29	38	64	64
Big Creek Marsh	ERCA Chatham	1110	243	867	20	17	89	9	58	8	68
Big Cr. Valley/ S.Walsingham	LPRCA Simcoe	567	246	321	22	19	92	11	44	38	67
Caistor-Canborough	Niagara	970	75	895	47	38	82	38	82	0	83
Canard River Kentucky Coffee Tree Woods	ERCA	99	40	59	2	2	100	1	90	0	94
Catfish Creek Slope & Floodplain Forest	CCCA	233	0	233	8	8	100	7	98	0	98
Cedar Creek	ERCA Chatham	247	54	193	22	17	90	7	61	16	70
Delhi Big Creek Valley	LPRCA Simcoe	352	17	335	16	13	90	8	55	0	57
Dorchester Swamp	UTRCA	548	307	241	57	37	78	31	65	0	85
Dundas Valley	HaRCA Cam.	1260	650	610	281	85	50 (est.)	68	32	0	67
Embro Upland Forest	UTRCA	110	2	108	10	10	100	8	72	0	73
Fonthill Sandhill Valley	NPCA Niagara	110	53	57	10	7	77	4	37	0	67
Grand River -Spottiswood	GRCA Cam.	767	296	471	65	39	64	36	56	0	73
Grimsby-Winona	NPCA Niagara	317	83	234	132	70	31	42	15	0	37
Iroquois Shoreline Woods	Oakville	39	39	0	0	0	0	1	0	0	100

Site	Lead Agency	Site Area (ha)			Private Landowner Contact			NHSA Agreements		Carolinian Canada Acquisition	Protected Area
		Total	Public	Private	# of Landowners	# Contacted at Least Once	% Private Area	#	% Private Area	(ha)	% Total Area
Jordan Valley	NPCA Niagara	193	56	137	59	52	88	18	28	0	49
Middle Island	Chatham	40.5	0	40.5	1	0	0	0	0	0	0
Middle Point Woods	Chatham	38.5	0	38.5	1	0	0	0	0	0	0
Ojibway Prairie Remnants	Windsor Chatham	238	200	38	?	0	0	0	0	19	84
Oriskany Sandstone	GRCA Niagara	239	0	239	7	7	100	4	13	0	13
Oxley Poison Sumac Swamp	Chatham	51	0	51	4	3	75	1	12	0	2
Plum Creek Upland Woodlots	SCRCA Chatham	177	0	177	15	14	97	10	80	0	80
Point Abino	Niagara	175	0	175	52	36	77	23	73	0	73
Port Franks and Forested Dunes	ABCA Chatham	1290	852	438	65	45	78	17	30	43	76
Rouge River	MTRCA	536	509	27	?	0	0	0	0	0	95
Sassafras Woods	HRCA Cam.	134	13	121	25	15	80	8	39	0	5
Shetland Kentucky Coffee Tree Woods	SCRCA	4	0	4	2	2	100	1	91	0	91
Sinclair's Bush	LTVCA	42	2	40	9	6	69	8	85	1.6	86
Skunk's Misery	LTVCA SCRCA	1053	657	396	17	14	82	8	36	41	76
St. Clair Marshes	SCRCA/LTVCA Chatham	2009	302	1707	14	13	97	8	28	0	39
St. Williams Dwarf Oak Forest	St. Williams Forest Stat.	81	81	0	0	0	0	0	0	81	100
Stone Road Alvar	ERCA/FON Chatham	79	79	0	0	0	0	0	0	79	100

Site	Lead Agency	Site Area (ha)			Private Landowner Contact			NHSA Agreements		Carolinian Canada Acquisition	Protected Area
		Total	Public	Private	# of Landowners	# Contacted at Least Once	% Private Area	#	% Private Area	(ha)	% Total Area
Sudden Bog	GRCA Cam.	89	4	85	7	6	87	2	10	0	14
Sydenham River	SCRCA	390	26	364	22	20	97	16	68	0	70
Willoughby Clay Plain Forest	Niagara	234	115	119	24	15	53	14	52	0	76
Totals		**16924**	**6155**	**10769**	**1177**	**716**	**83%**	**467**	**53%**	**419**	**66%**

Sites Under Indian Band Stewardship

Site	Lead Agency	Total	Public	Private	# of Landowners	# Contacted at Least Once	% Private Area	#	% Private Area	(ha)	% Total Area
Six Nations	Six Nations	8000	0	8000	N/A	–	–	–	–	–	–
Walpole Island	Walpole Island Band Council	810	0	810	103	48	24	0	0	0	0